VISIBILITY UNLIMITED

NATURE'S WEATHER FACTORY. Taken at 12,000 feet over New Orleans in mid-winter after climbing through about 2,000 feet of clouds. It was a cold, damp, rainy day on the ground.

ERNEST G. VETTER

Lieutenant, United States Naval Reserve

VISIBILITY UNLIMITED

*AN INTRODUCTION TO THE SCIENCE OF
WEATHER AND THE ART OF PRACTICAL FLYING*

With an Introduction by
GEORGE RUSSELL HARRISON

Dean of Science, Massachusetts Institute of Technology

Illustrated by the Author and
EARLE C. WENNER

NEW YORK
WILLIAM MORROW AND COMPANY
1942

Published December, 1942
Second printing, December, 1942

To

COMMANDER PAUL E. GILLESPIE, *United States Naval Reserve,* whose qualities of service and leadership, tempered with wisdom and justice, have set a high standard for his men. His guidance and counsel have had a profound influence on my naval career.

INTRODUCTION

MILLIONS of young men today are taking to the air. To them the atmosphere is no longer a tenuous canopy above the earth, now clear and brilliantly blue, now gray with the clouds of an approaching storm; it has become in addition a friendly and reliable medium through which to wing for a thousand miles of an afternoon or evening. The growing group of pilots who have flown the Atlantic a dozen times now finds its exclusiveness threatened by a still more select society of those who have spanned the vastness of that ocean twice in a single day! Breakfast in Newfoundland—a trifle early, to be sure—late lunch at an airfield in Scotland, and then to finish off the day a hearty dinner back at home in Canada—there's a schedule to make one realize how air travel has progressed since Orville Wright held his plane off the ground for twenty seconds a little under forty years ago.

When this war is over we shall all be flying. Air travel is still a trifle dangerous to suit the timorous, but the dangers are rapidly being lessened. To travel a thousand miles by train was fully as risky a few decades ago as a thousand-mile flight would be today, yet today travel by Pullman has become safer than staying at home. It is no shallow exaggeration, but a well-considered conclusion of able engineers, to say that air travel can and will be made as safe as Pullman travel.

Only occasionally do clues leak out as to some of the improvements in flying which scientists and technologists have in store for the post-war traveler. Planes whose pilots need have no fear of fog or darkness, because with new devices they can penetrate the murk for miles around; planes which fly of their own volition to airport or landing field, and when they reach this swing automatically into the wind and settle gently down to a smooth landing without benefit of any pilot's hand whatever; planes which refuse to collide with other planes no matter how inept the pilot of either, so that they cannot be forced together any more than the locomotive hauling the Twentieth Century Limited can be forced by a careless engineer to enter a block of track when the signals are set against it and its brakes automatically lock the wheels: these are things which most of us will live to see.

Many and great as are the ills chargeable to war, at least one benefit is coming from World War II. Into the next few years will be crowded improvements in the airplane and its use which in normal times would require decades. To those improvements in speed and safety about which we read in the daily papers add the great mass of scientific advances which are being kept secret by the warring governments, and it is not hard to realize that air travel in 1950 will be as far ahead of that in 1940 as automobile travel in 1930 was ahead of that in 1910.

If we are to realize to the full our usefulness as citizens of the post-war world we must come to know the air. To persons past middle age this may appear difficult, but a new generation is coming along which will be as much at home in the air as a Boy Scout is at home in the water after his first summer in camp. *Visibility Unlimited* is a handbook to help these new scouts of the air on their way. Its purpose is not to teach how to fly, but to help its readers to learn to find their way around the skyways, and to gain an understanding of that gamut of atmospheric emotions which we call the weather.

The air pilot needs to know his weather in a way no salt-water sailor ever dreamed of, for the weather of the airman is three-dimensional—his winds blow up and down in dead earnest, as well as from all points of the compass.

Meteorology, or the science of weather, is a very complex subject, but Mr. Vetter has here laid out its salient points in so cleverly simple a fashion that no air-traveler need hesitate to improve his understanding of atmospheric caprice on the grounds of lack of time or of scientific inclination. Reading of that part of the book which deals with the air, its makeup and behavior, should lead inevitably to improvement in ability at handling the most ancient, and to an airman most important, type of prophecy, weather prediction.

Not that weather prediction is yet entirely a science. There is the story of the Admiral who challenged the chief of the local Weather Bureau to a test of predicting ability. The challenge being accepted, it was agreed that each would deposit a dollar and a weather prediction for the day in a certain desk drawer each morning. Each evening both dollars were to be removed by the man whose prediction had come more nearly true. Day after day went by, until finally the Admiral was so many dollars ahead that the professional weather prophet asked to be let into the secret. The chief of the Weather Bureau had claimed to be right only 75 per cent of the time, but he had considered this the best predicting possible. Then the Admiral pointed out that he had been betting on a mathematically sure thing. He had noticed that the weather in that particular locality seemed to come in four-day cycles—a storm would be likely to last four days, while sunny days came in groups of four or eight. Thus if he always predicted that a given day would have the same kind of weather as the day before, he would be correct 80 per cent of the time, which gave a clear 5 per cent advantage over his opponent's 75 per cent!

This story should not be taken too seriously, and it must

not be forgotten that the Admiral was an old sea dog who was not above seasoning his routine predictions with a glance at the falling barometer or the red sky at sunset. Also this all occurred in an earlier day, when the chief of that local bureau had no such modern scientific aids as the polar front theory to help him.

The second part of this book gives an elementary yet comprehensive discussion of the common methods of aerial navigation. It is much easier to get lost in the air than one would suppose. This is not merely because the distances involved are greater than those to which the embryo navigator is accustomed, but because of the changed appearance of even familiar objects when seen from above. Between the one extreme of climbing your plane into the air, seeing your destination in the distance, and flying to it, and the other of merely setting a pointer on a chart and letting the mechanical pilot of the future carry the plane automatically to its destination, there are many intermediate steps and methods of aerial navigation. To a basic discussion of the more important of these Mr. Vetter has given that thoughtful care which comes only from the pilot who loves his work, his plane, and the medium through which he flies.

While reading this book I have often been reminded of the enthusiasm of a pilot friend when first he got his wings, back in the days of the original World War. I see him now, getting up at six o'clock on a clear summer morning, wheeling his tiny biplane out of its hangar, warming up the engine and taking off for some lark-winging exercises in cloud destruction. Climbing his plane slowly until he found himself a couple of miles above the still-sleeping countryside, he would select a small fleecy cloud, hardly more than a high-hanging wisp of lucent fog gently drifting a few thousand feet below. Diving at it, he would pull up sharply just above it so that his onrushing wings would carry him into it and through it. From the pressure of air before his plane the cloud would vanish! Filled with the sheer joy of power over the elements, he was off again to search for another bit of downy moisture over which to repeat his aerial cavortings.

Such is the release from earth-binding ties which is the heritage of those who will be reading *Visibility Unlimited*.

GEORGE RUSSELL HARRISON.

CONTENTS

CLOUD PHOTOGRAPHS

(Reference to the other illustrations will be found by subject in the Index.)

xv

CLOUD PHOTOGRAPHS

AUTHOR'S NOTE

THESE fore words are not written merely to conform with the custom of explaining why the book was written. It is hoped that *Visibility Unlimited* will stand on its own merits with its purpose self-evident. As a practical aviator I have made the study of meteorology and navigation a hobby and found them as fascinating as they are practical. If this book lifts the curtain on these two subjects for those interested in aviation, whether they fly or not, its purpose will have been served.

I wish to thank all those who have made this work possible, especially my associate officers in the Navy who have given of their time and experience whether at Pensacola, Philadelphia, New York, or New Orleans. Also lending a hand were independent operators, the Civil Aeronautics Administration, members of the Weather Bureau—they are top flight men in anybody's book—and my classroom and flight students. Mr. Clarence E. Kallquist, Manager of the Airport Weather Bureau Station at New Orleans, checked the section devoted to meteorology.

The Radio Corporation of America provided the illustrations of aircraft radio. The illustrations of the various navigation instruments were supplied by the Pioneer Instrument Division of Bendix Aviation Corporation and Kollsman Instrument Division of Square D Company. The chapter on instruments was read and verified by the Pioneer Instrument Division of Bendix Aviation Corporation. I am indebted to Julien P. Friez and Sons, Division of Bendix Aviation Corporation, for the photographs of the weather instruments. The

Sperry Gyroscope Co. furnished literature and illustrations of the gyro instruments, while the Jardur Chronograph and the flight calculator are the products of the Jardur Importing Co.

While this book treats of aeronautical meteorology and navigation, it will not make a pilot, nor a meteorologist, nor a navigator. No book can do that. Each is a science of its own and requires long study and experience. But, this book can add to one's general knowledge and make safer and better pilots if through no other means than by impressing one with the vastness of this thing called aviation.

The treatment of both subjects, while basic, is not exhaustive. An attempt has been made to start at the beginning, to be thorough, accurate, practical and to follow a logical sequence. The scope is that which is given in the basic training of the military services and the requirements for a civilian pilot's certificate.

ERNEST G. VETTER

New Orleans, La.

VISIBILITY UNLIMITED

ABOVE THE OVERCAST. Through large gaping holes, such as the one in the center foreground, we can see the earth below. These clouds, about 700 feet thick, were resting about a mile from the ground over Chicago in the middle of the winter.

1

A THING IN THE AIR

N_{OT} long ago I had to make a flight from New York to Philadelphia during the winter in an open observation plane. Leaving Floyd Bennett Field I climbed at once in order to have sufficient altitude to reach land in case of engine trouble while crossing the water. In order to conform with the air traffic rules I wanted to fly at even thousands on this course. At two thousand feet I was too low to cross the water over Sandy Hook and at four thousand feet it not only was very cold but I was just into the base of the clouds. I had several choices: to go lower, follow the shore line and take a longer route; to fly on instruments at four thousand feet and be much colder; to go back; or to go higher to see what would present itself. I decided that my observer and I could stand the cold for a few minutes to experiment, and we started up through the stratotype clouds. We broke into the sunshine at five thousand and continued up to six thousand feet. We immediately felt warm and my strut thermometer indicated that it actually was about 20 degrees warmer up there at six thousand feet than it was under the clouds. We enjoyed a very pleasant ride and were sorry to have to drop down into the cold again when we reached Philadelphia.

Going above the clouds on a drab winter day is one of the most striking experiences in an aviator's life. As he bursts into the dazzlingly brilliant sunshine, the depression of the earthbound is released and it is as if he were in a different world. However unemotional a man he may be, he cannot but be awed at the beauty of the spectacle even while he is forced to squint at the glittering whiteness of the unhampered sun on the upper surface of the clouds. The cloud surface is wavy, like soft cotton rolls, and off in the distance one can see a bluish white light indicating a predominance of infrared rays. The sky itself assumes an intense blue seldom seen on the ground, that contrasts markedly with the whiteness of the clouds. Occasionally the shadow of the plane on the clouds is encircled by the colors of the rainbow, which aviators know as a "glory." It is a never-to-be-forgotten experience and you take leave of it to return to earth with regret.

Such moments are among the compensations of an aviator's existence. But flying has its problems as well as its pleasures, and many of the problems have to do with the weather. Weather, the great unconquered factor in aviation, is still man's enemy as well as his friend. Our primitive ancestors hid in their caves from storms that brought disaster, or went forth in search of food made plentiful by sun and rain. It remained for Aristotle to attempt to pierce the mysteries of weather in his *Meteorologica,* and for the father of medicine, Hippocrates, to ponder the effects of climate on mankind. From these early observations to the present day there extends a thread of research that has been woven into one of the most complicated sciences known.

Columbus made use of meteorology on his voyages to the new world and about a century later Galileo invented the thermometer while his pupil, Torricelli, developed the barometer. These companion instruments are of immeasurable importance to meteorology and from the day they were given to the world the science of weather made rapid and steady progress.

While there are many complications in the meteorological scheme, each manifestation is the result of the rational operation of some physical law or combination of laws. It is in this confusion of detail and apparent contradiction that the fascination of meteorology lies. Weather is as endless as time—predictable but uncontrollable, fickle and yet at times stable and dependable.

Until recently two groups of men were vitally concerned with what the future weather might be. Men of the sea and men of the soil prospered or came to grief on their ability to guess what the next day would bring. There were no extensive meteorological facilities and knowledge of the weather was learned entirely from experience. In the form of proverbs, jingles and pet theories, this weather lore was handed down from generation to generation.

But today meteorology comes nearer to being an exact science. One has only to visit a field station of the United States Weather Bureau to find out what is being done about the weather. Today, not only seamen and farmers, but also a new class of men, men of the air, can have accurate and complete weather information.

Although the Weather Bureau is the most extensive and important weather agency in the United States, there are several other sources of meteorological data. The Army and Navy maintain weather services for their own use and the Civil Aeronautics Administration assists the Weather Bureau by collecting and reporting weather data along the airlines. Where the weather services of the government fail to meet the needs of the airlines, these lines rely on their own facilities. All of these organizations collect, study and distribute information about the weather. Weather information from the government agencies, while restricted during wartime, is free to the public under normal conditions.* In addition to the regular reports, special assistance is given to those who have a need for it. As a friendly gesture, the commercial airline companies have offered the use of their facilities to the private pilot.

If all of this information, necessary to flying and navigation, is so readily available, then why is it necessary for a pilot to know meteorology? It is necessary because there will be times when he will be out of touch with any weather assistance, and will have to decide for himself whether or not it is safe to fly. A proper understanding of the structure and movement of the atmosphere is necessary to make forecasts with any reasonable degree of confidence or accuracy. And even if one has all the weather data in the world they would be of no practical use unless one understood their significance. The study of meteorology can be a fascinating hobby. The subject is an intriguing one, which becomes more interesting and absorbing the further one goes into the science. The Federal Government wisely requires everyone who wants to become a pilot to pass an examination in elementary meteorology.

If weather cannot be controlled, it can be understood, and that is what is being done by experiment and development. Despite the complexities of the science, present-day forecasts by skilled meteorologists have an accuracy in excess of 85 per cent. Not only that, but with the modern knowledge of the pattern and movement of the great air masses of polar and tropical air across the Northern Hemisphere long range forecasts are rapidly becoming possible.

Meteorology is generally defined as the science of the at-

* In wartime authorized persons can obtain weather information upon satisfactory identification.

mosphere. To the average person this means weather and climate. Weather is the short-term condition of the atmosphere at a given place, while climate is the usual weather of a place over a long period of time. The term meteorology has an interesting origin. It comes from the Greek word *meteoron* which, literally translated, means a thing in the air. The ancients believed that weather phenomena came to the earth from outer space and logically gave the name meteorology to the science of weather.

Most of our weather changes are due to nature's attempts to equalize differences of temperature on the earth's surface. The heat that causes these differences in temperature comes almost entirely from the sun. Coming from the sun it has to reach us from outer space. In view of this, perhaps the name meteorology is still a very satisfactory term.

In reporting on the various phenomena, the weather man makes use of several terms called elements. With these he can ascertain and describe the condition of the atmosphere at any particular time and place. The most important of these elements are: the temperature of the air, its pressure or weight on each square foot of the earth's surface, wind direction and velocity, humidity of the air, the type and amount of clouds, and the amount and kind of precipitation. Of particular interest to the aviator are the additional elements of visibility, ceiling, and general state of the weather.

In order to make a flight in safety or to decide whether to make a flight or not a pilot must have certain meteorological information. He wants to know the existing weather along his route and what changes are likely to occur. More specifically he is interested in the height and thickness of clouds, the ceiling along the route, the wind, and the dew point and temperature. The aviator should have enough knowledge of meteorology to interpret weather signs and avoid trouble and delay caused by adverse weather conditions. He should know the structure and movement of the atmosphere, and understand the significance of clouds and other weather aspects. In addition to being able to read the weather map a pilot should be able to make simple forecasts with reasonable accuracy. Finally he should understand the workings of the Weather Bureau, the services available, and how to use them.

2

AIR, THE BLANKET OF LIFE

THE atmosphere, commonly known as "air," is a layer of gases completely surrounding the earth. It is a protective covering several hundred miles thick, turning as a part of the earth in its rotation and traveling with it in its revolution around the sun. The density of the atmosphere decreases with distance from the earth's surface. Shooting stars and meteors, which flare into incandescence when falling through the atmosphere, become visible around 150 miles above the earth's surface. The Aurora Borealis, which is caused by electrical discharges in the rarefied upper layers of the atmosphere, gives evidence that there is still some air at an altitude of 400 or 500 miles.

At the surface of the earth dry air is composed of about

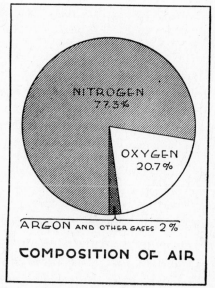

COMPOSITION OF AIR

77.3 per cent nitrogen and 20.7 per cent oxygen, the remaining 2 per cent being made up of argon, hydrogen, xenon, krypton, neon and helium. These gases exist in nearly the same proportions over all parts of the earth and up to a height of many miles. Far aloft, however, the composition changes so that at around 100 miles the atmosphere is composed almost entirely of hydrogen and a little helium. Although the gases at lower levels are thoroughly mixed it is a mechanical mixture and not a chemical combination. The gases are kept mixed by the intermingling horizontal and vertical air currents near the earth's surface.

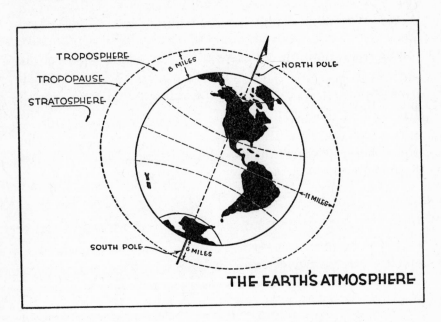

THE EARTH'S ATMOSPHERE

The atmosphere is divided into two main sections, the *troposphere* and the *stratosphere*. The dividing line, known as the *tropopause,* lies on the average about eight miles above the earth. It is the point where the temperature no longer decreases with altitude. The tropopause is found at an altitude of about 11 miles above the equator, 8 miles over latitudes 40 N and S, and about 6 miles above the polar regions.

The stratosphere is the section extending from the tropopause to the outer limits of the atmosphere. It is a region of slight density, low water vapor content, and a fairly constant temperature, with no wind, clouds, or storms. It is likely that the longer flights of the future will be made in this region. The larger airline companies have already completed extensive experimental work at altitudes bordering on the stratosphere, in the zone sometimes called the *substratosphere*. History will record that some of the air battles of the second World War were fought in the stratosphere or substratosphere.

The troposphere is the section between the earth's surface and the tropopause. This region, in which we live, is characterized by a decrease in temperature with altitude. It is here that we find the various weather phenomena—winds, clouds, storms, etc. As we shall be doing most of our flying in the troposphere, it is with that section of the atmosphere that we shall deal here.

3

INSOLATION VS. A FROZEN
UNIVERSE

BECAUSE it has so much effect on other elements, heat is
the most important factor in meteorology. Practically all atmospheric heat comes from the sun. The amount given off
by other celestial bodies and, in the reverse direction, by the
earth's interior is negligible. The manner in which heat comes
from the sun, enters the atmosphere and is distributed therein,
determines climate, weather, day and night, summer and winter, and actually life itself as we know it on the earth.

The sun sends forth a continuous stream of radiant energy.
That portion of solar radiation which strikes the earth is called
insolation. This term is a contraction of three words—incom
ing, solar, and radiation. Solar radiation is not heat while on
its way from the sun; it becomes heat only when it is absorbed
by the earth. Until it strikes the earth it remains in the form
of radiant energy.

Not all of the solar radiation directed towards the earth
reaches it, however. The proportion varies with the distance
of the earth from the sun, the turning of the earth on its axis,
and with the amount of dust, water vapor, and clouds in the
atmosphere. As the earth travels in its orbit around the sun,
it is nearly three million miles nearer the sun on January 1

than on July 1. About 7 per cent more insolation is received by the earth in January than in July.

As the earth rotates on its axis, giving us our days and nights, insolation is not received on one side of the earth. Likewise, the length of the day varies the amount of insolation in a given locality. In the latitude of New York State the length of the day varies from a little more than 15 hours in the summer to a little less than 9 hours in winter.

Under some conditions of cloudiness as much as 80 per cent of the sunlight falling on the earth may be reflected back into space by the upper surfaces of clouds. Under average conditions of cloudiness and dust content, over a period of time, perhaps 40 per cent of the radiation that reaches the outer atmosphere is lost by reflection and scattering. Another 20 per cent is absorbed by the atmosphere, and the remaining 40 per cent survives its journey and is absorbed by the earth's surface.

But the earth does not retain all of this absorbed heat. If it did, it would become hotter and hotter. This heat is released into the air that is in contact with the earth, causing the lower layers of the atmosphere to be heated. This process of heating the lower atmosphere by contact is called *conduction*. The air is a poor conductor of heat, however, and is rarely heated by conduction beyond three or four feet. Another process of heat release from the earth is by *radiation* in which the heat goes outward in waves, and also by *convection,* the most important single process in meteorology. Eventually all of the heat gained from the sun is gradually lost again into space by these three means, so that the heat received is balanced by the heat released.

It is the heating of the lower atmosphere that is responsible for life on the earth. Imagine for a moment the tremendous range of heat and cold in the universe and the comparatively narrow limits under which human life is possible. The surface temperature of the sun is estimated at 11,000 degrees F. Radiant energy, leaving the sun, passes through the vast reaches of outer space, where the temperature is 459 degrees F below zero. This is called the absolute zero of space and is the lowest possible temperature, corresponding to the total absence of heat. Now consider our world-record temperature. The highest ever recorded was 136.4 degrees F in the Libyan Desert. The lowest recorded was 90.4 degrees below zero F at Verkhoyansk, Siberia, or a difference of only 226.8 degrees F. Compare this narrow range with that between absolute zero and the temperature of the sun. Moreover, while man, with proper protection, is able to withstand temperatures from below zero to over 100 degrees for short periods, any doctor will tell you that a man dies when his body temperature goes below 95 degrees or above 105 degrees for any considerable time. So one can readily see how important our atmosphere is. Besides giving us vital oxygen it protects us from the intense heat of the sun, which would broil us to a turn in an instant, and from the extreme cold of space, which would freeze us stiff at nightfall. Without the earth's atmosphere, life on the earth as we know it would be impossible.

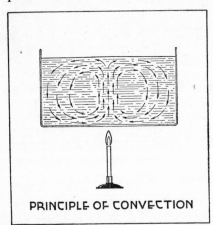

PRINCIPLE OF CONVECTION

Also, this heating of the atmosphere gives rise to the process already mentioned called *convection*, which is a very important means of transferring heat in the atmosphere. Convection is defined as the transference of heat within a liquid, or a gas, by circulation within itself (see illustration). Heat is applied to the base of a tank of liquid, causing the liquid just above it to be heated. The heated liquid expands, and as it decreases in density pushes upwards so that the colder and denser liquid on top flows, by the force of gravity, to the sides and bottom. There it is heated in its turn and rises, and thus a steady current is produced which distributes heat throughout the entire volume of the liquid. Substantially the same phenomenon occurs in the lower portion of the earth's atmosphere.

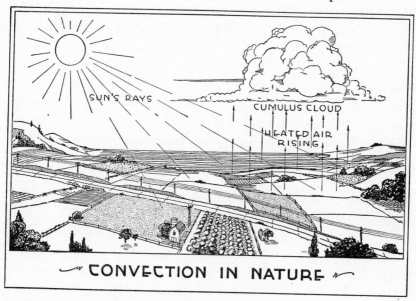

CONVECTION IN NATURE

The insolation received by the earth falls on a great variety of surfaces, which absorb heat at different rates. Generally speaking, dark and dull surfaces absorb heat readily while shiny or light-colored surfaces reflect the sun's rays. Wet bodies do not absorb much heat because the heat is largely used up in evaporating the liquid on the surface. The surfaces that absorb heat well, however, release it freely to the atmosphere, and the poor absorbers, having reflected it, do not have heat to release. This causes uneven heating of the air near the earth, which meets the requirements for convection. The air is heated at the bottom and in some places more than others. The result is a considerable number of localized convection currents over varying earth surfaces when the sun shines. The air in one place, being warmer than the adjacent air, expands and becomes lighter than the colder air. The heavier colder air forces the lighter air to rise by convection just as the liquid did in the tank. The air that rises from one place must eventually settle at another. These upward and downward moving currents make the air rough for airplanes.

The absorption of solar radiation by the waters of the earth is slightly different than by the land. Because the surface of the water does not vary, local convection currents are not prevalent. At sea, the oblique rays of the sun are largely reflected by the shiny surface and thus little heat is absorbed from them. The perpendicular, or direct, rays, however, penetrate to quite a depth, with the result that a large mass of water is heated. This heat is retained longer than land heat. Thus, in the tropics, where the direct rays strike the earth, we have vast oceanic heat reservoirs that are important factors in the climate of many countries farther north.

It is these same direct rays and oblique rays that make the tropics warm and the poles cold. The picture on page 17 shows how the sun's rays strike the earth. The distance BA is the same as CD. The lines representing the sun's rays are spaced equally and represent equal amounts of heat. It is readily seen that only about 5 units of insolation strike BA, while about 9 units strike CD. Obviously regions like CD that receive the direct rays of the sun get several times more heat than areas like BA which are reached by oblique rays. Consequently it is hot in the tropics and cold in the polar regions.

Now if both earth and sun stood still we would have half the world receiving heat and light and the other half receiving none. The half facing the sun would be warm and light; the other half, cold and dark. But the earth rotates on its axis once every 24 hours, giving us our night and our day. Owing to this regular rotation about the world's axis, the axis remains always in the same plane: gyroscopic action holds it there. Let's assume the position of this axis to be absolutely vertical, with the sun far off in a horizontal direction. We would then find,

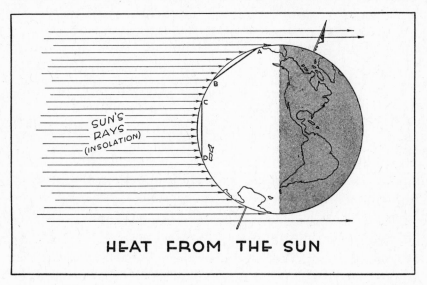

HEAT FROM THE SUN

if the speed of rotation were constant (which it is) that our nights and days would be of equal length—12 hours each.

In addition to its rotation every 24 hours, our earth has another circular motion. It is a planet, and therefore travels in an orbit around the sun. This orbit, or path of the earth around the sun, is in the form of an ellipse or flattened circle. Each revolution takes a year to complete.

At this stage in our reasoning, and still assuming that the earth's axis is vertical, if there were no complications we

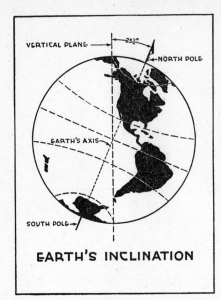

VERTICAL PLANE

23½°

←NORTH POLE

EARTH'S AXIS

SOUTH POLE→

EARTH'S INCLINATION

should have the earth rotating on its axis once every 24 hours, giving us night and day of 12 hours each. The earth would revolve once a year in its orbit, with the climate hot in the tropics, medium in what we call the temperate zones, and cold at the poles. This would be the same every day, month after month and year after year without change. There would be no seasons as we now know them.

But we do have one of those complications! The axis of the earth is not vertical. It is 23½ degrees off from perpendicular to its plane of orbit, as shown in the illustration. This angle is maintained throughout the earth's entire revolution around its orbit. It follows that as the earth rotates on its axis once a day and revolves in its orbit once a year—with its axis inclined—certain localities will alternate in being presented to the sun. The intensity and directness of the sun's rays will vary, and this explains why our days vary in length from 12 hours at the equator to 6 months at the poles. It also accounts for the change in seasons as the earth swings through its orbit. The polar day and night of 6 months each is the same as the summer and winter in these areas. The seasons north of the equator are just the reverse of those south of the equator.

These movements of the earth in relation to the sun have led geographers to put climate belts around the earth known as zones—frigid, temperate, and torrid according to latitude.

CREPUSCULAR RAYS. The sun is supposed to be "drawing water" when its rays are seen as they are here. Usually extending from the sun to the horizon in the late afternoon these Crepuscular rays are made visible by the illumination of particles of dust in the atmosphere. A rare shot made at high noon with the sun directly overhead.

The earth's axis is inclined 23½ degrees from the perpendicular, thus half of the year the sun will shine 23½ degrees beyond one pole and 23½ degrees short of the other, as is shown in the illustration. The reader will note that the earth,

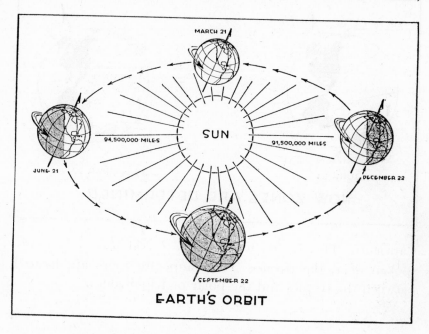

 MARCH 21

94,500,000 MILES   SUN   91,500,000 MILES

JUNE 21

DECEMBER 22

SEPTEMBER 22

EARTH'S ORBIT

as it revolves, has transcribed on it a circular area 23½ degrees from each pole, which locates the Arctic Circle in the north and the Antarctic Circle in the south.

In the illustration on page 17 the difference between direct and oblique solar rays was shown. Direct rays are those perpendicular to the earth's surface. There are definite geographical limits to the areas in which these direct rays strike the earth. These areas are determined in the same manner that the polar regions are located, by the earth's rotation and revolution. The boundaries of these areas are the Tropic of Cancer, 23 degrees 27 minutes north of the equator, and the

Tropic of Capricorn, 23 degrees 27 minutes south of the equator. The direct rays of the sun never strike the earth outside of the area between the Tropic of Cancer and the Tropic of

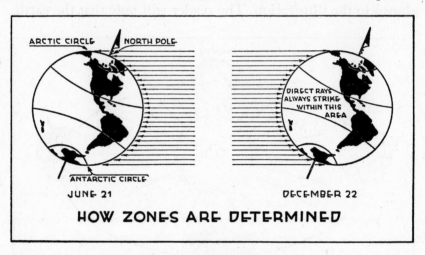

Capricorn. This region is called the torrid zone, commonly spoken of as the tropics. The temperate zones are located between the tropics and the polar or frigid zones.

4

HOME OF THE WINDS

*T*HE ancients thought wind came from some leather-lunged giant and that its force depended upon his mood. They would not have been far wrong if they had placed him at the equator and named him *convection*. With the sun pouring its rays down on the torrid zone the lower atmosphere becomes so heated that air rises in a great convection current.

Naturally air from some other locality must come into these areas to replace that which has risen. So cold polar air blows in from the poles. This air in turn is heated, rises and

then returns to fill the theoretical void at the poles. The result of this is a general movement of the atmosphere over the earth. When the atmosphere moves we have what we know as wind. Wind is air in motion. If the world were not rotating, this atmospheric movement would look like the illustration.

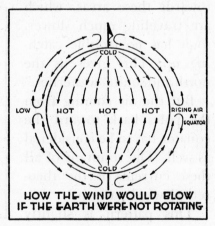

HOW THE WIND WOULD BLOW IF THE EARTH WERE NOT ROTATING

21

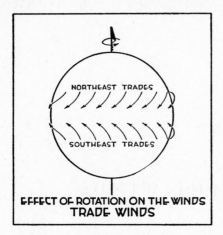

EFFECT OF ROTATION ON THE WINDS
TRADE WINDS

But, of course, the earth is rotating about its axis, which produces a centrifugal force outward from the center of rotation, as when mud flies away from a rotating automobile tire. This force assists in the rising of the air at the equator, but at the same time the rotation changes the orderly wind pattern in a manner which requires analysis.

The circumference of the earth is about 25,000 miles. Making a complete circle every 24 hours, a given point on the equator is traveling at a speed of 1040 miles per hour. The speed at the poles, of course, is zero. This variation in speed from the poles to the equator causes a veering of the atmosphere, resulting in fairly consistent air currents called trade winds. Thus we have the northeast and southeast trades.

Of course the air still has to return to the polar zones to fill the partial vacuum there. Accordingly the wind flows back towards these areas, which are traveling much slower, so it has no trouble catching up. This gives us the north and south "westerlies."

But the air coming from the poles back toward the equator has to be considered as well. The resultant of all these currents is the theoretical wind pattern.

This pattern is slightly

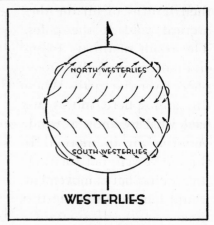

WESTERLIES

disturbed by the topography
of the land, water surfaces,
mountains, etc., creating the
actual wind system of the
earth as is shown on the map
on page 24. This changes
slightly with the seasons, but
remains generally the same
the year around.

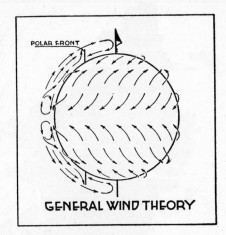

GENERAL WIND THEORY

Correlated with this sys-
tem of winds we have an-
other interesting phenome-
non. When air currents blow over water for a long period
of time, the water tends to move in the same direction as
the wind. This motion is accelerated by other factors such
as the earth's rotation, differences in temperature, and salinity
of the water. We therefore have in the ocean a system of currents or rivers—look at the map of ocean currents on page 25
and notice how closely the prevailing winds and the currents
coincide.

Slight deviations may appear where the topographical features, such as the contour of the seacoast, prevent the water
currents from following the air currents exactly.

Such currents have played an important role in the history
of mankind by rendering certain countries comfortably habit-
able that otherwise would be frigid. The best known of these
currents is the Gulf Stream. A river within the sea, 50 miles
wide and 2000 feet deep, it travels about five miles per hour,
bringing tropical heat up the eastern coast of the United States
and across the Atlantic. This strange current carries more
water than all the rivers of the world combined, and many
European countries owe their fertility and moderate climate
to it. Another important oceanic current is the Labrador

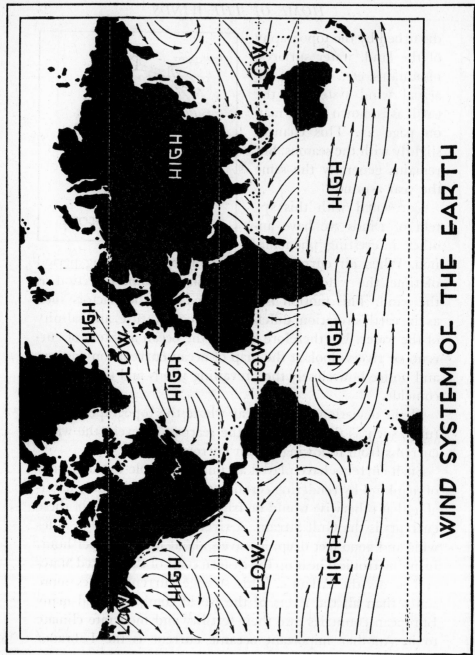

WIND SYSTEM OF THE EARTH

OCEAN CURRENTS

Current which may be considered the tail end of our Gulf Stream after it has traveled up through the Arctic. Coming down from Greenland, bearing cold water and ice, it meets the Gulf Stream off the coast of Newfoundland. One cold and uninviting, the other warm and hospitable, they meet in inevitable conflict. Here we find fog and icebergs, both of which have contributed greatly to the woeful nautical history of that section. The smaller icebergs are broken up with explosives by the ice patrol, but the larger ones float around, a menace to navigation, until they are melted by the warm waters from the south. The area is forbidden territory for ocean liners, but, like the ill wind, it blows good to the fishermen of that section. According to one theory the fish congregate at the feeding grounds formed by the junction of the Gulf Stream with the Labrador Current. Or it may be that the fish from the north, accustomed to cold waters, become torpid when they are swept into the Gulf Stream, and in this condition fall an easy prey to the nets of the fishermen of the Grand Banks.

On the west coast of our country we have another important current, impelled by the northeast trades, that endows Japan with its moderate climate. Swinging across the Pacific, it bestows its favor upon Alaska, keeping it warm enough for human habitation. Then, deflected by the protruding land mass of the western coast of North America, it travels southward and gives to California its agreeable climate—and its fog.

Although these currents are mentioned here, it should be noted that the currents themselves are not what affect our weather. They are themselves the results of the movements of the air and act as effects rather than causes. It is the movement of masses of air that causes the changes in weather and makes climate.

5

AIR MASSES—WEATHER BEARERS

T HERE are certain sections of the world where large quantities of air tend to stagnate or at least slow up in their movement. These large bodies of air assume the weather characteristics of the area in which they are resting. When the weather characteristics are approximately equal over a large horizontal area we have what are known to the weather man as *air masses*. The areas where these air masses are conditioned are called *air mass sources*.

These air masses travel with and as a part of the circulation of the atmosphere. On page 28 are shown the principal air masses that affect the weather of the United States in which we are most interested.

Until recently the air masses affecting the weather of the United States were classified according to the system developed by the Massachusetts Institute of Technology. Now, however, the international system developed by Bergeron, a Norwegian meteorologist, a system extensively used and understood abroad, is being used by the United States Weather Bureau. Actually in many ways the M. I. T. system is more descriptive and more interesting to students of North American meteorology. But as the Bergeron system will be found

AIR MASSES
OF
NORTH AMERICA

on the synoptic charts of the Weather Bureau, that is the one we shall use here. The most important air masses affecting United States weather are shown in the table on this page. Of less importance are the Arctic masses from the polar regions, which normally merge into the Polar; the Superior, hot and dry, from over Mexico; and the Equatorial from the south. These are not listed because of their relatively unimportant influence on our weather.

NATURE	SOURCE REGION	BERGERON CLASSIFICATION
POLAR CONTINENTAL	ALASKA, CANADA, AND ARCTIC	cP
	WHEN MODIFIED	cPw or cPk
POLAR MARITIME	NORTH PACIFIC AND	
	NORTH ATLANTIC OCEANS	mP
	WHEN MODIFIED	mPw or mPk
TROPICAL MARITIME	GULF OF MEXICO, CARIBBEAN SEA	
	AND MIDDLE ATLANTIC	mT
	WHEN MODIFIED	mTw or mTk

CLASSIFICATION OF AIR MASSES

Depending upon their geographical origin, air masses are classified as polar and tropical, respectively. Then they are further subdivided as to whether they come from the land or sea. Thus the symbol cP means continental polar, which, naturally will be cold and probably dry. The symbol mT indicates an air mass from the maritime tropics, warm and wet.

In addition to this, when the letter k is added to the symbol, it means that the air mass is colder (from *kalt*, German for cold) than the area over which it is traveling. Similarly the letter w added to the basic symbol signifies that the air mass is warmer than the area over which it is traveling. These letters usually denote that the air mass has been modified during its progress. In other words, it has lost some of its original characteristics and is beginning to assume the characteristics of the area over which it is passing.

As these air masses move into the United States, they bring with them widely different characteristics. The way they become modified, mix with others, or fail to mix, determines whether we will have good, fair, or bad flying weather.

Air mass analysis has opened up a whole new branch of weather science called *synoptic meteorology*—the study of weather conditions over a large area at a given time. The teletype and radio have made it possible to get simultaneous observations from a large number of stations. From these reports, synoptic charts or weather maps are made up which show existing atmospheric conditions over a wide area. The synoptic chart or weather map is the basic working tool of the meteorologist in making his forecasts.

Before we can understand the full importance of air masses and their effect on weather, and the significance of the synoptic chart, there are several other things we must know about. So we will leave air masses for the moment to discuss a number of subjects that will make air mass theory much clearer when we return to it.

6

DUST ALSO SERVES—WITH WATER

IN addition to the gaseous composition of the air, there are two other constituents that are extremely important. One is water vapor, the great variable element in the atmosphere, and the other dust, which plays a more important part in the genesis of weather than one would suppose.

The amount of water vapor in the air, or its humidity, varies with time and place. Despite its importance, it seldom exceeds four per cent of the volume of the air, and usually is around one per cent. It enters the air by evaporation and leaves by condensation or precipitation. The amount of water vapor that the air can hold depends upon the temperature— the higher the temperature, the more water vapor can be retained. The ability of air to hold water approximately doubles for each 20 degree increase in temperature. There-fore, air at 60 degrees F can hold four times as much water as it could at 20 degrees F. Water vapor itself is invisible, becoming visible only when it changes to the liquid state, in the form of rain, dew, clouds, fog; or solids, such as ice, snow, hail, etc. Coming from the waters and the vegetation of the earth, it returns to them in a ceaseless cycle of evaporation and condensation.

When water enters the atmosphere through evaporation, it absorbs heat to the extent of about 550 calories to each gram of water. This is known as the *heat of vaporization*. This is why sprinkling the pavements on summer nights makes them cooler. This added heat energy does not make the air hotter, it is *latent* and does not become evident until condensation occurs, at which time it is again returned to the atmosphere. In this manner heat is stored up and may be transported in the latent condition many hundreds of miles. A tremendous amount of the direct solar rays of the tropics are absorbed in evaporating water from the broad ocean surfaces in those regions. This is transported by air mass movement and released, often very violently, in other parts of the world.

Air, like a drinking glass, can hold only a certain amount of water. When the glass fills up, it overflows. The same thing happens to the air. When air fills up, or can hold no more water, it is said to be saturated. The temperature at which air is saturated is called the *dew point*. At the dew point, water condenses or precipitates in the form of rain, fog, dew, clouds, snow, etc. Now let us suppose that saturated air is heated. It will be affected in the same way as though our drinking glass were made larger—it will hold more water. Just the opposite happens when heat is taken from the air. The air is then affected in the same way as though our glass were made smaller—it will hold less water. So we can say that when any volume of air is at its dew point, any decrease in temperature will result in condensation, and any increase in temperature will enable the air to hold more water.

An illustration of dew point action is shown in your car in the winter. The warm air inside the automobile, moist from the occupant's breath, condenses when it comes in contact with the cold windshield. The glass steams up for the reason that the air near it has been cooled to the dew point.

Another way to define dew point is to say that it is the temperature to which a given body of air must be cooled for precipitation to occur. Let's take, for example, a weather report giving the temperature as 70 and the dew point as 60. In this case if the air were cooled to 60 degrees it would be at its dew point temperature and condensation would occur.

From the foregoing it should be plain that the relation of the temperature of the air to the dew point is extremely important to the aviator. When they are far apart, there is little likelihood of rain, fog, snow, etc., because the water just can't get out of the atmosphere until the air becomes full—reaches its dew point and overflows. When the dew point and the air temperature are close together, some kind of bad weather is imminent. If, simultaneously, the air temperature is at or below freezing level, there is danger of ice. Remember this— it is of utmost importance and will be discussed fully later. Dew point is always given with the air temperature in aviation weather reports. The farther apart the air temperature and dew point, the clearer the weather.

In measuring the amount of water vapor in the air, we use the terms *absolute humidity, relative humidity* and *specific humidity*. Absolute humidity is the weight of the water in a given volume of air. It is expressed in grams, or fractions of a gram, per cubic centimeter. In American units it would be given in ounces of water—actually fractions of an ounce— per cubic foot of air. Relative humidity is the percentage of saturation. It is the percentage of the water vapor that the air contains, compared to what it could contain at the same temperature. In other words, if air has only half the amount of water vapor that it can hold, or is half-way saturated, it has a relative humidity of 50 per cent. Specific humidity is the mass of water vapor contained in a mass of moist air. It is

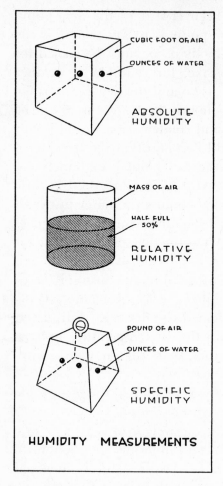

CUBIC FOOT OF AIR

OUNCES OF WATER

ABSOLUTE
HUMIDITY

MASS OF AIR

HALF FULL
50%

RELATIVE
HUMIDITY

POUND OF AIR

OUNCES OF WATER

SPECIFIC
HUMIDITY

HUMIDITY   MEASUREMENTS

expressed in grams of water vapor in a given number of grams of air. Or, to get away from the metric system, consider it as the number of ounces of water in a pound of air.

Humidity is measured by the use of a *psychrometer*. This instrument consists of a frame to which are attached two thermometers having cylindrical bulbs. These thermometers are mounted in such a way that they can be whirled by a hand crank. One of the thermometers has a muslin covering over the bulb. This muslin is wetted with pure clean water and the crank is turned, whirling the thermometers. As the water dries, the temperature in the thermometer with the wet bulb drops, owing to the release of the heat of vaporization from the muslin covering. The reading of the dry bulb thermometer does not change since it registers the true temperature of the air. The difference in readings between the two is called the *depression*. From the depression the dew point and humidity measurements can be obtained by reference to psychrometric tables.

Another type of psychrometer has the wet and dry bulb

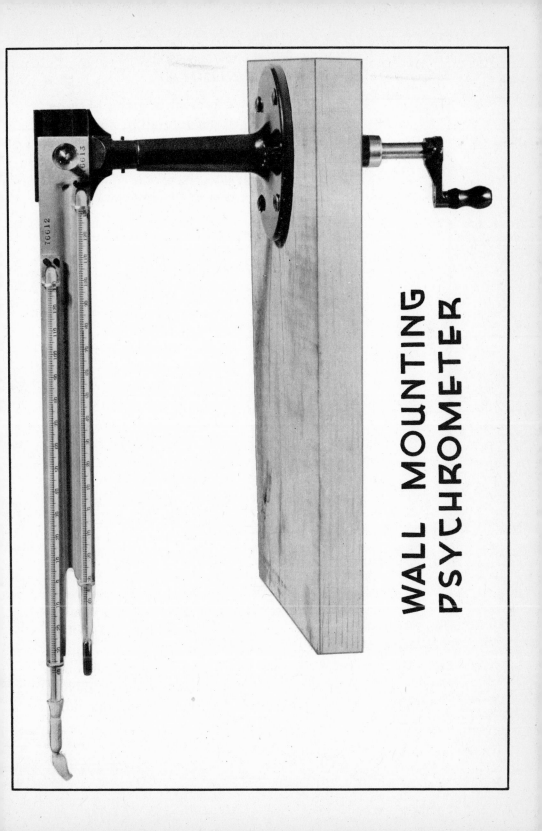

WALL MOUNTING
PSYCHROMETER

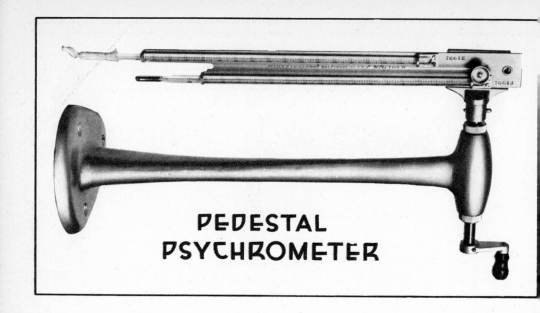

PEDESTAL
PSYCHROMETER

INSTRUMENT
SHELTER

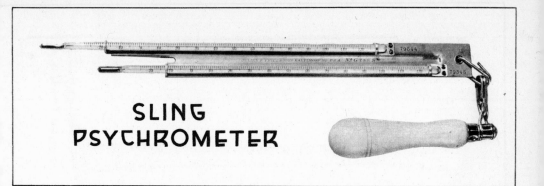

SLING
PSYCHROMETER

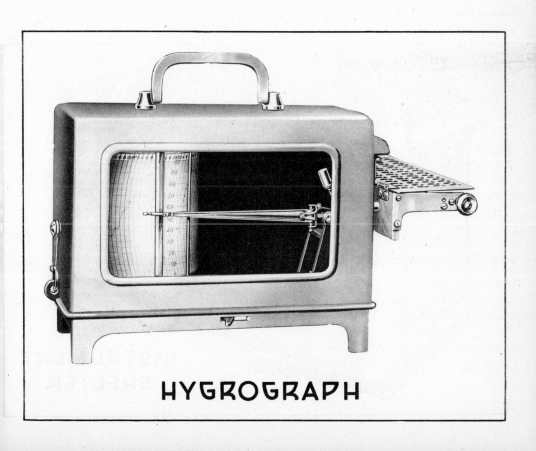

HYGROGRAPH

THE SMOKE OF INDUSTRY. In the foreground we see pure white smoke resulting from the chemical process involved in making cement. Described later on page 60, the direction of the smoke shows a lake breeze. In the background, the industrial plants of Lackawanna and Buffalo, N. Y., indicate the amount of dust particles sent into the air from the smoke of industry.

thermometers attached to a chain. The assembly is whirled by hand. The most common psychrometer, used by the Weather Bureau, is not of the whirling type. The two thermometers are mounted inside of an open shelter and cooling is accomplished by turning a hand fan. The principle, however, is the same for all types.

The *hygrometer* is an instrument that gives a direct reading of relative humidity. It is based on the contraction and expansion of human hair. An indicator shows changes in relative humidity as the length of the hair varies with the humidity. A *hygrograph* is a recording hygrometer.

It was stated at the beginning of this chapter that dust plays a part in making the weather. Dust-free air is unknown to nature. The dust in the atmosphere is of both meteoric and terrestrial origin. It is estimated that fully a thousand million meteors or meteoric particles enter the earth's atmosphere every twenty-four hours. Most of them are smaller than a grain of sand, but, even so, contribute to the total mass of fine solid matter in the air. The chief sources of terrestrial dust are volcanoes and the soil which is blown into the air by winds.

Volcanic dust is probably the most important dust from the earth itself. It is known that dust from large volcanic disturbances, such as the explosion of Krakatoa in 1883, may rise many miles into the atmosphere. In some instances it entirely surrounds the earth, and permeates the atmosphere for several years afterwards. However, nearly as important as volcanic dust is that from the earth's surface. Each year the winds charge the atmosphere with millions of tons of soil, most of which is picked up over deserts and carried great distances. In addition to this an immense amount of dust is sent into the air through the smoke of industry. Smoke is nothing else than finely divided particles of solid matter. Last, but not least, we have the products of life: spores, bacteria, diatoms, etc. Every hay fever sufferer can testify to the presence of billions of pollen particles in the air at certain seasons of the year. It would take a person a month to count the particles of dust, organic and inorganic, which he inhales in a single breath.

Contrary to common belief, dust does not "float." It is heavier than air and gradually settles to the ground, except where it is kept suspended and stirred up by air currents. Dust affects the distribution of light by scattering the sun's rays. If it were not for reflected, refracted, and scattered light, all objects not in direct sunlight would be in absolute darkness. Refracted light gives us our twilight after the sun is below the horizon.

Dust particles help to cause precipitation by acting as the nuclei for the condensation of water vapor. It has been proved that water vapor needs some sort of microscopic particles around which to condense. Not all dust particles are suitable for this, however. These nuclei must be hygroscopic, that is, be capable of absorbing water. Salt particles that have been blown into the atmosphere from sea spray and most kinds of smoke particles are highly hygroscopic, and therefore serve admirably as nuclei for condensation. While dust is a bugbear to the housewife, without it we could not live.

7

FAHRENHEIT AND CENTIGRADE

IN an earlier section, it was shown that heat gets into the atmosphere from the sun, and then is transferred horizontally by the movement of air masses and vertically by convection. The instrument used in observing the differences of temperature is the thermometer, invented in 1590 by Galileo.

The thermometer measures the level or degree of heat but not the amount of heat, just as a voltmeter measures electrical potential but not the amount of electricity. There are two thermometer, or heat measuring, scales in common use, the Fahrenheit and the Centigrade. The Fahrenheit scale gets its name from the German physicist, Gabriel D. Fahrenheit, who made the first mercury-in-glass thermometer. This scale is used largely for engineering and household purposes. The Centigrade scale was devised by Anders Celcius, a Swedish astronomer, and is universally used for scientific measurements. The temperatures of the surface atmosphere are given in Fahrenheit in weather reports but upper air data are given in Centigrade. It is therefore advisable to understand the relation between the two scales.

Using water, at sea level, as a standard, the range between freezing and boiling on the Fahrenheit scale is from 32 to 212

—a difference of 180 degrees. In the Centigrade scale zero is taken as the freezing point and 100 as the boiling point so that there is a difference of an even hundred degrees. There-

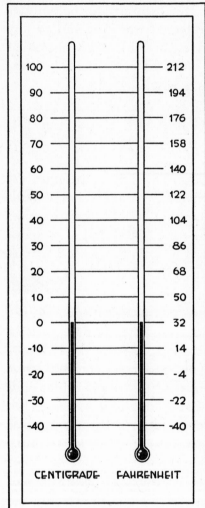

100	212
90	194
80	176
70	158
60	140
50	122
40	104
30	86
20	68
10	50
0	32
-10	14
-20	-4
-30	-22
-40	-40

CENTIGRADE   FAHRENHEIT

THERMOMETERS

fore, one degree Centigrade is equivalent to 1.8 degrees Fahrenheit. Since the freezing point of the Fahrenheit scale is 32 degrees Fahrenheit above the value for the freezing point on the Centigrade scale it is evident that this must be considered in changing from one scale to the other. In converting Centigrade to Fahrenheit it is only necessary to multiply the Centigrade reading by 1.8 and add 32. Thus 40 degrees C equals 40 times 1.8 plus 32 or 104 degrees F. To change Fahrenheit to Centigrade the process is reversed: 140 degrees F equals 140 minus 32 divided by 1.8 or 60 degrees C.

The most commonly used thermometer is the mercurial. Mercury expands and contracts uniformly; it is easily seen through glass and does not vaporize at the temperatures measured by a mercury-glass thermometer.

Since mercury freezes at a temperature of about 39 degrees F below zero, alcohol thermometers are used where temperatures below this value are expected. To give accurate readings a thermometer should have free exposure to the outdoor air and at the same time be protected from the sun or any other heat not normal to the free air. This is accomplished by placing these instruments in specially constructed shelters through which the air circulates freely.

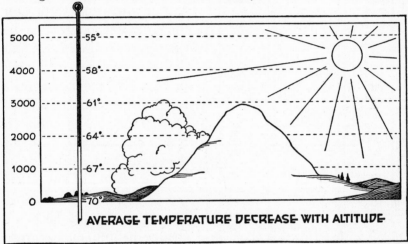

AVERAGE TEMPERATURE DECREASE WITH ALTITUDE

Horizontal temperature variation is shown on a weather map by *isotherms*. These are lines connecting points or areas having the same temperature, just as the contour lines on a topographical map connect points at the same altitude. Isotherms show the *horizontal temperature gradient*. (A gradient is a grade or slope; thus a temperature gradient is the slope, or rate of change, of the temperature.)

Just as it gets colder as we go away from the equator toward the poles, so it usually gets colder as we go upward into the air. The rate at which the temperature decreases with altitude is known as the *vertical temperature gradient* or *temperature lapse rate*. The average rate of decrease is 3 degrees for every

1000 feet of altitude, up to the tropopause above which the temperature remains constant or increases slightly. The stratosphere, above the tropopause, is sometimes referred to as the isothermal layer of the atmosphere because of this characteristic of equal temperature.

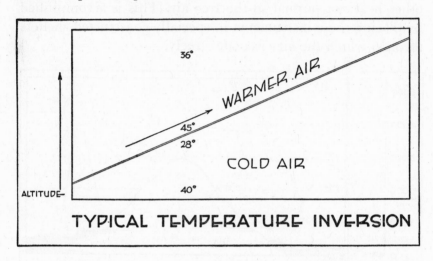

TYPICAL TEMPERATURE INVERSION

Although it is generally true that the atmosphere becomes colder with altitude, exceptions to this rule are encountered. There are frequent occasions when air at higher altitudes is warmer than that at lower levels. This phenomenon is called a *temperature inversion*. An inversion may occur, for example, on a clear night when there are no clouds to reflect the heat radiation back to the earth. The ground cools rapidly after the sun goes down, by radiating heat into space. The air in contact with the ground becomes cooled and being heavier tends to remain in place. The air above is warmer and a typical temperature inversion exists. Another cause of temperature inversion is warm air overrunning cold air in frontal formations; this will be discussed later. Whenever one sees *stratus* (flat sheets, from *strata*) type clouds in the atmosphere one can be sure that some sort of temperature inversion is present. Remember the Philadelphia-New York flight?

Until a few years ago meteorologists practically neglected the vertical movements of the air, in the mistaken belief that the horizontal movements were entirely responsible for weather changes. The modern theories and applications, however, regard weather as definitely a three-dimensional process. Thus, in addition to longitude and latitude we have altitude to consider in weather science. And it has been recently accepted that the vertical motions of the air are probably of more importance than horizontal movements in producing the more important weather phenomena.

The lapse rate of 3 degrees per thousand feet is the average rate of temperature decrease in a body of air that is not moving upward or downward. But in the atmosphere there are great quantities of air that are being raised mechanically—for example, being lifted over mountains. When this occurs, we have *adiabatic cooling,* which is measured by known adiabatic lapse rates.

Adiabatic means merely that if a gas is rapidly compressed, the temperature is increased, and, if a gas expands rapidly, the temperature is lowered. This is illustrated in the use of a bicycle pump, or an air compressor. When used, the pump gets warm, as does the tank of the air compressor. The same thing, and also the reverse cooling effect, takes place in a mechanical refrigerator, and on a larger scale in the atmosphere. As air is lifted, the pressure around it is lessened (we shall see in the next section why pressure decreases with altitude) and the air expands. Therefore, according to the adiabatic process, it should become cooler with altitude—and that is just what happens. When *unsaturated* air cools adiabatically (in a true adiabatic process there is neither gain nor loss of heat from the outside) the lapse rate is 5.5 degrees F for each thousand feet. This rate is called the *dry adiabatic lapse rate*.

When *saturated* air rises, the lapse rate is about 2.8 degrees F per thousand feet. This rate is called the *wet, pseudo,* or *saturated adiabatic lapse rate,* and is about half of the dry adiabatic rate. Other names for this lapse rate are *retarded* or *condensation* adiabatic lapse rate. Why should saturated air and unsaturated air cool adiabatically at different rates? When

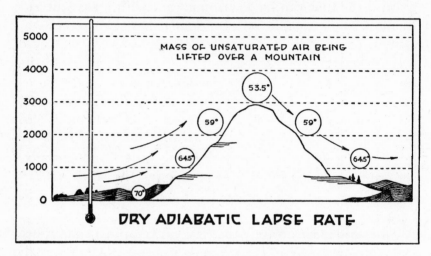

saturated air rises, condensation occurs because the air is at its dew point. It still continues to lose heat with altitude. With condensation, the latent heat of evaporation (remember the explanation of how 550 calories of heat per gram of water are stored up) is once more released. This quantity of heat is gained by the atmosphere; consequently air that is saturated cools more slowly as it rises than air that is dry. Air cools at the dry adiabatic rate until it becomes saturated, and then cools at the wet adiabatic rate until the stratosphere is reached.

The process of adiabatic temperature change is just the reverse when air is descending. The air is heated at the same rate as it was cooled when ascending, except that when descending it will always be heated at the dry adiabatic lapse rate since condensation cannot occur while the temperature is being raised. This effect is shown in the illustrations.

The actual temperature decrease with altitude for any given mass of air does not necessarily have to be the same as the adiabatic rate. The observed lapse rate of a given mass can vary over fairly wide limits. What this lapse rate happens to be at the time can be determined by instruments sent aloft by pilot balloon, radiosonde, or airplane.

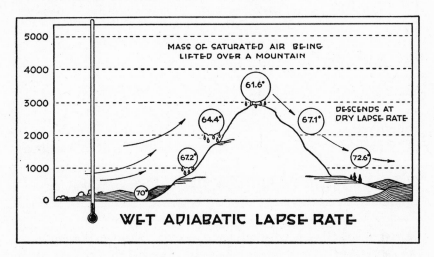

But when air is cooled adiabatically it is always at the dry adiabatic rate, if unsaturated, or at the pseudo adiabatic rate if saturated. The dry adiabatic rate is always 5.5 degrees per thousand feet, while the wet adiabatic rate varies slightly with temperature. Thus within one mass of air we might have another mass of air rising, having a different lapse rate from that of the surrounding air. At any given level, by noting the difference in temperature between an upward moving mass of air and the surrounding air mass, one can tell whether the atmosphere is stable or unstable. If the temperatures of the

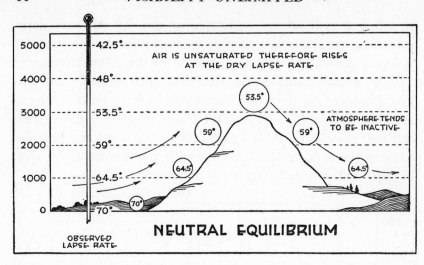

rising air and the surrounding air are equal there is a state of neutral equilibrium, which will neither resist nor favor vertical currents.

When the lapse rate of air is less (when it cools more slowly with altitude) than the dry adiabatic lapse rate, any mass of air forced to rise within it will be colder and heavier and

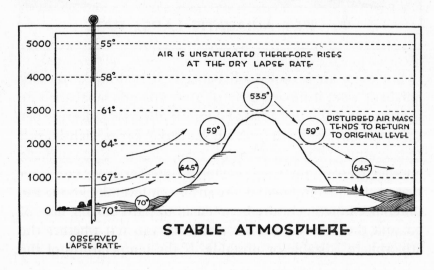

therefore will tend to return to its original level. This is known as a stable condition.

When the observed lapse rate of the surrounding air is greater (when it cools more quickly with altitude) than that of the dry adiabatic lapse rate the rising air, being warmer, will tend to keep on rising. This indicates an unstable condition.

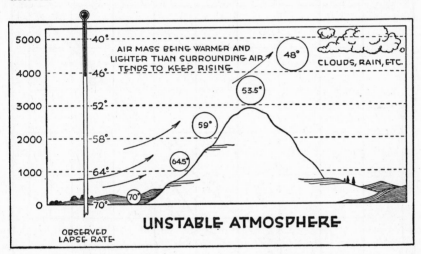

When vertical currents actually exist because of such differences in lapse rates, the rise of air does not continue indefinitely. It will continue until the rising air and the surrounding air have the same temperature, and then come to rest.

Up to now we have been considering vertical movements of a small mass of air having definite lapse rates, upwards through surrounding air having a different lapse rate. The conditions disclosed definite cases of stability and instability. Very often, however, it happens that the lapse rate of the atmosphere is such that it is stable as long as air is unsaturated, but when condensation occurs and continues the condition may become unstable. In the illustration on this page the line AB represents the lapse rate of a given mass of air as observed and reported by airplane, pilot balloon, or radio-

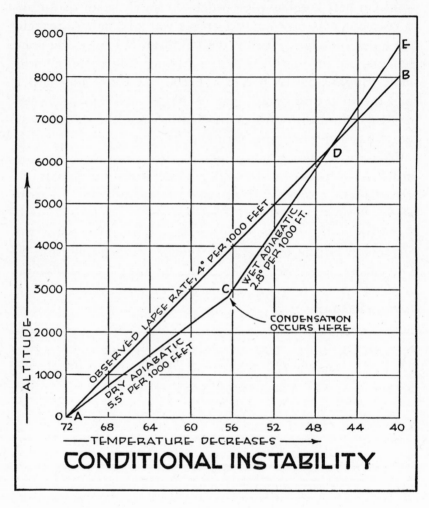

CONDITIONAL INSTABILITY

sonde. Line ACDE represents a small mass of air that is being forced to rise. It is clear that the rise of this mass must be forced in that it is colder and therefore heavier than AB, the surrounding air. From A to C it cools at the dry adiabatic rate of 5.5 degrees per 1000 feet. In this example the vapor content is such that the dew point is reached at 2800 feet (at point C); here condensation occurs. From C the air continues to rise, but it is now cooling at the wet adiabatic lapse rate of 2.8 per 1000 feet. Until it reaches point D it is still heavier than the air through which it is passing, and therefore still stable. But at point D this mass becomes warmer and lighter than the surrounding air, and no longer needs to be forced up. It continues upward of its own momentum and thereby the atmosphere becomes unstable.

From the above we may conclude that when the lapse rate of the air lies between that of the dry adiabatic and that of the wet adiabatic a state of conditional instability exists. In areas where vertical currents are frequent, such a state of conditional instability indicates the probability of intense upward currents, resulting in violent turbulence and thunderstorms. The reader is advised to keep this in mind, as it will be brought up again when we discuss conditions contributing to thunderstorms.

8

ATMOSPHERIC PRESSURE

THE immediate impelling factor in the movement of the atmosphere is pressure. Atmospheric pressure is nothing more or less than the weight of the column of air over a given area. It used to be supposed that the atmosphere had no weight, hence the saying "light as air." But air does have weight and if you could take a cubic foot of air and weigh it, you would find that it weighs about an ounce and a quarter. A cube-shaped room 30 feet on a side holds no less than a ton of air. The column of air extending up as far as there is air, resting on a square inch of the earth's surface, weighs 14.7 pounds, which is another way of saying that at sea level the atmospheric pressure is 14.7 pounds per square inch, or over a ton to the square foot. This is about the same weight as a layer of water 34 feet deep. This weight, or pressure, becomes less with altitude for the obvious reason that the higher we go, the less air there is above.

Look at the pile of blocks in the illustration. The weight at point A would be the weight of all of the 10 blocks. At the point B the weight would be that of only 4 blocks. The same thing would hold true in any given volume of air, except that the blocks, being solid, will retain their original shape, while

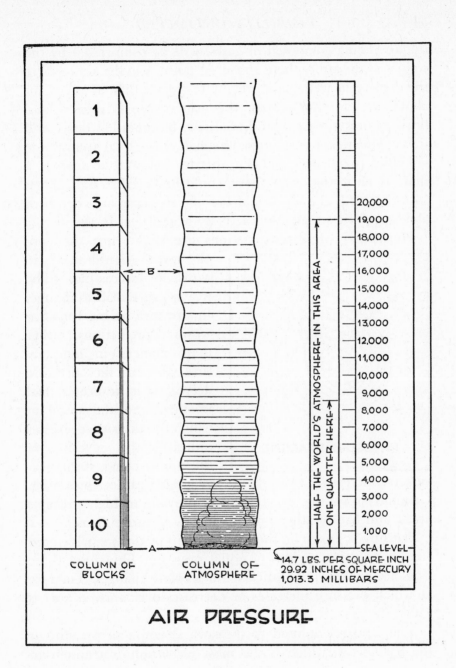

Column of Blocks

1
2
3
4
5
6
7
8
9
10

B

Column of Atmosphere

A

HALF THE WORLD'S ATMOSPHERE IN THIS AREA

ONE QUARTER HERE

20,000
19,000
18,000
17,000
16,000
15,000
14,000
13,000
12,000
11,000
10,000
9,000
8,000
7,000
6,000
5,000
4,000
3,000
2,000
1,000
SEA LEVEL
14.7 LBS. PER SQUARE INCH
29.92 INCHES OF MERCURY
1,013.3 MILLIBARS

COLUMN OF BLOCKS   COLUMN OF ATMOSPHERE

AIR PRESSURE

the air, being composed of gases, will be compressed by the weight of the atmosphere above. At point A in the atmosphere the density, as well as the weight, is greater than at any point above it. In other words, the atmosphere is densest and heaviest near the earth and gradually becomes less dense and lighter the higher up you go. One half of the total atmosphere is below 19,000 feet and one quarter below 8500 feet. If a shaft, open to the atmosphere, could be bored straight down into the earth the air would become so dense at a depth of almost 35 miles that wood actually would float in the air.

Horizontal pressure variations are slight, but they are

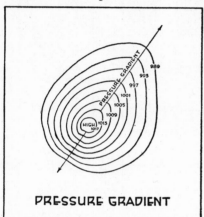

PRESSURE GRADIENT

of great significance in weather forecasting. The weather man utilizes changes in pressure as his basis for weather predictions, rather than changes in temperature. When the pressure decreases it indicates bad weather, and the speed at which the pressure decreases indicates the severity of the approaching storm. Inversely, increasing pressure means good weather is coming. Generally speaking, good weather prevails in high pressure areas, and bad weather prevails in low pressure areas.

Pressure is shown on the weather map by *isobars,* which are lines connecting regions of equal pressure. The closer these lines are together, the quicker the pressure changes. The rate at which pressure increases or decreases over a given area is called the *pressure gradient.*

The instrument used to measure atmosphere pressure is the barometer, which is the most important instrument in

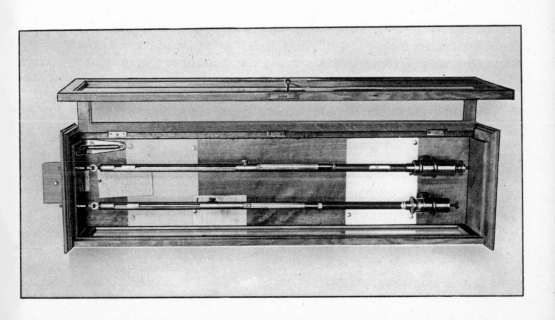

ANEROID BAROMETER

BAROGRAPH

forecasting. The barometer "weighs" the atmosphere in somewhat the manner that the scale in a grocery store weighs potatoes. Barometers are of two kinds, mercurial and aneroid. The principle of the mercurial barometer is very simple. A glass tube, closed at one end, about 3 feet long and ⅓ inch in diameter, is calibrated near the closed end in thousandths of an inch. This tube, filled with mercury, has been inverted into a small cuplike container partially filled, also with mercury. The mercury in the tube flows down into the cup until the pressure of the air on the surface of the

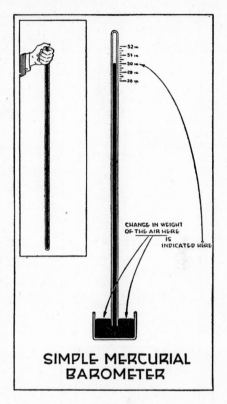

CHANGE IN WEIGHT
OF THE AIR HERE
IS
INDICATED HERE

SIMPLE MERCURIAL BAROMETER

mercury equals the pressure of the mercury left in the tube. The height of the column of mercury, read at the calibrated end of the instrument, shows atmospheric pressure in inches of mercury. The standard sea level mercury reading is 29.92 inches, which is equivalent to a pressure of 14.7 pounds per square inch.

Atmospheric pressure is now being recorded on the United States Synoptic Chart in terms of *millibars*. European meteorologists have long been using this measurement, and the adoption of this method in 1939 by the United States Weather Bureau makes its use universal. The sea level standard in millibars is 1013.3, which is equal to 29.92 inches of mercury. The use of millibars (mbs.) instead of inches in measuring

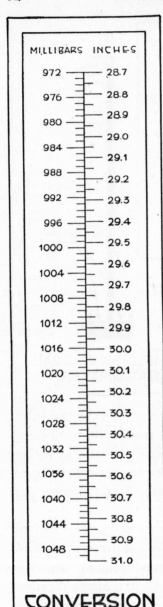

MILLIBARS	INCHES
972	28.7
976	28.8
980	28.9
	29.0
984	29.1
988	29.2
992	29.3
996	29.4
1000	29.5
	29.6
1004	29.7
1008	29.8
1012	29.9
1016	30.0
1020	30.1
1024	30.2
	30.3
1028	30.4
1032	30.5
1036	30.6
1040	30.7
1044	30.8
	30.9
1048	31.0

CONVERSION SCALE

pressure is sound, for the bar is the standard unit of pressure while inches are primarily units of length. A bar is equal to 1000 millibars.

The aneroid barometer is made in various sizes varying from a 3- or 4- to a 12-inch face. The main feature of an aneroid is a flat circular metal box or cell, from which most of the air has been removed. This cell is corrugated in order to make it flexible, and a spring is provided to balance the air and prevent collapse. Changes in pressure make the cell contract or expand and these slight movements are magnified and transmitted through a system of links and chains to a pointer. This pointer moves on a dial graduated in inches of mercury or millibars of pressure. The aneroid is not quite as accurate as the mercurial barometer but is more convenient to carry around.

A *barograph* is simply a recording barometer. The indicating hand is fitted with a pen that rests on a revolving cylinder. As the cylinder rotates the pen leaves a record of the changes in barometric pressure as the changes occur on a sheet of paper which has been attached to the cylinder.

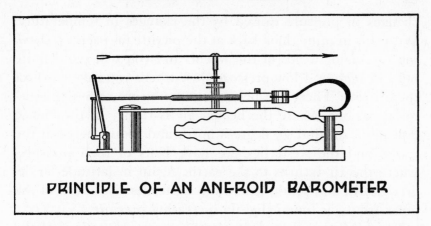

PRINCIPLE OF AN ANEROID BAROMETER

Although pressure is not constant for any elevation, fairly consistent changes with altitude can be expected. Therefore pressure, like temperature—because they are so closely related—has a vertical as well as a horizontal pressure gradient. Under average conditions, pressure will be reduced at the rate of about one inch per one thousand feet for the first ten thousand feet. In studying convection currents, we saw how heat changed the density and pressure in a liquid or in a gas like the atmosphere. In adiabatic lapse rates it was shown that moisture makes a difference in the rate of cooling of saturated and unsaturated air. We know, then, that the amount of heat and the amount of moisture in the air govern the atmospheric pressure. It is interesting to note that while pressure varies both horizontally and vertically with changes in temperature, there still can never be an inversion of pressure as there are inversions of temperature.

The annual variation in any locality is usually less than 2 inches of mercury, or about 68 millibars.

In our earlier explanation of the circulation of the air it was shown that warm air rises and flows into cooler sections. It can now be seen that, while the difference in temperature brings about this circulation indirectly, it is actually due to changes in pressure caused by the changes in temperature. With this in mind, look back at the picture on page 24, showing the major winds of the world, and you will see definite belts of high and low pressure, just where you might expect them to be. There are belts of low pressure over the equatorial regions, where the heated air is rising. In the "horse latitudes," around 35 degrees north and south, between the trades and the westerlies, we have belts of high pressure, where the air returns to the earth. Again in latitude 60 degrees north and south, where the westerlies rise ahead of the polar fronts, is found slightly increasing pressure.

In addition to these belts there are certain sections of the earth containing high or low pressure areas that are more or less permanent. These areas of regional "high" and "low" are called "centers of action."

The relationship of heat to pressure and wind now becomes clearer. It is nature's tendency to equalize the pressure differences induced by temperature variations that gives us our circulation of the atmosphere.

9

SURFACE WINDS

THE ancient Greeks, trying to solve the mystery of the wind which brought their ships safely into port or battered them in fury against a rocky coast, built a Tower of the Winds and topped it with one of the oldest known weather instruments —the weather vane. Greatly improved since the days of ancient Athens, the vane is an important source of data on surface winds, which must be distinguished from mid-air or high altitude conditions. A mass of air moving steadily and evenly over the earth's surface is rare, although wind currents do remain fairly constant and orderly at high altitudes.

Air, like water, tends to follow the land over which it flows. Striking a mountain it bounds upwards; it falls down into a valley. The downdrafts in the lee (downwind) side of hills are often strong, depending on the velocity of the wind, and should be avoided by airplanes. In too many cases downdrafts have been the direct cause of serious accidents.

Wind directions may be changed by obstructions such as mountains and bodies of water. Later we shall encounter spiraling winds, blowing clockwise and counterclockwise in the cyclones and anticyclones. Along the coast line land and sea breezes contribute to the turbulence of the air. During the

SEA BREEZE

day the land gets warm more rapidly than the sea. Convection currents are set up over the land and then sea air flows in to the land to replace the air that has risen.

At night when the air over the water is warmer than the air over the land, the reverse of this process takes place. Convection currents are then set up over the water and the cooler air from the land replaces that which has risen from the water. These winds are rarely felt more than 30 miles inland.

LAND BREEZE

In certain parts of the world the wind changes direction with the seasons. Winds of this type, called *monsoons,* occur in India, Australia and Spain.

Highways, railroads, power lines, etc., release the sun's heat into the air, which on hot days can be seen moving upward in convection currents. Streams of water, the evaporation from forests, etc., cause downward currents. Such disturbances, tending to make the air turbulent and to rock or jolt planes in flight, are called *air bumps.* They are sometimes referred to as "air pockets," but this is a misnomer. There is no such

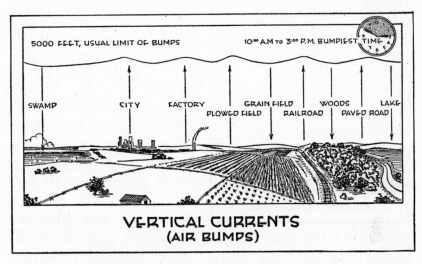

VERTICAL CURRENTS
(AIR BUMPS)

thing as an "air pocket." It was formerly believed that there were places in the atmosphere where no air existed, and that an airplane flying into these areas would fall. On the basis of our previous consideration of atmospheric pressure we can readily see that such a condition is impossible, since the pressure of the air would fill any such rarefied space. However, the varying air currents sometimes rise to about 5000 feet and often make the air very rough. Rough air in itself is not necessarily dangerous, but the pilot should stay away from

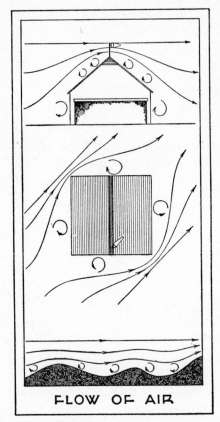

FLOW OF AIR

downdrafts and use extra care in landing or taking off when the air is "gusty." Also in climbing out of an airport or gliding in for a landing, when the air is turbulent it is advisable to have a little extra speed for better control.

It is an excellent plan for every flyer to visualize the streams of air as they flow over the country. Try to imagine how the winds will be affected by the various hills, trees and buildings so that, combined with your actual flying experience, you will be able to foretell where updrafts and downdrafts may be expected. The effects of downdrafts and gusts are most noticeable near the ground. Do not take off directly toward trees, buildings, hills, etc., unless you have a reserve of power and *KNOW* that you can clear them. Downdrafts, being on the downwind side of objects, will be directly in your path when you take off, as you should, into the wind. And, if you are a private pilot, don't think that because a Navy or an Army pilot does it with his high-powered ship you can do the same thing with your less powerful airplane. He has hundreds and in some cases thousands of horsepower in his engine.

On the other hand, if you know where to find the updrafts

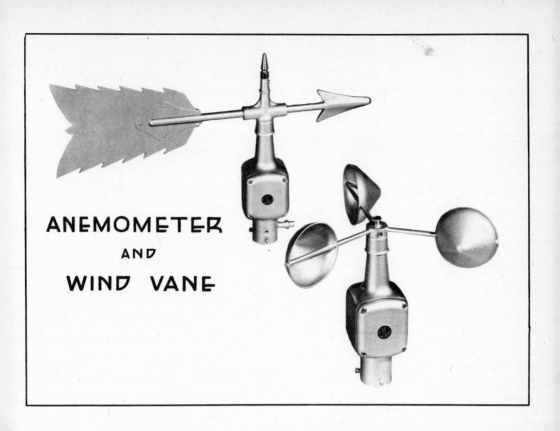

ANEMOMETER
AND
WIND VANE

WIND DIALS

"THE WIND IS PASSING BY." With a steady wind this particular smoke column from a factory near our main training field sometimes extended in a straight line for nearly fifty miles. This is pointed out to each new student on his indoctrination flight as the most common and most natural wind direction indicator.

WINDS ALOFT BALLOON AND THEODOLITE

RECORDING PATH OF BALLOON CHARTS AT THE WEATHER BUREAU

under a cumulus cloud and
on the right side of the hills,
you can gain altitude in a
hurry when you want to.
But this comes only with experience and should not be
attempted until you fully
understand the pitfalls involved.

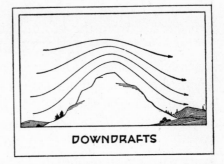

DOWNDRAFTS

It is these air currents that are utilized by the pilots of
gliders in keeping their motorless crafts aloft. Their training,
however, is such as to make them proficient in making the most
of each irregularity of terrain and the resulting air conditions.

On an early cross-country flight I approached a dark cloud
that was separated from the top of the hills by what appeared
to be about three hundred feet. As I came nearer the plane
seemed to be settling. I advanced the throttle and pulled the
ship up. We settled more rapidly. I kept advancing the throttle
and trying to climb but still the ship went down. By this time
I was too close to the hill to turn back. It looked hopeless. Just
as I was about to crash I passed over the ridge and an updraft
hit us and forced the plane violently upward.

After my scare had worn off and I returned to normal I
remembered my instructor's lecture on downdrafts and I re-
solved never to be caught
that way again.

Because of even heating
and the absence of ter-
rain irregularities the air is
usually smooth over water,
except when there are
numerous currents under
clouds. Even over land

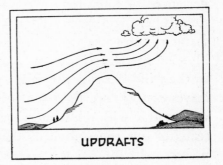

UPDRAFTS

the air tends to become smoother with altitude, as the plane gets further from the ground disturbances.

The most common wind instruments are the *anemometer* and the *wind vane*. The anemometer consists of three or four hemispherical metal cups at the ends of arms that are attached to a rotatable vertical rod. As the wind blows, it catches the cups, whirling them and the rod to which they are attached. A pointer connected to the rotating rod indicates the approximate wind speed on a dial. The indicating dial may be located on the instrument tower or in the office below.

Usually located near an anemometer is a wind vane, resembling a large metal arrow and pointing in the direction *from which* the wind is coming. A wind is named by the direction from which it comes, not by the direction in which it is going. Thus a north wind is a wind coming from the north and going southward. A pointer on a dial in the flight office gives a remote reading of the direction of the wind.

While air is invisible, its passage as wind is not entirely unseen. The effect it has on objects tells us its story of where it goes and whence it came. In the words of Christina Rossetti, "when the trees bow down their heads, the wind is passing by."

The student pilot flying cross country is sometimes at a loss to know in which direction the wind is blowing. With experience one looks for the common signs that tell wind direction. There is almost always factory smoke or a bonfire not many minutes away to show you the wind. Clothes, flags, dust blowing are clear indicators, and in the fall the waves made by the wind blowing through a grain field point the way. The leaves of trees are lighter on the upwind side and waves on water curve with the wind. Occasionally a lonesome windmill searches out the source of that which gives it motion and power.

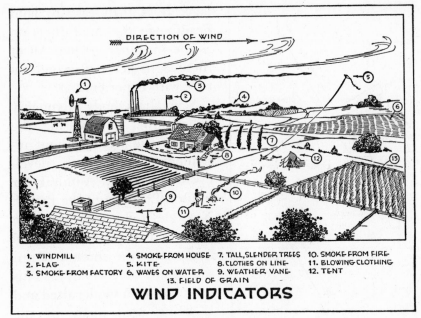

DIRECTION OF WIND

1. WINDMILL	4. SMOKE FROM HOUSE	7. TALL, SLENDER TREES	10. SMOKE FROM FIRE
2. FLAG	5. KITE	8. CLOTHES ON LINE	11. BLOWING CLOTHING
3. SMOKE FROM FACTORY	6. WAVES ON WATER	9. WEATHER VANE	12. TENT
	13. FIELD OF GRAIN		

WIND INDICATORS

A surprising number of pilots have confessed to me that it took them some time to be certain of the wind direction, even from the common signs at airports. The proper use of these signs is shown in the illustration. Some airports have smoke coming from the center of the field making it easy to tell how to land. The common *wind sock* or *wind cone* gives trouble until you get used to it. Remember to land so that the small end of the sock is toward you and you will be right. When one becomes familiar with each individual wind cone he can roughly estimate the strength of the wind by the way the cone blows. It takes a strong wind to make a heavy cone stand out horizontally. A light wind will lift it gently and listlessly. The *wind Tee* is quite common at large airports. This is a device turning with the wind and resembling an airplane. To use it correctly, think of the cross part of the Tee as the wings of an airplane and the long part of the Tee as the fuse-

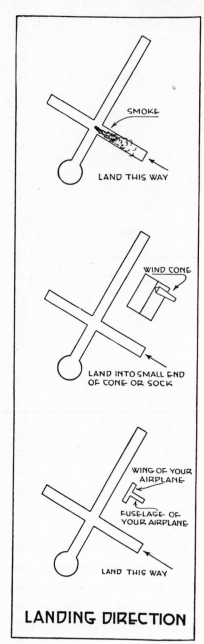

SMOKE

LAND THIS WAY

WIND CONE

LAND INTO SMALL END
OF CONE OR SOCK

WING OF YOUR
AIRPLANE

FUSELAGE OF
YOUR AIRPLANE

LAND THIS WAY

LANDING DIRECTION

lage. It is then easy to land heading in the same direction as the imaginary plane. All of these signs become second nature with experience.

Several methods of roughly determining and stating the force of the wind without instruments have been developed. In 1805, Admiral Sir Francis Beaufort of the British Navy devised a scale based on the speed of an old-fashioned frigate and the amount of sail she could safely carry. This scale has been modernized and is being used today by the United States Weather Bureau on its weather maps. It provides a means for a pilot to estimate the velocity of the wind when no instruments are available. This will be covered more thoroughly in the later section on weather-map data. (See illustration on page 131.)

It is common practice to speak of wind direction in terms of degrees. This is difficult to visualize at first but with a little practice it becomes easy to understand. It is difficult to talk about or locate a

certain point on a circle. All points are alike. Therefore there
must be some system of locating points in relation to one
point taken as a standard. As you look around the horizon it
becomes apparent that you are in the exact center of a circle
all points of which are on the horizon. There are two points

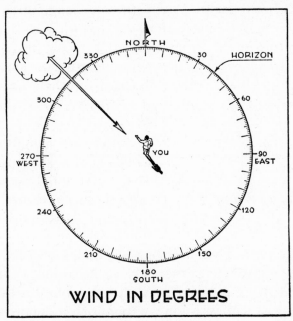

WIND IN DEGREES

where a vertical plane passing through the earth's axis would
intersect the periphery of this circle. One of these points is the
zero point, or North. Starting clockwise from this point and
making a complete trip around the horizon, on returning to
the zero point we shall have traveled through 360 degrees.
One quarter of this would be 90 degrees or East, one half
would be 180 degrees or South, and three quarters of our
circle is 270 degrees, or West. A wind may be named by the
reading in degrees at the point where it crosses the horizon on
its way to you in the center. For instance, a NW wind would
be a 315-degree wind, as shown in the illustration.

A theodolite is used to get information on the winds above the surface of the earth. This is a telescopic instrument designed to measure angles—practically the same as a surveyor's transit. When the meteorologist releases his helium-filled balloon he sights through the theodolite on the rising balloon until it is lost to sight. As the balloon changes direction and rate of ascent, the observations are recorded on a large circular plotting board. From these data, tracing the path of the balloon, it is possible to determine the directions and velocities of the winds aloft. This information is then made up into a report called the *winds-aloft report,* which is available to pilots.

The ascent of one of these helium balloons discloses an interesting cross section of the atmospheric movement as the balloon is caught and carried on by the different wind currents. The speeds of the winds are as a rule slower near the earth because of friction and the turbulence caused by the unevenness of the land. As the balloon rises it may go to the left or the right, rise faster or slower, all of which show the air movement characteristics. The most marked change is the increase in wind velocity with altitude. While this increase of wind speed with altitude is substantial, it is not as great as was formerly supposed. It used to be believed that wind velocities of 200 or 300 miles per hour prevailed at high altitudes. This has not been borne out by many thousands of observations over a period of years. High winds are encountered in thunderstorms and particularly in tornadoes, where velocities probably reach 400 to 500 miles per hour, but these are unusual conditions. In the United States, there is a fairly steady increase in velocity and a change in direction with altitude which leads up to and merges into the general west to eastward prevailing winds at around 25,000 feet.

A cross-country flight of mine, which was not in any way

unusual, will illustrate how this sort of information can be of value to the pilot. I wanted to fly from Elmira to New York City and called at the Elmira Weather Bureau station to get weather information. The surface wind was blowing about 20 miles per hour from the southeast which would be almost on my nose. Looking at the winds-aloft chart I found that the wind swung around so that at 6000 feet there was a wind from the northwest of 18 miles per hour. This was almost an exact tail wind, so, the rest of the weather report being favorable, I lost no time getting to 6000 feet. My speed over the ground was 38 miles per hour faster at 6000 feet than it would have been near the surface.

A sample of a winds-aloft chart is shown in the illustration on page 139 and will be discussed in a later chapter.

10

SIGNPOSTS OF THE SKYWAYS

WHEN air is saturated, it is in a critical condition for some sort of condensation. The condition of the air at the time as regards absolute humidity, temperature, etc., and the nature and degree of the change that causes condensation, will determine whether fog, clouds, dew, rain, hail, sleet, etc., will result. With saturated air a decrease in temperature, or a decrease in pressure (which would automatically bring about a decrease in temperature) will cause the water vapor in the air to condense on the hygroscopic dust particles present. If this condensation takes place at or near the ground, fog will form. At higher altitudes, the fog produced will be called clouds. The only difference between fog and clouds is the altitude at which they occur.

If the absolute humidity is high (large quantities of water present in the air) the condensation process will continue. The particles of water increase in size until they are heavy enough to fall in the form of rain, which strikes the earth at speeds varying from 8 to 18 miles an hour, depending on the size of the drops. Showers have the highest speed, drizzle the lowest. If the temperature is below freezing in the stratum where this condensation occurs, the water vapor crystallizes

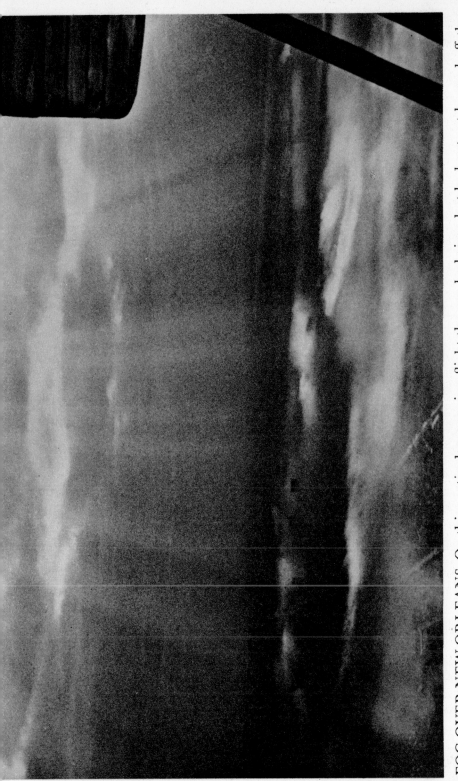

FOG OVER NEW ORLEANS. On this particular morning flight the sun had risen but had not yet burned off the advection, or morning, fog below. The matutinal rays passing through interstices in the clouds above light up patches of the fog blanketing the city.

A FOREBODING. Cirrus tufts—wispy, delicate and silky. Several miles high where temperatures are always below freezing they are made up of tiny ice crystals. Cirrus clouds appear in varied forms and warn of the coming of bad weather.

MARE'S TAILS. This form of Cirrus cloud is descriptively called "mare's tails." In the lower part of this picture the Cirrus is merging into Cirrostratus. This combination adds to the certainty of an approaching warm front with its attendant poor flying weather.

SILHOUETTE. Another Cirrus merging into Cirrostratus in the southwest. About eighteen hours after this shot a steady rain started which lasted several hours. As seen here the clouds are high and thin. They gradually thickened and lowered until with the arrival of the warm front the ceiling was near the ground and visibility poor.

"NURSLINGS OF THE SKY." Real Cirrocumulus clouds are rare and are often confused with Altocumulus which they resemble except that the Cirrocumulus masses are much smaller. This photograph had a high degree of enlargement, making the patches look a little larger than when in the sky. Crack weather men agree that these are Cirrocumulus.

MOUNTAIN MEADOW. Captured in the mountains of West Virginia, this photograph shows above the thin whitish veil of Cirrostratus covering the sky at around 30,000 feet. Like the Cirrus, they are composed of ice crystals. Because of their thinness they do not obstruct the sun or moon. With the sun or moon behind Cirrostratus clouds, halos are visible. The Altocumulus below are quite common.

LAMB'S WOOL AND BUTTONWOOD. A good example of Alto-cumulus floccus. This is one of the many variations of Altocumulus clouds, made up of tufts resembling small Cumulus clouds without a base and more or less ragged.

CELESTIAL CITY. Note the more or less parallel bands of clouds below and the patches above. In the middle cloud family these would also be classified as Altocumulus.

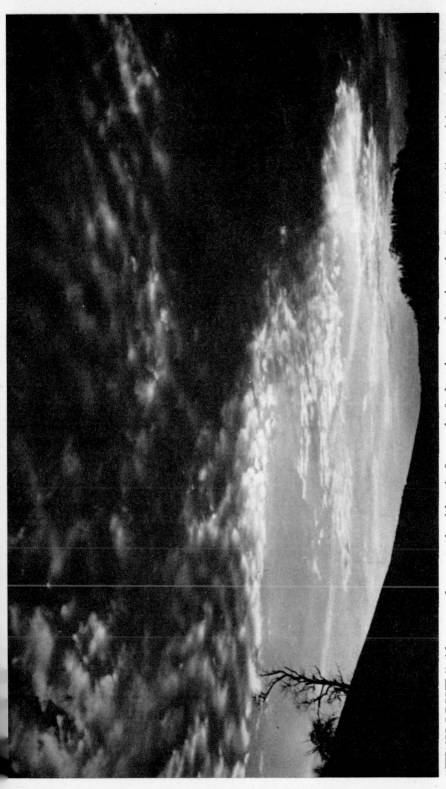

"TWILIGHT." Altocumulus translucidus is formed of clouds ranging in color from dazzling white to dark gray because of the varying degree in thickness. The variability of the color makes the identification of this type positive. Because of the angle of the sun in the late afternoon this contrast is not as apparent as it would have been in the middle of the day.

OVER THE PENNSYLVANIA HILLS. Altocumulus opacus is an Altocumulus sheet which is continuous at least over the greater part of the layer.

SUMMER CLOUDS. Soft clouds, Altocumulus floccus, evaporating into the thirsty air over Western New York and breaking up into poorly defined globular masses.

LATE AFTERNOON. Another study of Altocumulus opacus.

BLACK AND GRAY. The Altostratus cloud is a striated or fibrous veil more or less gray or bluish in color. It is like a Cirrostratus, but thicker and does not show halo phenomena. With the sun high and strong enough to penetrate these clouds, it is like light seen through ground glass.

A SILVER LINING. Stratocumulus vesperalis, the flat elongated clouds often seen forming about sunset as the final product of the diurnal changes of Cumulus. A special specie of Stratocumulus.

SUNSET ON LAKE ERIE. Another striking example of Stratocumulus vesperalis. Not an uncommon sight in New York State along the shores of the lake, where every clear or nearly cloudless day presaged a sunset of brilliant color.

THE CLOUDS HANG LOW. Stratocumulus clouds are defined as a layer of globular masses or rolls, arranged in groups, lines or waves, aligned in one or in two directions. Very often the rolls are so close that the edges join, and when they cover the whole sky present a wavy appearance. An unusually good example of Stratocumulus opacus.

INVICTUS. Behind this lone sentinel standing against the force of a gale, Stratocumulus translucidus are swept along at 40 miles an hour.

LOW CEILING. Sometimes the difference between fog and a cloud is hard to recognize. Fog is a cloud resting on the ground, while a Stratus cloud, low as the layer may be, does not rest on the ground. Take your choice here; but it seems like a Stratus cloud, and flying in this neighborhood would be unwise.

VISIBILITY LIMITED. When anything like this looms ahead you would be very wise to fly around it. There is heavy rain and poor visibility near clouds of this type and they are very likely to have high winds in and around them. This resembles somewhat a Nimbostratus cloud but is actually the base of a Cumulonimbus.

FAIR WEATHER. Cumulus of fair weather are quite common and develop on clear days over land areas. The result of diurnal convection currents, they appear in the morning and then seem to dissolve again towards evening.

A GIANT. A Cumulus cloud is puffing and swelling into a Cumulonimbus. It cannot properly be classified as a Cumulonimbus, however, until the "anvil" develops as the top begins to spread out into a cloud of the Cirrus type.

A STORM IS BORN. For miles around, the sky is dark and rain falls steadily out of the disturbed air of an occluded front. A break in the clouds shows momentarily the sun shining on the Cumulonimbus cloud just forming, which will later give forth torrents and thunder and lightning.

THE ANVIL IN THE SKY. The top of a Cumulonimbus shot at 18,000 feet over Pensacola in mid-winter. The top is spreading out on both sides into the anvil shape which positively identifies this cloud as a Cumulonimbus.

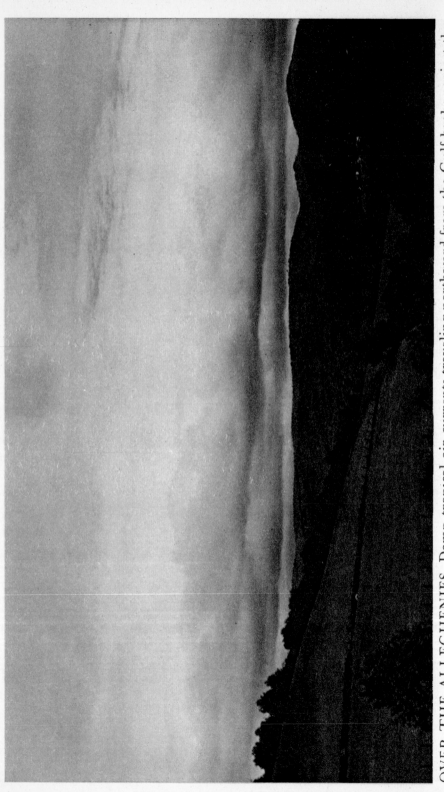

OVER THE ALLEGHENIES. Damp tropical air currents traveling northward from the Gulf broke against the ridges of the Allegheny Mountains and formed this cloud formation. As the air rose to climb over the summits, it cooled and upon reaching the dew point was converted into the Stratocumulus clouds seen in the lower part of this picture. The clouds above are Altostratus.

into snow. It takes from 8 to 12 inches of snow to make the liquid equivalent of one inch of rain.

Where strong vertical currents exist, falling raindrops may be picked up and carried back into air which is below the freezing point. Freezing into small pellets, they fall through humid areas, picking up more moisture. They may then again

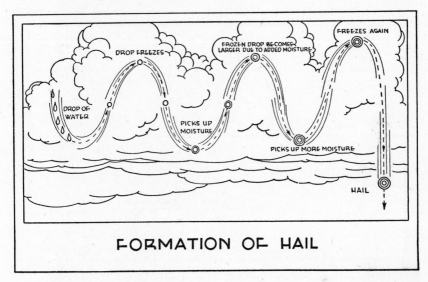

FORMATION OF HAIL

be caught by rising currents and raised upward, and after this process has been repeated several times the pellets become so heavy that they fall to the earth in the form of hail. Hail is almost always associated with thunderstorms.

In the winter rain may form at a higher altitude, which because of a temperature inversion is warmer than the freezing air at a lower altitude. This rain, falling into the freezing air below, turns into solid ice particles known as sleet. Sleet may also result when snow passes through a warm stratum, melts, and later passes through a lower cold stratum and freezes.

There are times when the earth and the adjacent atmosphere are at or slightly below the freezing point, and an inversion of temperature exists, permitting an upper stratum to be above freezing. If precipitation occurs in the upper layer, the resulting rain will freeze and stick to everything it strikes on the ground, covering it with ice. The frozen deposit is known as glaze. It is under similar conditions that ice forms on air-

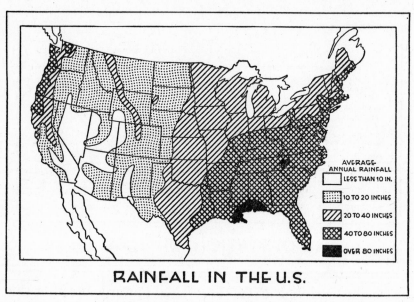

AVERAGE
ANNUAL RAINFALL
LESS THAN 10 IN.
10 TO 20 INCHES
20 TO 40 INCHES
40 TO 80 INCHES
OVER 80 INCHES

RAINFALL IN THE U.S.

craft in flight, presenting a serious hazard to navigation. A later section will be devoted to aircraft icing conditions.

The process of precipitation often asserts itself in violent demonstrations such as thunderstorms, sleet storms, blizzards, etc. Even in some of its milder forms it always makes itself known, as the woman who is caught in the rain with a new hat, or the man whose car is stuck in a snow drift, can testify. On the other hand, evaporation goes on unobtrusively, with few persons aware of its existence. Yet these two processes, in the long run, exactly equal each other—another phase of nature's great system of checks and balances. It is astounding to realize that the amount of precipitation occurring over the world averages about 16,000,000 tons per second. One inch of rainfall weighs 100 tons to the acre, or 64,000 tons per square mile. Back and forth, into and out of the atmosphere—so it has been since time began—so it will be until time ends.

Although there are several ways of classifying fogs, they can all be placed under one of two headings, *radiation fog*

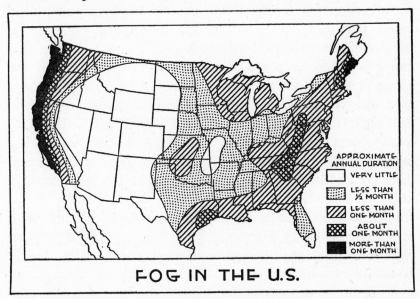

FOG IN THE U.S.

and *advection fog*. Radiation fog is found when humid air is cooled through radiation and advection fog is found when warm humid air is cooled by moving over colder surfaces. The resulting fogs are the same, the difference being only in the way they are formed.

Radiation fog, sometimes called summer fog or land fog because it occurs on land in the summer or autumn, forms on clear, cool nights when there is little or no wind. During the day and early night, the atmosphere may become relatively humid through evaporation. During the night, the air and the earth lose heat rapidly to the clear sky through radiation. If enough heat is lost, and the dew point is reached, condensation into fog will take place at or near the surface of the earth. This type of fog usually does not extend very high and "burns off" by about 9 or 10 A M the following day. The conditions under which you may expect radiation fog are on clear summer and autumn nights when the air is warm and humid.

Advection fog results when air that is warm and humid moves over a cold surface of land or water. The warm humid air passing over the cold surface is cooled, and, when the dew point is reached, condensation into fog occurs. This is the cause of the fog off the Grand Banks and on the west coast that was mentioned in connection with the Gulf Stream and other ocean currents. The warm damp air from the south passing over the colder water from the north is cooled below its dew point and fog is formed in those regions. Advection fog may also be caused by a mass of cold air moving under a mass of warm humid air (cold front). Advection fog is also known as winter or sea fog, depending upon where and when it occurs. When an extremely heavy fog exists to the extent that you cannot see forward or upward, the condition is said to be one of *zero-zero ceiling* and *visibility*.

Visibility is defined as the greatest distance at which conspicuous objects can be seen and identified by eyesight alone. Visibility is affected by the amount of moisture and foreign matter in the air. Since water vapor itself is invisible, it must condense into some of its visible forms such as mist, fog, rain, etc., to affect visibility. Although foreign matter is important in this connection, the conditions arising out of condensation are the chief causes of poor visibility. It may be said that visibility is inversely proportional to the relative humidity. Foreign matters affecting visibility are smoke and dust, and in some localities smoke which has united with moisture to form a condition called smog. Visibility is given in weather reports in miles or fractions of miles, and is of paramount interest to the pilot.

CLOUDS

Clouds can very appropriately be called the "signposts of the skyways." Every phase of weather, except total clearness, is shown by a cloud of some kind. To the skilled weather man, the understanding of the different cloud forms and their significance is a great help in forecasting. It is difficult for the amateur, however, to identify the various types and to achieve accuracy in determining their meaning. Clouds appear in an infinite variety of shapes and combinations. Their height varies with the type, with latitude, the season of the year and the nature of the land below. Trying to predict weather by clouds alone will not give consistently accurate results. Coordinated with other weather information, however, cloud analysis can be very helpful to the pilot. When a little interest, some unconscious knowledge and a great deal of observation and practice are brought to bear, the clouds have a message for the flyer.

The greatest contributing cause of clouds is vertical convection. Convection may be either thermal or mechanical. Thermal convection is the rising of heated air. Mechanical convection is caused by air turbulence, by air forced up the slopes of mountains or lifted by underrunning currents of colder air.

When air rises, it cools either adiabatically (as has been shown) or by losing heat to the surrounding atmosphere. At some point in its rise, the air temperature has been lowered so that it equals the dew point—that is, the air has become saturated. At the level at which this occurs, condensation starts and clouds are formed.

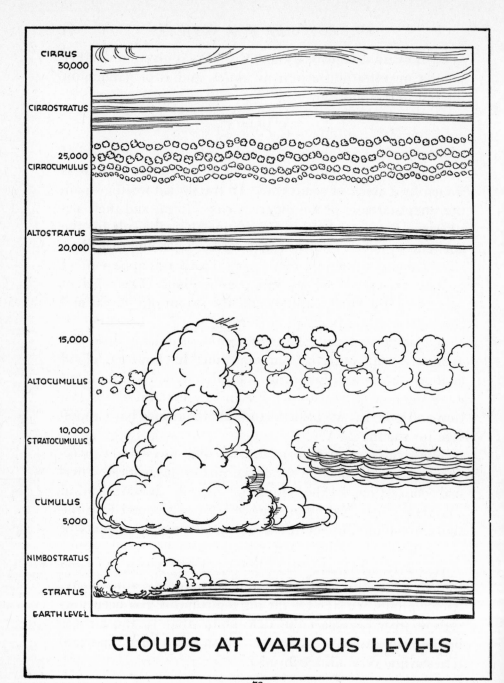

CIRRUS
30,000

CIRROSTRATUS

25,000
CIRROCUMULUS

ALTOSTRATUS
20,000

15,000

ALTOCUMULUS

10,000
STRATOCUMULUS

CUMULUS
5,000

NIMBOSTRATUS

STRATUS

EARTH LEVEL

CLOUDS AT VARIOUS LEVELS

Clouds are classified according to their form and appearance. Consideration is also given to the physical processes forming them and the heights at which they appear. There are ten basic cloud types commonly used and these are divided into families according to the altitude at which they are commonly found.

Family A are the high clouds whose lower levels average 20,000 feet. In this group are the cirrus, the cirrocumulus and the cirrostratus.

In family B, we have the middle clouds, altocumulus and altostratus. These clouds range from 20,000 feet down to 6500 feet.

The low clouds are family C, whose tops are below 6500 feet, with bases close to the ground. Stratocumulus, stratus and nimbostratus make up this group.

The fourth group is family D, clouds with vertical development. These clouds, cumulus and cumulonimbus, may extend from 1500 feet upward to 20,000 feet.

As highest of all clouds, it is fitting that the *Cirrus* (Ci) come first in any cloud discussion. The word comes from the Latin meaning "curl" or "ringlet," but cirrus clouds appear in many other shapes. We find them in the form of white featherlike plumes, scrolls, isolated tufts, and as delicate white cobwebs.

Cirrus clouds also appear as lines drawn clear across a blue sky and as short curved lines ending in tufts commonly known as "mare's tails," which they resemble somewhat. All of these forms have two things in common, one of which is responsible for the other. They fly at a height of six, seven and even eight miles where the temperature is from 50 to 90 degrees F below zero. Because of this extreme cold cirrus are always made up entirely of small ice crystals. At this height these clouds are very thin and when they cross the sun hardly diminish its brightness. As long as they can be seen good weather prevails.

Unfortunately, the good weather is then but temporary for the cirrus is an almost infallible warning of coming bad weather. A few strands of cirrus have little significance. They may be the condensation from a local disturbance or a remnant of a past storm. But if the cirrus are quite pronounced and gradually thicken toward the western horizon, merging into a formless sheet of cirrostratus cloud, it means that bad flying weather will appear, sometimes in eight, usually in twelve, often in twenty-four and occasionally in forty-eight hours. When cirrus clouds appear it means that off to the south or west, perhaps a thousand miles away, warm air has left the ground and is rising up over a long wedge of cold air. Forced along the cold air layer it rises higher and higher as it travels northeastward with the prevailing movement of the atmosphere. As the warm air rises it condenses into clouds at various levels along its path. The last cloud formed is the cirrus which becomes the first one we see as the entire formation moves toward us from the south and west. The normal progression of clouds is cirrus, cirrostratus, altostratus, stratus, and nimbostratus, all gradually lowering as they appear. Rain usually starts with the altostratus, continuing with the stratus and then becoming steady with the nimbostratus of the storm center. This storm warning cloud sequence will be brought out again when we come to frontal formations.

Cirrocumulus (Cc) clouds are small globular masses with either very light or no shadows. The average height is about 22,000 feet, but they may appear as low as 10,000 or as high as 35,000 feet. They are often arranged in groups or lines, but oftener in ripples like sand on a seashore. If they appear alone it is nearly always as a fair weather cloud dissolving in the morning to leave a clear blue sky. Often, however, they merge into the stratified cirrostratus which will shortly bring the bad weather of the low pressure area. Commonly called "mackerel sky," because of its resemblance to the pattern on the backs of certain species of mackerel, this formation is the result of upper air instability. This cloud is rare.

Second in sequence after cirrus in predicting a coming storm is the *cirrostratus* (Cs). The cirrostratus are usually attached to the cirrus. They are merely a thickening continuation of the cirrus in the west, but usually do not fly quite so high. Averaging about 30,000 feet, and also composed of ice crystals, they form a thin whitish veil presenting the appearance of a milky haze. Because of its thinness the sun and the moon shine through the haze, producing halo phenomena. If these clouds lower rapidly it is only a question of a few hours until precipitation begins.

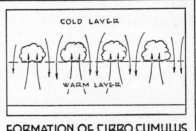

FORMATION OF CIRRO CUMULUS AND ALTO CUMULUS CLOUDS

Commonly known as "sheep herd" cloud, the *Altocumulus* (Ac) fair weather clouds appear after the rain has passed. They are globular masses, white or grayish, arranged in groups or lines, and often packed closely together. Usually appearing around 10,000 to 15,000 feet they are larger and thicker than the cirrocumulus which they resemble. These clouds are also the result of upper air instability.

Next in order of storm warning clouds are the *altostratus* (As). Like cirrus and cirrostratus, which they follow, they are a stratified cloud resulting from warm air overrunning cold air. They appear as a thick sheet of more or less gray or bluish color. These clouds are similar to cirrostratus but lower, thicker and darker. The sun and the moon show through very dimly and without halo phenomena. The average height is about 20,000 feet but they have a wide range of from 6000 to 32,000 feet. Rain or snow may fall from altostratus, but when precipitation becomes heavy, the clouds usually lower and thicken to become nimbostratus or rain clouds.

Stratocumulus (Sc) clouds form in a layer of dark rolls or dark globular masses. Often, when in the form of rolls, they are so close together that the edges join and they have a wavy appearance. Stratocumulus may be distinguished from nimbostratus by their lumpy or rolling appearance, and by the fact that they generally do not tend to bring rain. These clouds are the result of instability of the air in lower levels.

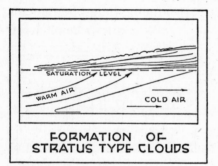

FORMATION OF STRATUS TYPE CLOUDS

Stratus (St), from the Latin, meaning "spread out," are a uniform layer of cloud resembling fog, but not resting on the ground. Nevertheless they are always found at low levels, averaging around 1000 feet. They are completely formless and very difficult to illustrate. Rain can fall from stratus in the form of a light drizzle. These clouds are formed by the lifting of relatively warm humid air, by underrunning cold air, and by warm air flowing over cold air.

In our cloud storm sequence, the altostratus thicken and settle, becoming the *nimbostratus* (Ns) or rain clouds, a thick, nearly uniform layer of shapeless gray. Typically storm clouds, they usually give forth steady rain or snow, and appear around 1000 feet.

Poets or artists proclaim the beauty of the *cumulus* (Cu), or "wool pack" clouds. Cumulus means "heap" in Latin. These are large domelike clouds with flat bases, often of great

beauty and highly photo-
genic. Cumulus are purely
convectional clouds, and
form in cold air masses,
often over mountain ridges.
They are fair weather
clouds. Appearing after a
storm has passed they usually
mean a clear spell. If the

**FORMATION OF
CUMULO TYPE CLOUDS**

summer afternoon cumulus clouds do not decrease in size as
evening approaches, showers can be expected during the
night. They range in height from one thousand to ten thousand feet, averaging about 5000 feet.

The outgrowth of strong convectional currents, the *cumulonimbus* (Cb), has violent currents within it. Nimbus means
rainstorm in Latin and this name tends toward understate-
ment. Cumulonimbus clouds are commonly known as "thun-
derheads." One can watch them build up into huge masses,
boiling and churning, storing up violence and meanness.
Lightning, thunder, hail, wind and heavy showers come from
cumulonimbus. The base is flat and dark, hardly distinguish-
able, under most circumstances, from nimbostratus. While
the base is low, the top can extend many thousands of feet
into the air. These clouds form at the meeting place of a
warm air mass and a cold air mass, or along mountain ridges.
When the cold air pushes under the warm air the differences
in temperature cause the fierce upward currents. Their violence exists throughout their volume and pilots are well-
advised to stay away from them.

Cumulonimbus clouds are often the outgrowth of the beautiful and harmless cumulus. Under conditions of strong vertical convection, along mountain ridges and on the wind
shift line, cumulus clouds often swell and darken to become

cumulonimbus. These are the thickest of all clouds, ranging in depth commonly from 1 to 3 miles, and occasionally, in tropical regions, even to 8 or 9 miles. Generally speaking it is inadvisable to try to fly over them.

In addition to the type of clouds, the weather man reports the amount of sky cover in one of four different degrees. *Clear* means that less than one-tenth of the sky has clouds. *Scattered clouds* is a condition of cloud coverage of from one-tenth to five-tenths. *Broken clouds* are from five-tenths to nine-tenths and *overcast* means that more than nine-tenths of the sky is covered by clouds.

The height of the lower level of the clouds is called the *ceiling*. It is said to be unlimited when there is no cloudiness below 9751 feet. This figure is not as arbitrary as it may first appear. The hypothetical point for determining unlimited ceiling is 10,000 feet. Up to 5000 feet, the ceiling is measured in 100 foot intervals; above 5000 feet, safety permits the ceiling to be measured in 500 foot intervals such as 7000, 7500, 8000 feet, etc. Using this system a ceiling reported as 9000 feet would actually be anywhere between 8751 feet and 9250 feet. If the ceiling were reported to be 10,000 feet, the base of the clouds would be between 9751 feet and 10,250 feet. Therefore, with 500 foot divisions, the standard unlimited ceiling of 10,000 feet starts at 9751 feet.

The altitude of the ceiling is usually determined by estimation which requires considerable experience and practice. It is determined by actual measurement when making regular balloon observations for upper air data, on the basis of the length of time it takes the helium-filled balloon to disappear from sight. Knowing the rate of rise of the balloon, and observing the time it takes to reach the base of the clouds, one may readily compute the height of the ceiling. When the ceiling is low smaller-sized ceiling balloons are sent aloft for

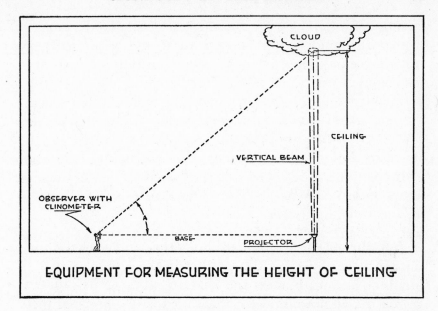

EQUIPMENT FOR MEASURING THE HEIGHT OF CEILING

special reports. At night, a light called a ceiling projector, is directed straight up at the base of the clouds. The observer, at a known distance away from the projector, measures the angle between the horizontal and the line between himself and the spot of light in the clouds. Knowing the distance between himself and the projector, the observer can compute the height of the ceiling.

11

AIR MASS SIGNIFICANCE

THE illustration on page 28 shows the sources of the various air masses affecting the weather in the United States. In ascribing to an air mass the characteristics of its "source" region, we do not mean that the air actually originated there without ever having been anywhere else. Air, as has already been emphasized, is continually in circulation. What is meant is that the air has slowed up temporarily, long enough to acquire the definite characteristics of certain areas.

Obviously an air mass that has spent some time in the north will be colder than one from the tropics. And it is just as apparent that an air mass that has been a long time over the ocean will contain more water than one whose source region is over the continent. Accordingly we would expect an air mass from the northern continent to be cold and dry. This area is almost entirely covered with ice and snow. Coupled with this, the area is protected by mountains on the west so that none of the moist and warmer Pacific air gets in. The characteristics of this air mass are responsible for a great portion of our United States weather, particularly in the north and east.

The air that is conditioned over the Northern Pacific is

cold, yet warmer than that of the polar continental air. This maritime Pacific air is high in moisture content and plays an important part in determining the weather of the entire West Coast. With its high moisture content it is responsible for precipitation on the West Coast and the Rocky Mountain section. After it passes over the Rockies, it is warmed adiabatically and becomes warm and clear. Fog found on the West Coast is from this air mass.

On the eastern side of the continent there is another polar maritime air mass from the Northern Atlantic. It is a relatively infrequent visitor to the United States, because it enters contrary to the prevailing wind direction. When it does penetrate, however, bringing with it cold air, wet and dense, it is an important factor in the weather of the Northeast United States. It is known as the "Nor'easter" to natives of New England.

The Gulf of Mexico is the breeding place of an air mass of great importance to United States weather. Since the air here is warm it has a great capacity for absorbing water, particularly at the surface. This gives it an "unstable" quality that is responsible for the development of strong vertical currents.

The air mass formed over the Middle Atlantic in the region of the Sargasso Sea has characteristics so similar to Gulf air that these two masses can be discussed together. Bringing to the United States their plentiful supply of moisture, they are responsible for a great part of the precipitation and cloudiness in the eastern half of the United States.

The hot air from continental Mexico is dry and enters the United States infrequently. Also the air mass of the Middle North Pacific is a relatively unimportant visitor. Although possessing characteristics similar to those of the Gulf and Middle Atlantic air masses, Pacific maritime is not nearly so effective in developing disturbances.

While air masses generally carry their source characteristics with them as they move into this country, they undergo certain modifications, usually near the earth. These modifications are caused either thermally or mechanically.

Thermal modifications occur when the air mass passes over a cooler or a warmer area. The bottom of the air mass is cooled or warmed as the case may be. In passing over bodies of water or dry ground an air mass changes in water vapor content. It will either absorb or expel water, depending on the condition.

Mechanical modifications are caused by turbulence, by air being lifted over land irregularities, or by sinking.

Because of the frequency of thermal modifications, temperature inversion is very common in air masses.

Let us consider an example. While the following phenomena may, and probably do, happen just as outlined, again it must be mentioned that this is an ideal condition. The theory follows accepted patterns and the air masses chosen to illustrate the principles do meet frequently as shown. The only qualification is that in nature there are countless details and complications.

We will return to our Polar Continental air mass in Northern Canada and Alaska. Also we will take our Tropical Maritime air mass from the Gulf of Mexico. Using the symbols for brevity, the northern cold dry air mass is cP, and the southern air mass, warm and wet, is mT.

The air mass cP brings what is known as a "cold wave." As it moves southward into the United States, it becomes warmer and therefore can hold more water, which it absorbs from the Great Lakes. Passing on to be lifted over the Allegheny Mountains, it gives up some of this moisture in the form of clouds and precipitation. By this time the bottom, at least, of the air mass has undergone considerable change.

It is now over a different kind of country and tends to become agitated.

The air mass mT leaves the Gulf on its trip northward. Because of its high relative humidity it does not have to be lifted very high or cooled very much to reach the dew point. Naturally, going farther north it cools. In addition to this, when it is lifted mechanically over the Appalachians it cools adiabatically. Condensation and precipitation result. With its normally unstable nature to start with, it is a pretty touchy animal, and continues in this state as it moves northward.

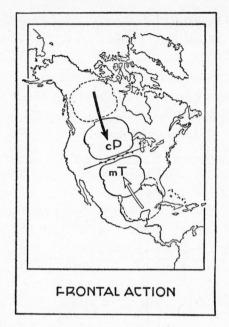

FRONTAL ACTION

At this point we have two masses of air of widely varying characteristics approaching each other head on. Several things can happen. These two masses may meet head on with equal pressure, neither of them gaining nor losing, with a "fight it out on this line if it takes all summer" attitude. What usually occurs, however, is that either the cold air mass or the warm air mass predominates. In either case the warm air is lifted up over the cold air and a definite line of discontinuity exists between them. This line of discontinuity is called a *front*. If the warm air is stronger it pushes over the cold air, forcing it backward and resulting in what is known as a "warm front." If the cold air is stronger it pushes under the warm air and forces the warm air back. This is called a "cold front," the same as the popular "cold wave." There is a clash or battle regardless of which type of front develops, but the cold front is much more violent. Either way the warm air, being lighter than the cold dense air, is forced to higher altitudes, and therefore cools adiabatically. When it reaches the altitude where the dew point is reached, condensation occurs and clouds form. At a later stage with continuing condensation we have rain or snow.

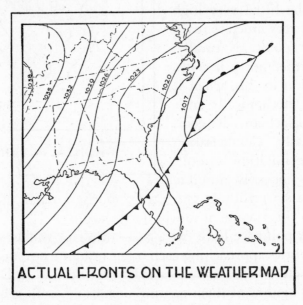

ACTUAL FRONTS ON THE WEATHER MAP

Therefore in frontal formations we can expect to find shifting winds, changes in temperatures, clouds and different forms of precipitation. Atmospheric fronts are sloping surfaces, and the line on a weather map indicating a front is merely where this sloping surface meets the earth.

The slope of the cold front is usually much steeper than that of a warm front. The air forming a cold front assumes a rounded shape called a *squall head*. It assumes this rounded shape owing to the fact that at the earth's surface the air is retarded by friction, while above there is nothing to retard it except the warm air it is pushing back.

The approach of a cold front is heralded by darkening of the horizon to the west and north. The ceiling lowers rapidly and rain falls, usually with high wind, depending on the magnitude of the difference in temperature. The air cools off and thunderstorms are likely to appear, particularly if the cold front is pushing back Tropical Gulf air. Tornadoes are the result of marked cold fronts meeting tropical air. Fog may

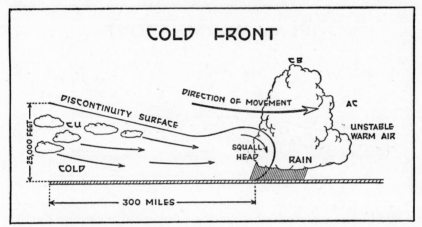

form and, in winter, ice. The wind changes from a southerly or southwesterly direction to a northwesterly direction from which the name *windshift line,* that every old pilot knows, comes from. This is also called the *squall line* and the thunderstorm is known as a *line squall.*

After the passage of the front, clearing is rapid and a marked rise in pressure is noted. Clouds of cumulus and stratocumulus formation are found after the passing of the cold front, and usually fair weather.

Due to the prevalence of high winds, low ceilings, precipitation, strong vertical currents and the likelihood of ice or thunderstorms, cold fronts should be avoided by pilots.

It has already been said that cold fronts assert themselves more violently than warm fronts. One reason for this is the steepness of the slope of the cold front as compared with that

of the warm front. Looking at the illustration on page 85 of
the ideal cold front, the slope is shown reaching 25,000 feet
in about 300 miles, or a slope of about 1 to 60. On the other
hand a warm front has a much more gradual slope. In the diagram the slope of a warm front is shown reaching 25,000 feet
in 1000 miles or a slope of 1 to 200. The figures are average
and can vary greatly.

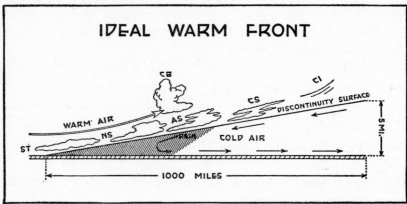

Owing to the gradual slope the temperature change during
warm front conditions may be relatively gradual. Also the
wind discontinuity may not be pronounced. Rain or snow
usually descends from the altostratus clouds after the cirrus
clouds have passed on. This rain continues until the front has
passed the surface. The rain falling from the warm air above
the discontinuity surface down into the cold air often causes
clouds in the latter. The sequence of clouds cannot be noted
by an observer on the ground, consequently it is difficult to
identify warm fronts. The chief danger to a pilot is the sud-
denness with which these lower clouds form when warm air is
overrunning cold. Every experienced pilot has seen rain coming from high altostratus quickly form into lower clouds, thus
reducing the ceiling and visibility.

Warm stable air from continental Mexico has very little

moisture and therefore involves little condensation and that only at high altitudes. On the other hand the warm, wet, unstable air from the Gulf and Atlantic requires but slight lifting to disgorge its torrents. The ascent of this air over the cold wedge becomes violent enough to produce thunderstorms. This tropical maritime air is responsible for the greatest percentage of thunderstorms in the Appalachian Mountains. If the synoptic chart shows the presence of this type of air in the Alleghenys in summer, thunderstorms can be expected during the heat of the day.

Note the diagram of a warm front and see the usual cloud formations. All along the line of discontinuity, as the warm air keeps climbing, clouds of different types keep forming. This is because of the continual drop in temperature as the air moves higher, cools adiabatically and results in condensation. The different types of clouds aid the forecaster in locating these fronts. Far ahead of the line where the warm front meets the ground are cirrus clouds which are the sign of an oncoming warm front. This usually means that rain or snow will come within 24 hours as the clouds change from cirrus to cirrostratus, altostratus, stratus, and nimbostratus with the approach of the front.

In the movement of air masses fronts build up, go through their cycle and die out. The process of building up fronts is called *frontogenesis*. When fronts have reached the point where they die out it is called *frontolysis*. There are certain areas where it is common for fronts to form, other locations where they meet with other fronts, and other places where they die out. The entire scheme with its twisting and turning moves across the country as a part of the general west to eastward movement of the atmosphere.

One of the interesting phenomena of the meeting of fronts is the forming of cyclones and anticyclones.

12

CYCLONES AND ANTICYCLONES

CYCLONES and *anticyclones* with local surface winds form the secondary circulation of the atmosphere, and, although related to the great regional highs and lows, they should not be confused with them.

A cyclone may be defined as the system of winds that accompany and surround any considerable area of low pressure. It must not be confused with the violent but short-lived storm that people call a cyclone, but which is actually a tornado or "twister." True, a tornado is an area of low pressure, but the conditions are different and it is a rare occurrence, while the passage of the true cyclones and anticyclones makes up our everyday weather. An anticyclone is the system of winds that accompany and surround any considerable area of high pressure. On the synoptic chart, or weather map, cyclones are called "lows" and anticyclones are called "highs." Low pressure areas are also known as depressions.

Because their passage brought changes in pressure, and therefore changes in weather, the movement of the "highs" and "lows" until recently was the most important factor in forecasting. For years meteorologists had been telling us what our weather would be because they knew that low pressure areas brought one kind of weather and high pressure areas brought other kinds. There was, however, no definite understanding of just what caused these peculiar phenomena. There have been various theories offered, but with the knowledge derived from the study of air mass movement and fronts, it is now pretty well understood that cyclones are formed, at least at the earth's surface, as a result of the meeting of fronts. Therefore the location, movement, and characteristics of the fronts become the most important factors in forecasting.

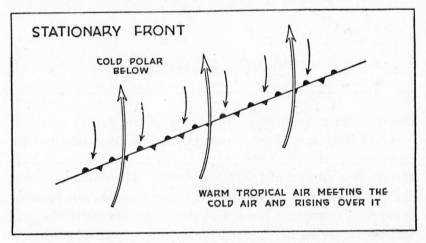

To understand how cyclones can be formed by the action of fronts let us return to our example of cold polar air meeting warm tropical air. It has already been shown how either a cold front or warm front is caused by either a cold air mass or warm air mass forcing the other back. While a state of absolute equilibrium rarely, if ever, exists, sometimes the fronts are comparatively well balanced in intensity. When this occurs, they remain fairly stationary. But nature will not long permit inaction or stagnation, so something must give. Somewhere along the line of discontinuity the front starts to break. This may be aided by some ground inequality such as a lake,

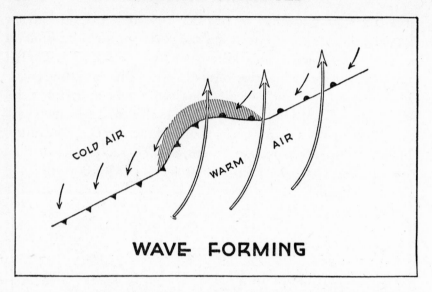

WAVE FORMING

desert or mountain, or by the effect of the earth's rotation.

The illustration shows a normal line of discontinuity in a state of equilibrium. Cold polar air has met warm tropical air along a line approximately NE and SW. The warm air meets the cold air and flows right on up over the cold air. Neither is exerting a stronger force than the other. Owing to the prevailing winds in the United States this whole formation is moving generally from the west slightly northeastward.

Now, in the illustration above, we see a bulge in our line of continuity. The warm air still flows up over the cold air but in the center it has started to push the cold air back. Precipitation has begun and the cold air is being forced around the bulge as shown by the dark arrows. The symbols representing fronts are standard symbols used on printed charts and are shown in a later figure.

Once the warm air has started to push the cold air backward it gains momentum like water spilling over a breaking dam. By this time we have a readily recognizable warm front

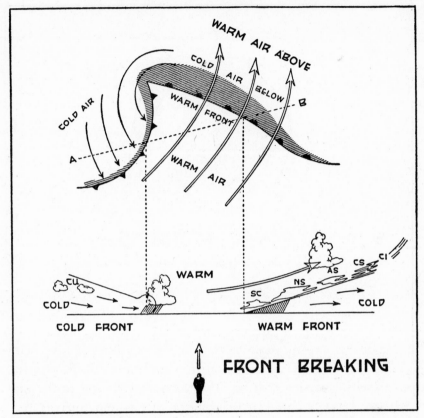

with its attendant precipitation. But the warm air rushing out tends to leave an area of low pressure behind it and this accelerates the cold front in the western section. The cold front gains speed because of the tendency for cold air to rush in to fill the space emptied by warmer air.

In order to give some idea of what this would look like on the ground, suppose you were standing looking in the direction of the arrow in the diagram above. You would see the warm front on the right closely followed by the cold front on the left. The dotted lines connect the same places on the top view and side view of the fronts where they would

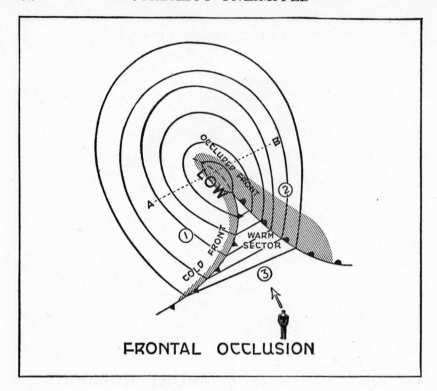

FRONTAL OCCLUSION

be touching the earth at the time of the observation.

It can be seen that our original front has bent in two and now instead of one inactive front we have two smaller but active ones. But our cold front is still moving faster than the warm front and it catches up. When it does it causes a secondary frontal formation called an *occlusion*. An occlusion is represented by the center section in the illustration above. The air is cold in both sections 1 and 2, since they are of the same origin. But because of the changes that have taken place one is probably colder than the other. The air in area 3 is warm and is called the warm sector. Now, if the air in area 1 happens to be colder than that of area 2, when the fronts occlude, area 1 (cold air) will continue to push under

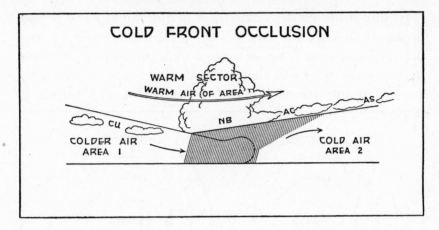

the air in area 2. The warm air of area 3 will be carried aloft between the fronts.

This is called a cold front occlusion, and the figure represents the way these different air masses would look along the line AB if seen by the observer.

On the other hand, if the air of area 1 is warmer than the cold air of area 2, when the fronts occlude, area 1 air will climb over area 2 air. This is shown in the warm front diagram below.

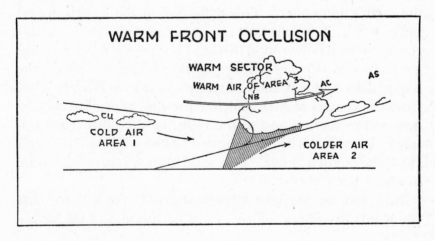

In our study of the circulation of the atmosphere it was brought out that the flow of air is toward an area of low pressure and away from an area of high pressure. The winds in a cyclone (low) will then blow inward toward the center, and in an anticyclone (high) the winds will blow outward,

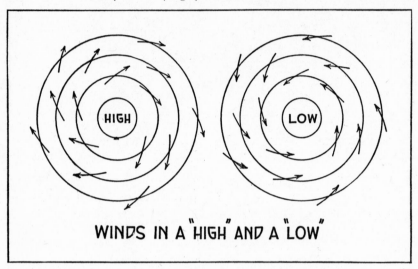

WINDS IN A "HIGH" AND A "LOW"

away from the center. In Chapter 4 it was brought out that the centrifugal force of the earth's rotation caused a deflection of the earth's atmosphere. This deflection of the earth's atmosphere results in a definite wind pattern for the earth. It also results in the winds around high and low pressure areas having a whirling or twisting motion. As the illustration shows, the winds then will not blow directly toward or directly away from the centers of high and low pressure areas, but will be deflected to the left and to the right. In the northern hemisphere the winds will flow counterclockwise into a "low" and clockwise out of a "high." This wind motion is reversed in the southern hemisphere.

Now look at the next illustration and you will see that the winds have been added to our occlusion and we have a

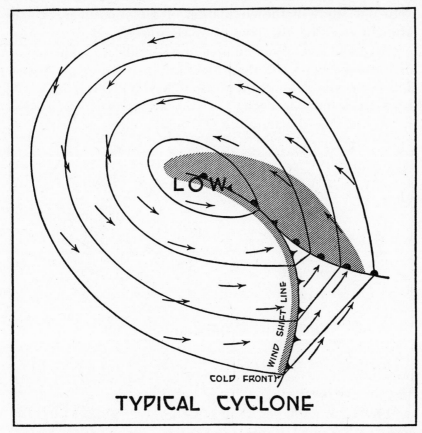

TYPICAL CYCLONE

typical cyclone. The process of cyclones forming is called *cyclogenesis.*

The relation of wind direction to high and low pressure areas is brought out in Buys-Ballot's law, which states that if you stand facing the wind in the northern hemisphere, the low pressure area will be on your right and the high pressure area will be on your left. This also is reversed, of course, in the southern hemisphere.

As the "highs" and "lows" approach and pass over a given point it can be seen how, as the pressure changes, the wind changes direction. Winds that shift their direction counterclockwise are called *backing winds*. Winds that shift their direction clockwise are called *veering winds*.

In speaking of the flow of winds around a "high" and a "low," as far as we are concerned they are surface phenomena. But the curious student is going to wonder where the winds come from and where they go in order that this spiral motion may exist. The illustration will complete the mental picture.

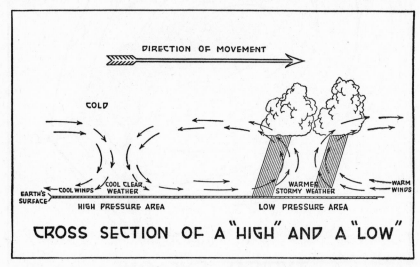

CROSS SECTION OF A "HIGH" AND A "LOW"

With the general movement of air masses in mind and the way in which they meet to form fronts, one can understand why cyclones form fairly regularly in certain regions of the United States. Then, considering the prevailing west to eastward movement of the winds of the United States, it is easy to visualize the birth, life and death of the cyclone's cycle. Cyclones are named according to the region in which they first appear. The passage of the cyclones affecting the climate of the United States is shown in the following diagram.

The rate of movement of the cyclones, as well as the direction of movement, is practically the same as that of the prevailing winds. It is interesting to note that on account of the prevailing winds airlines require about 15 per cent more time and 15 per cent more gasoline on their westward trips than on their eastward flights. More cyclones occur in winter than in summer, and they also move faster in the winter. The average rate of movement is 30 miles per hour in winter, 21

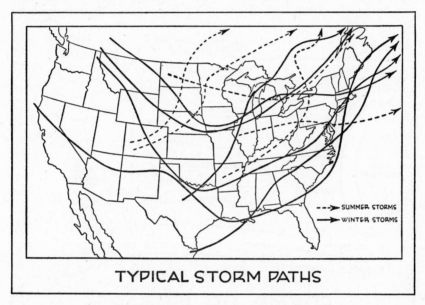

TYPICAL STORM PATHS

miles per hour in summer, and 24 miles per hour in spring and fall. These are only averages, as cyclones may stagnate over an area for several days, or may move as much as 1000 miles in 24 hours.

Cyclones are of two general classes: the tropical and the extratropical, so named because of their location. The tropical cyclone is found in the tropical area between latitude 30 degrees north and latitude 30 degrees south. The extratropical cyclone is found between latitude 30 degrees north and the north pole and between latitude 30 degrees south and the south pole.

The area covered by an extratropical cyclone may be from

400 to 2000 miles across, with an average diameter of 1200 miles. The center of a cyclone is the area of lowest pressure, and while this varies, the average pressure in the center is 29.6 inches, or 1002 millibars. A circle or isobar encloses this center area on the weather map. (Look at illustration on

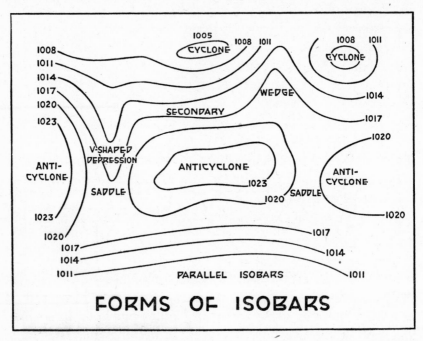

FORMS OF ISOBARS

page 132.) Every 3 millibars, another isobar is drawn, indicating that much change in pressure. Isobars indicating low and high pressure areas vary in shape. The shapes that they assume may be circular, V-shaped, oval, and sometimes nearly straight for some distance. In a cyclone the surface winds (see picture on page 95) blowing inward and upward, cross the isobars at angles of from 15 to 40 degrees. At around 2000 feet the wind velocity usually doubles, and the wind begins to flow nearly parallel to the isobars. As altitude increases, the whirling motion tends to diminish until at about 20,000 feet the winds straighten out and merge into the prevailing west to east winds. The cyclone is a formation of levels below 25,000 feet.

Irregularly shaped isobars have descriptive names as classified by the noted British meteorologist Abercrombie. Little was known about the upper air in his day but he was able to associate weather with the shapes of the isobars.

A *secondary low* is a small area of low pressure on the border of a large or "primary" low. The secondary may develop marked intensity surpassing the parent cyclone. The latter may even disappear.

A *trough* is an elongated area of low barometric pressure.

When the isobars change direction abruptly to form a V-shaped depression this indicates the location of a cold front with its cloud, rain and squalls, followed by a change in wind and then clear cooler weather.

When the isobars bend to form an inverted V this is called a *wedge* and is usually found with lows to the east and to the west. Wedges are nearly always regions of good weather, but are of short duration because of the lows which follow them.

A *saddle* or *col* is a neck of relatively low pressure between two anticyclones. Conditions in the saddle are usually unsettled, sometimes with fog and thunderstorms.

Frequently the isobars on the outer edge of a low appear on the weather map as straight or slightly curved lines between the low and the adjacent high. The kind of weather that prevails depends upon the season, the location of the center of the low and the direction in which the isobars run.

Normally, high winds are more prevalent in low pressure areas than in high pressure areas.

Because of its counterclockwise motion, the winds striking the south and east sides of a cyclone will be coming from the south. Southern winds are naturally warmer and contain a large amount of water vapor. These warm humid winds make the south and east sides of a cyclone warm and cause fog and rain in those quadrants. Almost all types of clouds are present in a cyclone from the high cirrus to the nimbostratus, which is directly responsible for rain and poor visibility. The cyclone is the area of variable weather, inherently so. It usually has cold, warm and occluded front formations in various stages of development. Each type of front causes its own weather changes so that practically any kind of weather can be found in a "low," from the violence of the line squalls in the windshift line (cold front in the low) to the fine weather after its passage.

An anticyclone is in many respects the opposite of a cyclone. An anticyclone, or high, is generally associated with good flying weather. The average pressure in the center of a high is 1036 mbs. which may vary between 1016 and 1050 mbs. The usual shape of a high is in the form of an oval, but the isobars are frequently irregular in shape. As a general rule, an anticyclone is colder than a cyclone. There are two reasons for highs being cooler. They usually form a little further north and also, owing to the general absence of clouds, heat radiation is greater through the clear air.

Although anticyclones are usually associated with fair weather, clouds and precipitation do occur in connection with them. The absolute and relative humidity are both high in the southwest, consequently that is where clouds and precipitation will appear. When clouds are found in the eastern and western boundaries of a high, they are lingering remnants of a cyclone that has just passed, or the beginning of a new cyclonic area.

In general, anticyclones are larger than cyclones, and travel slower. They range from 700 to 2500 miles in diameter, with an average of 2000 miles. Their speed of travel averages 25 miles per hour in winter, 20 miles per hour in summer, and 23 miles per hour in spring and fall. Anticyclones, like cyclones, occur more frequently in winter. The movement across the United States of anticyclones is similar to that of cyclones. Anticyclones move almost directly west to east. As a rule they

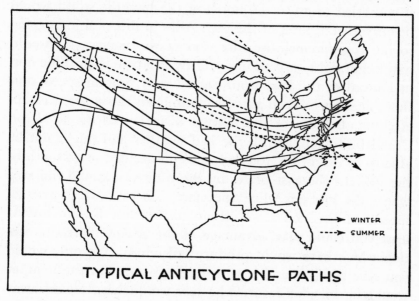

TYPICAL ANTICYCLONE PATHS

form farther north and leave the United States a little farther south than cyclones do. Anticyclones are known by their place of origin, as are cyclones. Compare picture on page 97 with the one above.

In the relation between cyclones and anticyclones, one leads to the other. As a low passes, a high usually follows. While the rule is subject to variation, it is generally true.

As a practical illustration of how a knowledge of cyclonic formations is of help to a pilot, consider a type of question that is common on pilots' examinations. The candidate may be asked, "If you were flying due east, and a low pressure area was on your direct course, would you fly to the north or south of it? Why?" In answering this question, consider the general movement of the low itself and the direction of the winds in a low. We already know that the low would be moving from the west to the northeast, and at a rate of speed up to perhaps 45 miles per hour. Even at 30 miles per hour, if you tried to go to the north of the low, the storm would be on your tail most of the way. Also, in this position, owing to the counterclockwise direction of the winds, you would have them right on your nose. These headwinds, plus the normal speed of the low, would make your ground speed very slow, tending to keep you indefinitely in the storm area. In addition, because of the normal direction of the low, you would be traveling with the bad weather and might not be able to fly out of it. Now suppose you decided to go south of the low. In the first place, by the time you got to the area where the low was when you started, because of its normal speed and direction, it would probably be out of your way. At least you could take advantage of the counterclockwise motion which here would produce tail winds. Not only would you save gasoline and a great deal of time, but the weather would be in your favor. The low would have passed away from your course, and the pressure would probably be increasing to a high. On analysis of the conditions, the answer to the question thus becomes obvious. Go to the south of the low and enjoy a quick, direct, pleasant flight, under good weather conditions.

Meteorology is not an easy subject, but by now the reader should begin to see the interrelationship of all the various processes—how each function fits into its proper place, depending upon the process before it, and building up the next step in the never ceasing cycles of weather. It is difficult to explain any one process separately because of its dependence upon and correlation with all the other factors. To decide which element is the most important or which came first is like trying to answer the question: "Which came first, the chicken or the egg?" All of the steps are important, and it will be necessary to reread certain sections, shuttling the material back and forth in your mind until it becomes clear just how the various factors dovetail and depend upon one another.

13

HAZARDS TO AVIATION

EVEN if thunderstorms were not so important to aviation, they would still demand special attention in any discussion of the weather. They are so stupendous in their development, and so dynamic and potentially destructive that they cannot be ignored. But to aviation they are more than that, they represent one of the greatest hazards to safe aerial navigation.

The thunderstorm is always associated with a cumulonimbus cloud. In this cloud are found strong ascending and descending winds blowing in opposite directions alongside one another. Flying in such a cloud is extremely dangerous and may result in destruction of the airplane by the shearing effect of these winds. Electrical discharges are violent and the hail, which often accompanies these storms, may do irreparable damage. Furthermore the rain is very heavy and the visibility is poor. In addition to all of this there is the likelihood of ice formation. The danger in these storms is proportionate to their size and intensity.

Generally speaking thunderstorms are of two kinds, those caused by local convection and the frontal types developed by the meeting of air masses. The formations of the two types are considerably different but the characteristics are identi-

104

cal. Local convection storms are caused by thermal convection where the ground is heated unevenly, thus forming upward currents, and by mechanical convection where air is forced over a mountain. Frontal thunderstorms can form at cold fronts, warm fronts and occluded fronts; those on a cold front, called line squalls, being the most violent. The main essential for thunderstorm formation is a strong upward current of air. For vertical currents to exist it is necessary that the air be in unstable equilibrium. (Do you remember our discussion of stability and instability of the air and how vertical currents are developed or checked?) A further requirement for thunderstorm intensity is a high moisture content in the air.

As an example of local thermal convection, let's consider the sun heating a plowed field adjacent to a wooded area. The air over the plowed field is heated more than that over the woods and as a result becomes lighter and is forced up by the cooler air around it. As this rising air moves upward it expands and cools adiabatically. It will continue to move upward as long as it is warmer than the surrounding air. If there is a large amount of moisture in the air, it will soon be cooled to its dew point and condensation will occur, forming a cumulus cloud. If convection continues, and the moisture content of the air is high, the cumulus cloud swells and darkens into a cumulonimbus cloud and a thunderstorm is born.

The rate of cooling from the ground to the base of the cloud, where condensation occurs, is at the dry adiabatic rate of 5.5 degrees per thousand feet. As soon as the cloud starts to form, the heat of vaporization is released and the rate of cooling changes to the wet or saturation adiabatic of roughly 2.8 degrees per thousand feet.

As soon as this type of storm starts to travel with the wind it is removed from the source of heat that formed it. The rapid condensation in the cloud serves to prolong it for a time, but unless replenished with more heat, it tends to wear itself out eventually. This is a purely local-type storm, not likely to form at night when the sun no longer heats the ground. The thunderstorm that develops from thermal con-

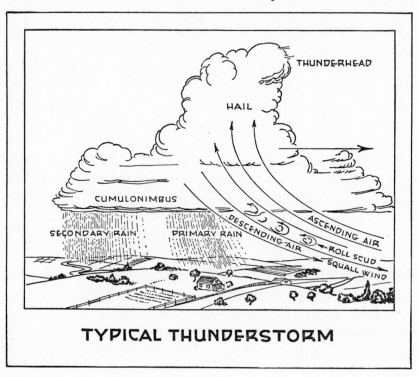

TYPICAL THUNDERSTORM

vection is a seasonal storm occurring most frequently during the summer and early fall.

The magnitude of a thunderstorm depends upon the strength and endurance of the vertical currents and the amount of moisture in the air. The normal shower and the thunderstorm differ only in intensity. A shower becomes a thunderstorm, and is generally recognized by the Weather Bureau as such, when thunder is heard.

It is generally accepted that the breaking up of the drops of water in a cloud by the strong upward currents is the cause of lightning. The velocity and turbulence of the air split and resplit the water drops in such a manner that positive and negative ions of electricity are produced. The smaller droplets, or spray, gain a positive charge of electricity and the air around them a negative charge. The positive ions in the water

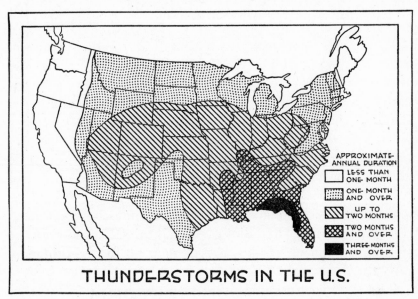

APPROXIMATE
ANNUAL DURATION

LESS THAN
ONE MONTH

ONE MONTH
AND OVER

UP TO
TWO MONTHS

TWO MONTHS
AND OVER

THREE MONTHS
AND OVER

THUNDERSTORMS IN THE U.S.

tend to settle while the negative ions of the free air rise to other parts of the cloud. The earth itself is negatively charged. When the differences in potential between certain areas of the cloud, or between the cloud and the earth become great enough, lightning flashes across the gap in an attempt to restore the electrical balance. This flash is accompanied by a report that we know as thunder.

Because the speed of light and that of sound are entirely different you can estimate how far the storm is away from you by noting the elapsed time between the lightning flash and the resulting thunder. When we see the flash and hear the thunder at the same time, the storm is upon us. If there is an interval the storm is some distance away. The flash from the lightning reaches you instantaneously at the speed of light, 186,000 miles per second. The sound of thunder travels one mile in five seconds. All you have to do is start counting in seconds when the flash appears, and divide by five when you hear the thunder. The result is the distance in miles that you are from the storm.

While lightning does strike aircraft the known instances are rare. Also the observed effects seem to indicate that the airplane was struck solely because it happened to be in the path of the lightning, not because the aircraft attracted the charge. Cases are known where the discharge has burned a clean hole through a wing, leaving the rest of the plane intact. A certain airplane in a formation has been struck while all others were untouched. An associate of mine on patrol had his entire electrical system fused by a bolt, leaving him and the rest of his plane unharmed. Several cases have been reported of damage to radios where lightning has followed the trailing antennae. While cases of damage by lightning are rare, the danger of being struck should not be minimized.

The thunderstorms resulting from mechanical convection start differently but end up with the same type of storm as those of thermal convection. In thermal convection storms the air is unstable to begin with, or is made unstable by the heating of lower levels. In mechanical convection the vertical currents are formed by air being forced over mountains. If the air is stable and fairly dry it rises over the mountain and comes to rest at about the same level on the other side. It rises and cools at the dry adiabatic rate on one side of the mountain, settles and warms on the other side at the same rate, and continues on its way without disturbance.

But if the air is conditionally unstable (turn back to illustration on page 46 showing the lapse rate between the dry and wet adiabatic) and the relative humidity is high, conditions are critically different. The air forced up the mountain unwillingly (because it is heavier than the air around it and therefore stable) is cooled at the dry adiabatic and reaches its dew point part way up. When condensation occurs the cooling rate with altitude changes to the wet adiabatic. The rising air, still being forced upward, is then cooling with altitude at a rate slower than that of the surrounding air. At this rate the rising air reaches a point where it is no longer cooler than the surrounding air, but on the contrary becomes warmer. Then instability results, the vertical currents continue without being forced, and a thunderstorm develops just as with thermal convection, which it now is. This type of storm is also called an *orographical thunderstorm*. These are common in certain mountainous localities where the prevailing winds blow over the mountains regularly. These storms are local because the means of lifting the warm air to form them are local. They tend to die out as they move away from the mountain, the cause of the lifting. But as new fresh air moves up thunderstorm conditions may prevail for long periods in certain mountainous localities.

Frontal types of thunderstorms are formed in the same way as orographical storms or those of mechanical convection. In the case of the frontal storm, however, the warm air is forced up over a mass of cold air which is moving, instead of up

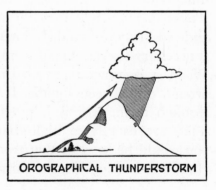

OROGRAPHICAL THUNDERSTORM

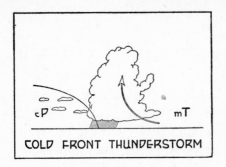

COLD FRONT THUNDERSTORM

over a stationary mountain. These are not local storms, but travel as a part of, and as natural phenomena of the frontal system. As long as the conditions prevail that form the fronts, these storms are continually replenished with the main requirements for thunderstorms, moist and rising air. As they are not directly dependent upon the heat of the sun for the necessary vertical currents, these storms occur just as frequently at night as during the day.

Because they are more severe, the thunderstorms found along cold fronts are better known than those of warm fronts. Their violence comes from the greater speed of the cold front and the steepness of the slope of cold air, which forces the warm air ahead of it to rise sharply. When the cold front is well defined these disturbances may form as a continuous line of thunderstorms known as "line squalls." The front itself, usually occurring in the southeast quadrant of a cyclone, is often referred to as the "squall line" or "windshift line." Cold front thunderstorms are confined to an area about 50 miles wide along the front. There is usually small excuse for a pilot to get caught in a line squall. They are visible far off and can easily be avoided. There are times, however, when it is necessary to cross a cold front in order to complete a flight. When it is necessary to do this the flight should be made around or between squalls. It is not advisable to try to fly through them. Nor is it practical to try to fly over them. They are usually so high that by the time they are seen you would be so close that too much time would be wasted climbing. Besides this, the storm is moving, and even if your

airplane had ceiling enough
to climb over the storm, you
might be far off your course,
and perhaps lost, by the time
you reached sufficient altitude to fly over it. If you cannot get around or between
squalls the most sensible
thing to do is to land, stake

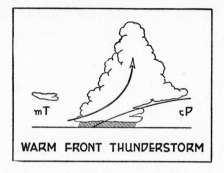

WARM FRONT THUNDERSTORM

your airplane down, wait for the storm to blow over and continue your flight in the good weather in back of the cold front.
The more severe the storm, the quicker it passes.

Owing to the flatter slope and slower movement, the thunderstorms found ahead of warm fronts are not as violent as
those in cold frontal formations. Warm-front thunderstorms,
however, are scattered over a wider horizontal area and are
accompanied by longer periods of poor visibility and rain.

Upper-front or occlusion-type thunderstorms are produced
in the same manner as surface-front thunderstorms. In the
upper-front type there is a layer of cold air underneath the
storm cloud where there is little or no turbulence. Cold-front,
warm-front and convectional thunderstorms have rough air
from the ground to very high levels.

TORNADOES

The most violent and destructive, and yet the briefest of
all storms in this country, is the tornado or "twister," so
called because of its twisting circular motion. In some localities where this type of storm occurs it is called a cyclone but
this is not the proper name for it.

The winds of a tornado blow in a counterclockwise direction around an area of extremely low pressure. The velocity

of the wind and the extent of the pressure drop can only be estimated, for whenever instruments have happened to be in the path of a tornado they were destroyed by the storm itself. The velocity of these winds has been estimated at from 200 to 600 miles per hour, while the storm itself travels from 20 to 50 miles per hour.

The entire life history of a tornado seldom extends over an hour and its path of destruction is usually less than a hundred miles in length and from 100 to 2000 feet in width. Tornadoes are highly localized and at any given place along the path the whole thing is quickly over.

The conditions favoring the development of tornadoes are easily recognizable from the synoptic chart. Tornadoes are closely associated with, and occur under the same conditions that produce the most violent thunderstorms. Therefore they are likely to appear in extratropical cyclones that have a well-defined cold front or windshift line. Cyclones having V-shaped isobars indicate this condition on the weather map. They occur most frequently in the central portion of the Middle West but have been reported from every State in the Union. Despite the indications on the weather map, predicting tornadoes is difficult. Because of their localized nature and short extent most weather men do not attempt to predict tornadoes.

It is obvious that it would be suicidal to fly into a tornado. But the hazard of tornadoes to aircraft is, or should be, small. The most distinctive thing about a tornado is the black funnel-shaped cloud which extends downward from the heavy cloud masses toward the earth's surface. It may or may not touch the earth's surface. It can be easily seen and avoided by the aviator. Tornadoes almost always travel toward the northeast at a fairly steady speed and on a straight course. Under these conditions there is no excuse for an aviator ever to become involved with a tornado.

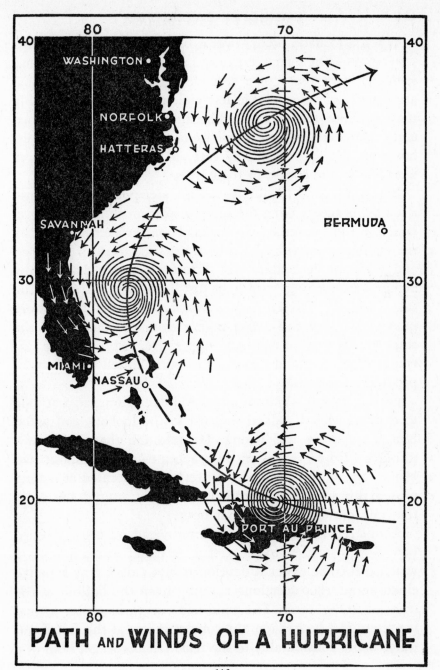

PATH AND WINDS OF A HURRICANE

When a tornado occurs over a body of water it is called a waterspout. The characteristics of a waterspout therefore are identical with those of a tornado, except that waterspouts are usually of considerable less violence. They are probably more common than is realized because most of them are born and die unseen. In the experience of the individual observer, however, they are decidedly rare. Many sailors have never seen one in the course of their lives.

It was my good fortune to see a waterspout on Lake Erie a few years ago. Taking the night boat from Buffalo to Cleveland for the National Air Races, I was awakened early by the rolling of the ship. Unable to get back to sleep I dressed and went on deck about six o'clock. It was a dismal gray September morning, with light just beginning to show in the east. The sky was entirely overcast. Although there were moderate waves and a fair breeze from the motion of the ship, the air seemed dead and oppressive. A bluish haze surrounded the ship and the water to port showed the effects of peculiar air currents.

Feeling that this was an unnatural condition, but not able to explain why, I walked forward to the lookout and asked him if anything was wrong. He told me that just a few minutes before I came on deck a beautiful waterspout had broken up off our port bow. Bitterly disappointed at having missed this spectacle I strolled unhappily around the deck, the only passenger up at that hour.

About ten minutes later, looking ahead off the starboard bow, I was startled to see a strange cloud formation. As I watched it come closer it developed into a dark gray ropelike cloud about 1800 feet long running from the bottom of the overcast to the water. The wind had curved its center so that it presented a bow-shape, the contact points at the cloud and water being considerably to the rear. Unable to get hold of a

AN AMERICAN "TWISTER." Confined almost exclusively to this country, the tornado passes over a place in less than a minute, but is, nevertheless, the most violent and destructive type of storm. Always associated with a severe thunderstorm, it occurs in the warmer months and during the hottest part of the day. Easy to see, they can be readily avoided by aviators.

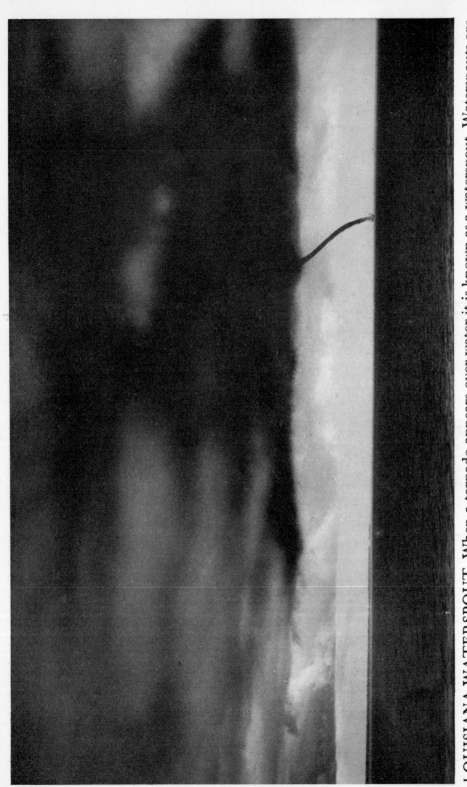

LOUISIANA WATERSPOUT. When a tornado appears over water it is known as a waterspout. Waterspouts are not as rare as is generally supposed, since most of them are born and die unseen at sea. They occur quite frequently in the Gulf of Mexico. This one was caught over Lake Pontchartrain where they occur often during the summer.

camera, I had to be content with watching this phenomenon pass about a half mile from the ship, finally to dissipate about 20 minutes later off in the northeast.

HURRICANES

Cyclones that originate in the tropics are logically called tropical cyclones. These have many characteristics in common with the extratropical cyclone but are usually much more violent. They are known by various names in different parts of the world. The disturbances that originate in the Gulf of Mexico, the Caribbean, and the tropical Pacific and Atlantic Oceans are known as "hurricanes." The word hurricane, of Mayan Indian origin meaning "evil spirit," usually implies a wind of destructive force. In the China Sea the hurricane is known as a typhoon. This is the same as the baguio of the Philippines, and the cyclone of the Indian Ocean. The only differences between these storms is in the names.

Tropical cyclones develop almost exclusively in the belt of equatorial calms called the doldrums. They form only over the water where the intense heat of that area permits the absorption by the air of immense quantities of moisture. The combination of great quantities of heat and moisture results in widespread convection. The prevailing wind system of the earth carries this upward rising mass of warm moist air westward with the trade winds. Being of low pressure, the winds blow counterclockwise toward the center in the northern hemisphere and clockwise toward the center in the southern hemisphere. The speed of movement is very moderate, around 10 or 15 miles an hour. Sometimes such cyclones may even remain stationary for a time. Upon reaching the vicinity of latitudes 20 or 25 they swing away from their westerly direction and turn poleward. Later when they move into the

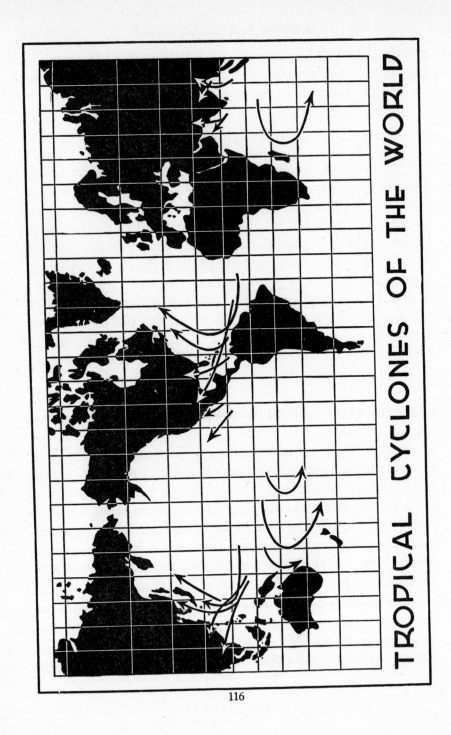

TROPICAL CYCLONES OF THE WORLD

middle latitudes or over land areas they lose some of their intensity, die out, turn eastward, or become modified into extratropical cyclones.

Not all tropical cyclones attain hurricane intensity. Less severe storms are called tropical disturbances and are described as slight, moderate, considerable, etc. The destructive effects of a real hurricane are caused by the high winds, which sometimes reach a velocity over 100 miles per hour. Along the seacoast there is the additional hazard of the sea being raised and blown overland by the force of the wind. This is known as a tidal wave, or more correctly a sea wave, since it has nothing to do with the tides. I went through the hurricane of September, 1926, in Miami. At one time during the night, I stood on the street in water up to my chest with the wind blowing so hard that it was absolutely deafening. The water was blown in from the bay and practically covered the streets of the city. The sky was black and spewed forth torrents of rain with a stinging velocity. The loss of life was enormous and the damage to property ran into many millions. The next morning the sun shone brilliantly on a scene of appalling destruction.

The isobars of a hurricane are nearly circular and close together, which accounts for the high wind velocities. There are no cold or warm fronts in tropical cyclones. In fully developed hurricanes the barometric pressure nearly always falls below 29 inches and there have been many readings below 28 inches. The lowest pressure recorded in the United States was during the 1926 hurricane at Miami when the barometer got down to 27.61 inches. The hurricanes that affect the weather of the United States are those starting in the West Indies. The season when these can be expected is during September, October and early November. During the 1941 season, while I was training Navy pilots at New Orleans, I remember at least four occasions when hurricanes of destructive force were moving in the vicinity.

Hurricane winds increase gradually as the center approaches. At the center there is an area called the "eye of the storm," where there is little or no wind. In this area the skies clear and the sun is visible by day and the stars by night. When a storm passes directly over a place and this center

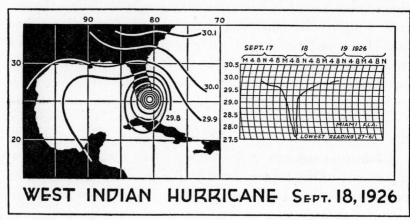

WEST INDIAN HURRICANE Sept. 18, 1926

appears with its clear sky people come out rejoicing that the storm is over. But this is only a respite. Suddenly the winds begin to blow in the opposite direction, leading to the belief that the storm has returned or that another one has come along. This ignorance of the characteristics of the hurricane resulted in additional loss of life in Miami in 1926. The storm passed directly over the city and the second part caught many of the people who thought it was all over.

The diameter of the area of destructive winds in a hurricane varies. The smaller ones do not exceed 25 miles, while in others the diameter may be as much as 400 to 500 miles. The possibility of an airplane pilot becoming involved in such a disturbance is rather remote. Hurricanes are confined to a relatively small area of the United States and their frequency is not very great even during the few weeks in the fall when they are most likely to occur. The excellent hurricane warning system of the Weather Bureau, which operates in peacetime, gives ample notification of any possible disturbance.

But you never can tell about a hurricane. Gulf Coasters, well trained in hurricane lore, like to tell of the inexperienced Long Islander and his cottage. He thought it would be nice to lend a nautical air to his abode, so he bought a barometer. The first day he hung it out it registered a hurricane low. He packed up the fool gadget and wrathfully took it back to the city to demand a refund. That was in September, 1938 —and that was also when his cottage blew away.

ICE

Ice is a menace not only to the outside surfaces of the airplane, but to the engine as well. The public is aware of the fact that ice will build up on the wings and propellers of aircraft but few realize the extreme danger of carburetor icing. Carburetor icing is far more vicious than outside icing because it does not require winter conditions. The prerequisites for the formation of wing and propeller ice are more or less apparent but carburetor icing may occur when the very thought of it seems ridiculous. Before there was very much known about this phenomenon, I had three forced landings, in mid-summer, as a result of carburetor icing.

The conditions necessary for the formation of ice on the outside surface of the airplane are quite definite and obvious. The temperature must be below freezing and there must be moisture in the air in a visible state, such as mist or fog. It would seem that if the temperature were below freezing the water droplets would just go ahead and freeze and present no danger. But it has been found that clouds, even in temperatures below freezing, do not necessarily freeze. Strangely enough clouds have been known to remain in an unfrozen state at temperatures considerably below zero Fahrenheit. But, these clouds are in a very unstable condition and ice will form when something disturbs them. An airplane flying into

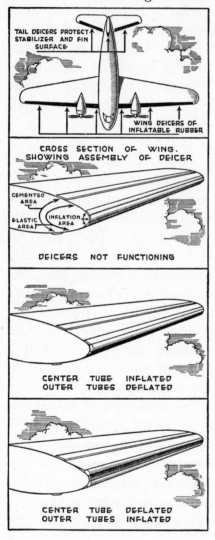

TAIL DEICERS PROTECT STABILIZER AND FIN SURFACE

WING DEICERS OF INFLATABLE RUBBER

CROSS SECTION OF WING. SHOWING ASSEMBLY OF DEICER

CEMENTED AREA

ELASTIC AREA

INFLATION AREA

DEICERS NOT FUNCTIONING

CENTER TUBE INFLATED OUTER TUBES DEFLATED

CENTER TUBE DEFLATED OUTER TUBES INFLATED

such a cloud provides this disturbance and the droplets of water stick to it and freeze. Ice also forms when an airplane flies through a stratum of freezing rain.

When freezing weather exists do not fly through clouds. When the free air temperature is 36 degrees F or below and water droplets are present ice formation can be expected on the aircraft. With droplets of water in the air ice can be expected between the temperatures of 36 degrees and —5 degrees F.

Engineers have been able to combat wing and propeller icing on airplanes, except under extreme conditions, by installing rubber casings on the leading edges of the wings and tail surfaces. Inner tubes inside the casings alternately expand and contract when compressed air is forced into and out of them.

This changes the shape of the airfoil and breaks the ice off as it forms, guarding against the accumulation of a dangerous amount. Ice formation is prevented on the propellers by the release of a mixture of alcohol and glycerine onto the blades. This is called a *slinger de-icer* because the anti-freeze liquid

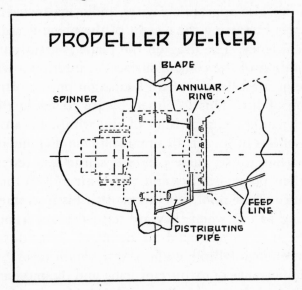

is released near the hub and is carried out to the blades by centrifugal force.

The ice that forms on the outside surfaces of an airplane is of two kinds, clear ice or *glaze,* and *rime ice.* Glaze, formed under the above conditions, is a hard, clear ice that becomes heavy and destroys the aerodynamic qualities of the airfoil by

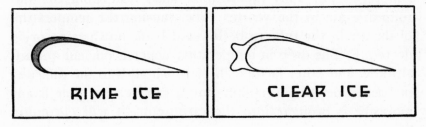

building up into uneven shapes. Rime, an opaque white snowlike ice softer than glaze, builds up evenly on the airfoil. Ice formations on aircraft are usually a mixture of rime and glaze.

In addition to forming on the wings, propeller and tail surfaces, ice also appears on wires, radio masts, instruments, etc. Besides increasing the weight of the plane it reduces the engine efficiency. The drag on the plane is greatly increased and operation of the control surfaces is interfered with. Perhaps the greatest danger of ice formation on the plane is the reduction of lift. This is caused by ice changing the shape or aerodynamic characteristics of the wings. It can be seen that the effects of ice are all unfavorable and cumulative. To make matters worse, these conditions usually present themselves when poor visibility and rough air add to the mental disturbance of the pilot, who knows that his instruments may fail, owing to ice, when they are needed most. Venturi and pitot-static tubes are heated on airline equipment, but even so they are not infallible under severe conditions.

The importance of carburetor icing and the mechanics that cause it have only recently been realized. Many new pilots are still unfamiliar with the problem.

What occurs, briefly, is this. The purpose of a carburetor is to vaporize the fuel and mix it with the proper amount of air so that it can be converted into power by the engine. As the fuel enters the carburetor, it is drawn through fine jets and vaporized. This vaporization takes heat from the surrounding air in the venturi tube, causing the temperature of the air in the tube to be lowered by as much as 50 or 60 degrees F. The drop in temperature depends on fuel quality, altitude, and other factors, all of which adds to the difficulty of predicting ice formation. But it can be seen that if any moisture is brought into the carburetor, it will encounter

ON A TREE—OR AN AIRPLANE. Just above this tree is the formless Stratus cloud with its icy cargo. Highly saturated with moisture it rested upon the trees and passed on, leaving a filigree of glaze. Glaze or clear ice forms on an airplane under the same conditions, but the temperature must be at freezing or below and there must be visible moisture in the air.

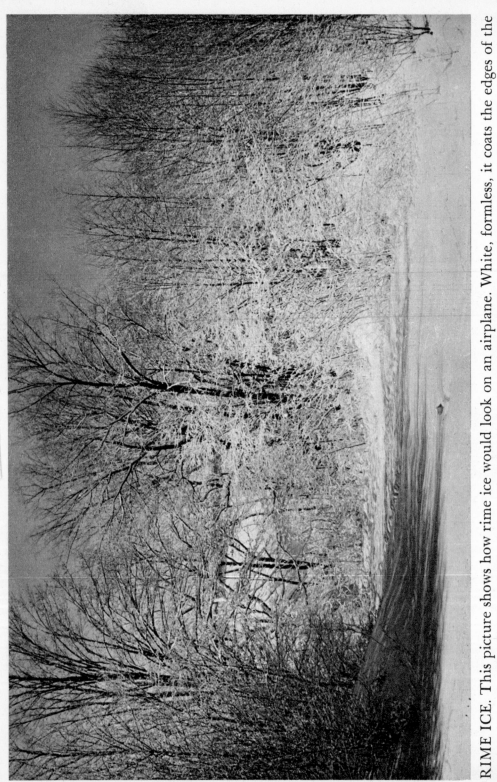

RIME ICE. This picture shows how rime ice would look on an airplane. White, formless, it coats the edges of the wings and control surfaces changing their shape and their aerodynamic characteristics.

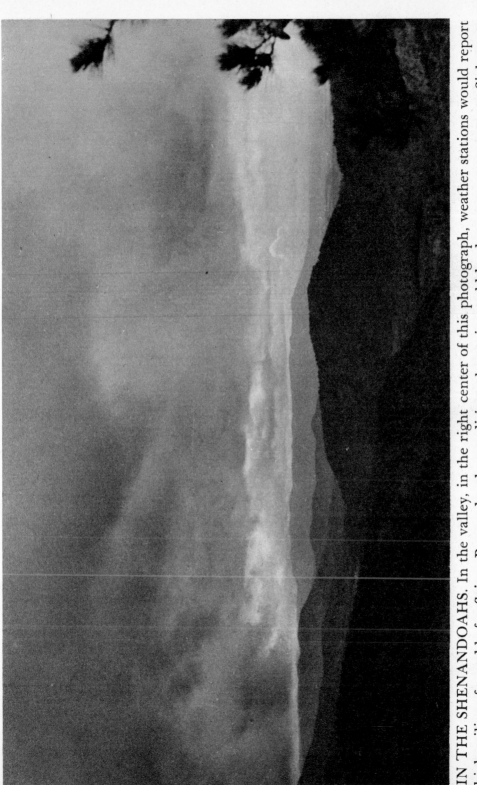

IN THE SHENANDOAHS. In the valley, in the right center of this photograph, weather stations would report high ceilings favorable for flying. But under the conditions shown it would be dangerous to attempt a flight over the mountains toward the left. In the valley the clouds are Altostratus; those in the hills, Nimbostratus.

freezing temperatures and may form ice, even in the summertime. The ice gradually builds up in the venturi tube and cuts down the supply of air, enrichening the gasoline mixture excessively and reducing power. It may also adhere to other inner parts of the carburetor, cutting off the supply of the life-giving vapor to the cylinders.

If nothing is done to stop or retard this formation of ice the power continues to be reduced. Under certain atmospheric conditions serious ice accumulation may occur without warning in amounts sufficient to cause motor failure. In many cases ice will form during a glide so that when the pilot has to use his engine he finds that he either has no engine or very little power. This is particularly serious if he has undershot the field or has to go around again.

Usually, however, carburetor ice is formed slowly and with a little warning of impending trouble. The first indication is usually a drop in the engine revolutions, which may be accompanied by roughness of the motor caused by the rich mixture. Larger commercial ships and military planes have carburetor heat gauges which warn of icing conditions. Modern airplanes have carburetor heat controls which heat the incoming carburetor air so that ice formation is prevented. When ice formation is suspected in flight, either through a drop in power, a falling off of r.p.m.'s, or a roughness of the engine, the heat should be applied in sufficient quantities so that the symptoms disappear. In light airplanes the heat should be put on full at the first indication or suspicion of ice. As heat reduces power it should only be used when required to prevent icing.

There are other methods of combating the carburetor ice hazard. One is through the use of an injector, such as is used on Diesel engines, which injects fuel directly into the cylinders. These are now being used on some gasoline engines.

Another method is to inject alcohol into the carburetor air intake. This acts as an anti-freeze, preventing ice formation. These methods are not in common use, however, and the problem of carburetor ice still remains with most of us.

Under certain conditions it is possible to predict with certainty that ice will form. Other conditions might lead one to believe that ice is a possibility. Ice on the airplane surface can be predicted with a much greater degree of certainty than carburetor ice. Under conditions of temperature inversion, in freezing rain, the plane will take on outside ice. Whenever mist, fog or clouds are encountered in freezing temperatures, surface ice must be expected. Carburetor ice may be looked for when the temperature is less than 50 degrees and with the dew point within 6 degrees of the temperature. Thus the temperature can be that of summer on the ground and carburetor ice can still form. One cannot tell merely by looking at the weather whether or not carburetor ice may form, because even in clear weather the danger exists. The humidity may be high enough so that the reduction in temperature and pressure in the venturi tube will precipitate moisture inside the carburetor. If the temperature is below freezing, ice is sure to appear.

Nearly all outside surface icing conditions occur in frontal zones. In the western states icing conditions prevail in frontal areas or in the mountains. Frontal formations are characterized by precipitation and when accompanied by freezing temperatures meet requirements for icing. Where mountains act as the lifting agents the effect is the same as if a cold front were present. The moisture content in the lower levels of the mP air mass is great enough so that in winter icing conditions frequently result over the mountains of our western states. When air of the mT air masses, with their plentiful supply of moisture, encounters a polar front in the Appalachians in winter, icing conditions are almost sure to result. The mountains themselves contribute to the development of icing conditions. In general, therefore, icing tendencies are more likely to exist and to be severe in mountainous country.

While icing conditions are prevalent in all frontal formations, they are not all of the same extent. Because of the range of the warm front the icing conditions are apt to cover a wide area. Flights in a warm front are likely to be of long duration, with the consequent increased hazard of dangerous icing. The distance across a cold front is relatively less, hence the time in which icing conditions may be encountered is diminished. But as under summer conditions, while the duration is shorter the characteristics of a cold front are apt to be more intense. The ice is of the hard clear variety and the rate of accumulation is higher. This makes flying in the area of a cold front in winter extremely hazardous. Generally speaking, it is well to look for ice when frontal formations are in the path of the flight, temperatures at the flight level are at or around freezing, and the air has a high relative humidity. Most ice forms at temperatures between 26 and 35 degrees.

If a little sound judgment is used pilots should not have too much difficulty with ice. If a study of the weather map indicates the possibility of severe icing conditions it will be wise to cancel the flight. In the event freezing rain is encountered it usually can be avoided by climbing up into the warm air where the temperature is above freezing.

If the carburetor starts to ice up when the weather appears good, use the heat control, as previously advised. It is a good idea to make it a rule to put on the carburetor heat before closing the throttle when making a long glide. If you are making a landing into a small field under conditions where you might need your engine in a hurry, be sure to have the heat on before closing the throttle, regardless of the outside temperature. To avoid ice formation use full heat all of the time when the ground temperature is 50 degrees or below. Full heat should also be used when high humidity or rain is present and the outside temperature is 70 degrees or less. High humidity is indicated by visible moisture, such as mist, fog, clouds and damp air. The directions in the service manual should be read to determine the specific recommendations of the engine manufacturer regarding the use of heat on that particular engine. If there is no carburetor heat control on the plane, and icing conditions are known to exist, don't fly.

FROST

Frost can hardly be considered a serious hazard to aviation, yet at least one airline accident in my recollection has been attributed to it. Frost forms instead of dew when the temperature is below freezing. It consists of small separate crystals of ice in a relatively thin layer. It is not important while in flight but if it forms on the wings while the plane is on the ground it should be thoroughly cleaned off before a takeoff is attempted. The slight coating on the upper side of the wings changes the lift characteristics of the ship enough so that the plane may not be able to get off the ground in the space available. Many pilots who have left their airplanes out all night in the fall have wondered why the ship just would not leave the ground the next morning.

VISIBILITY

Visibility is both horizontal and vertical. The vertical visibility is given on weather reports in hundreds and thousands of feet up to 9751 feet. If there is no overcast below 9751 feet the vertical visibility or ceiling is said to be unlimited. It is determined in the daytime by balloons and estimation and at night by ceiling projectors. The horizontal visibility is measured in miles and is considered as unlimited when over 10 miles. The term CAVU means, in pilot talk, *ceiling and visibility unlimited.*

There are very definite rules laid down by the Civil Aeronautics Administration regarding minimum ceilings and visibilities. These vary under different conditions such as night or day, whether off or on the airlines, and whether or not it is raining. At first these regulations may be a little confusing but they must be learned. There is no other way to learn them than to sit down and commit them to memory. They are designed for the safety of those who want to fly.

Visibility is good or poor depending upon condensation and precipitation. Whether it is called fog or cloud makes little difference. The main thing is that you cannot see far enough to fly safely when the visibility is below the minimums prescribed by the government.

It is important that the pilot know the country over which he is going to fly. Very often weather stations are located in valleys and a report from one of these indicating a ceiling above the minimum does not always mean that it is clear in nearby hills. The various reporting stations are likewise located at different elevations. While operators conscientiously try to anticipate such matters, when there is any doubt about the ceiling or the visibility being adequate, the flight should be canceled. In mountainous country one should be doubly careful. The very strictest rules of the Civil Aeronautics Administration are those that deal with the minimums of ceiling and visibility. If during flight, conditions are encountered that are known to be below the minimum a landing should be made at once.

14

THE SYNOPTIC CHART

THE average person has little idea of the colossal amount of work carried on by the United States Weather Bureau. The collection of data, the distribution of reports and the prediction of what the future will bring is as endless as weather itself. In the ceaseless efforts to master weather and to render as complete a service as possible a vast organization and a marvelous system have been built up.

The Weather Bureau has established nearly 600 stations spaced at fairly regular intervals along the civil airways of the United States. In addition to these there are over 250 other stations distributed uniformly off the airways. Another 150 stations from Canada, Cuba, Hawaii, Alaska and Central America co-operate to give a total of over a thousand that make weather observations.

Observations are taken every hour throughout the 24 hours at most of the stations located on the airways, and special observations are taken whenever marked changes occur in the weather. At the stations located off the airways, observations are taken every 3 hours. The reports are made on the general weather conditions prevailing at the time, and include evaluation of the various weather elements.

The elements of visibility, state of the weather and the types and amounts of clouds are determined without the aid of instruments. The observations of the temperature, pressure, wind direction and velocity, ceiling, humidity and precipitation are made with the instruments described.

The information so obtained is all surface data. In addition over one hundred of the reporting stations are equipped for obtaining upper air information. The wind directions and velocities at various levels up to the ceiling are obtained by pilot balloon.

During the first World War a system of obtaining weather data by airplane flights was started. This method has now been largely replaced by the use of a device called the radio sonde. Basically, the radiosonde is a small radio transmitter carried aloft by a special helium-filled balloon. As the balloon rises the radio begins a continuous broadcast, reporting the prevailing temperature, barometric pressure and humidity at various levels, back to the ground station.

As the balloon ascends into the area of decreased pressure, it gradually increases in size, until it bursts. Then a small parachute is released, permitting the radio transmitter to descend safely to earth. The return address is on the case with a notice of a reward to be paid to the finder when the instrument is shipped back to the Weather Bureau. There are now about thirty stations in the United States where radiosonde observations are taken daily.

Just as soon as all the data are gathered at the different stations they are arranged in orderly fashion and transmitted by various means to central points for distribution. The stations along the airways send in their reports by the teletype system of the Civil Aeronautics Administration. Stations off the airways send their reports by telegraph or telephone to certain of the above stations selected as relay points.

These reports are gathered into orderly sequences in the order that they appear along airways. When these sequences are collected for a certain area they are relayed to other circuits, which transmit other sequences in return. Thus, a short time after observations are made every important airway terminal is informed of the weather all over the country.

Four times a day, at 7:30 and 1:30 A M and P M, Eastern

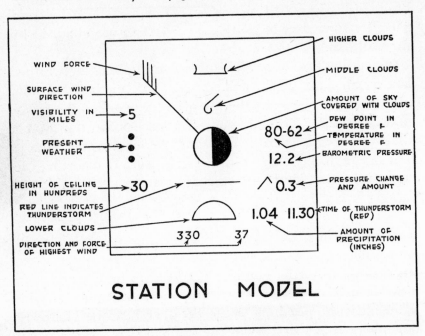

STATION MODEL

Standard Time, the weather map is made up at around 200 of the larger airport stations. This map is known as the synoptic chart. It gets its name from the fact that it presents a synopsis of the weather conditions prevailing in the entire country at one time, the time at which the observations were taken.

With a picture of the prevailing weather before him the meteorologist is in a position to make forecasts of the future

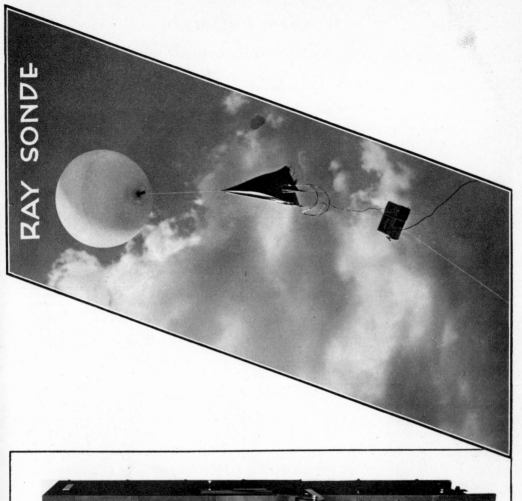

RAY SONDE

RAY SONDE RECEIVER

CHARTS AT THE WEATHER BUREAU

weather. Knowledge of the rate and direction of movement of the weather renders it possible to make accurate predictions for several hours in advance. Airway forecasts are made for 8 hours ahead.

BEAUFORT NUMBER	MAP SYMBOL	DESCRIPTIVE WORDS	VELOCITY	GUIDE FOR ESTIMATING VELOCITIES
0		CALM	LESS THAN 1	SMOKE RISES VERTICALLY.
1		LIGHT AIR	1 TO 3	DIRECTION OF WIND SHOWN BY SMOKE BUT NOT BY WIND VANES.
2		LIGHT BREEZE	4 TO 7	WINDS FELT ON FACE; LEAVES RUSTLE; ORDINARY VANE MOVED BY WIND.
3		GENTLE BREEZE	8 TO 12	LEAVES AND SMALL TWIGS IN CONSTANT MOTION, WIND EXTENDS LIGHT FLAG.
4		MODERATE BREEZE	13 TO 18	RAISES DUST AND LOOSE PAPER; SMALL BRANCHES ARE MOVED.
5		FRESH BREEZE	19 TO 24	SMALL TREES IN LEAF BEGIN SWAY; CRESTED WAVELETS FORM ON INLAND WATER.
6		STRONG BREEZE	25 TO 31	LARGE BRANCHES IN MOTION; WHISTLING HEARD IN TELEGRAPH WIRES; UMBRELLAS USED WITH DIFFICULTY.
7		MODERATE GALE	32 TO 38	WHOLE TREES IN MOTION; INCONVENIENCE FELT IN WALKING AGAINST THE WIND.
8		FRESH GALE	39 TO 46	BREAKS TWIGS OFF TREES; GENERALLY IMPEDES PROGRESS.
9		STRONG GALE	47 TO 54	SLIGHT STRUCTURAL DAMAGE OCCURS (CHIMNEY POTS AND SLATE REMOVED.)
10		WHOLE GALE	55 TO 63	TREES UPROOTED; CONSIDERABLE STRUCTURAL DAMAGE OCCURS.
11		STORM	64 TO 75	RARELY EXPERIENCED; ACCOMPANIED BY WIDE SPREAD DAMAGE.
12		HURRICANE	ABOVE 75	

THE BEAUFORT SCALE

Although drawn by different people, who are many miles apart, all charts are identical because all are made up from the same data and by an identical process. The chart is drawn by taking the weather data of each station and entering it on the map in a designated order at the station's location. This order is shown in the illustration on page 130.

The wind force is given in terms of Beaufort numbers. The force is shown by barbs on the end of the shaft. Each full-

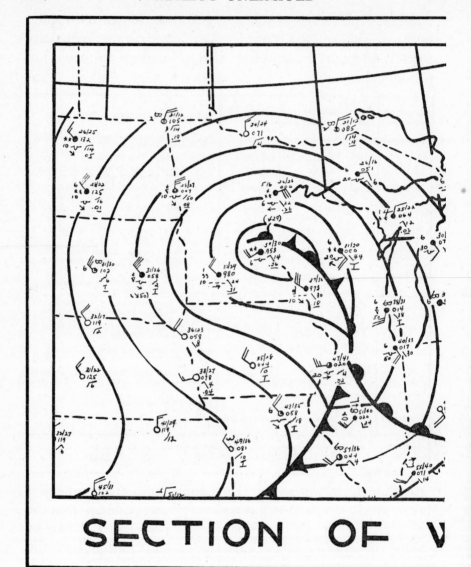

SECTION OF V

length barb is equal to 2 units of force, and a half barb is
equal to 1 unit. The direction of the wind is shown by the
shaft flying toward the center of the sky-cover circle in the
middle of the diagram. If there is no wind a circle is drawn

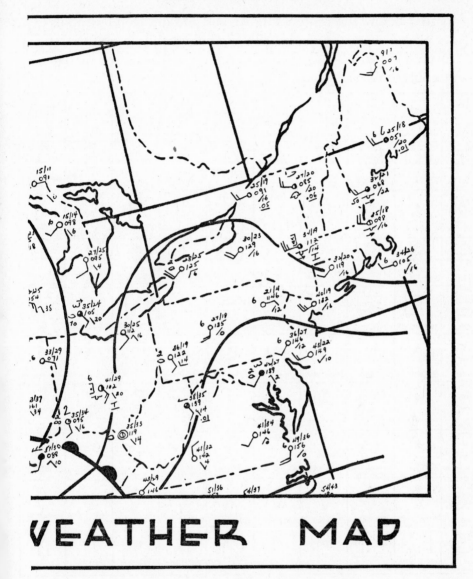

VEATHER MAP

around the center. See the Beaufort Scale on page 131.

General weather existing at the time of taking the observation is shown by one of the symbols at the left center of the station model. The type of lower clouds is shown by symbols located below the center. Higher and middle cloud symbols are placed above the center. The symbol for the amount of sky covered is placed directly in the center, and pressure change symbols to the right center.

CLOUDLESS	PARTLY CLOUDY	CLOUDY	OVERCAST	LOW FOG	HAZE	DUST DEVILS SEEN	DISTANT LIGHTNING	LIGHT FOG	FOG AT DISTANCE
PRECIPITATION WITHIN SIGHT	THUNDER WITHOUT PRECIPITATION AT STATION	DUST STORM WITHIN SIGHT BUT NOT AT STATION	UGLY, THREATENING SKY	SQUALLY WEATHER	HEAVY SQUALLS	WATERSPOUTS SEEN IN LAST 3 HOURS	VISIBILITY REDUCED BY SMOKE	DUST STORM	SIGNS OF TROPICAL STORM (HURRICANE)
PRECIPITATION IN LAST HOUR	DRIZZLE IN LAST HOUR	RAIN IN LAST HOUR	SNOW IN LAST HOUR	RAIN AND SNOW MIXED IN LAST HOUR	RAIN SHOWERS IN LAST HOUR	SNOW SHOWERS IN LAST HOUR	HAIL OR RAIN AND HAIL SHOWERS IN LAST HOUR	LIGHT THUNDERSTORM IN LAST HOUR	HEAVY THUNDERSTORM IN LAST HOUR
DUST OR SAND STORM	DUST OR SAND STORM HAS DECREASED	DUST OR SAND STORM, NO APPRECIABLE CHANGE	DUST OR SAND STORM HAS INCREASED	LINE OF DUST STORMS	STORM OF DRIFTING SNOW	SLIGHT STORM OF DRIFTING SNOW GENERALLY LOW	HEAVY STORM OF DRIFTING SNOW GENERALLY LOW	SLIGHT STORM OF DRIFTING SNOW GENERALLY HIGH	HEAVY STORM OF DRIFTING SNOW GENERALLY HIGH
FOG	MODERATE FOG IN LAST HOUR	THICK FOG IN LAST HOUR	FOG SKY DISCERNIBLE HAS BECOME THINNER DURING LAST HOUR	FOG... SKY NOT DISCERNIBLE HAS BECOME THINNER DURING LAST HOUR	FOG, SKY DISCERNIBLE, NO APPRECIABLE CHANGE DURING LAST HOUR	FOG, SKY NOT DISCERNIBLE, NO APPRECIABLE CHANGE DURING LAST HOUR	FOG, SKY DISCERNIBLE, HAS BECOME THICKER DURING LAST HOUR	FOG, SKY NOT DISCERNIBLE... HAS BECOME THICKER DURING LAST HOUR	FOG IN PATCHES
DRIZZLE	INTERMITTENT... SLIGHT DRIZZLE	CONTINUOUS SLIGHT DRIZZLE	INTERMITTENT... MODERATE DRIZZLE	CONTINUOUS MODERATE DRIZZLE	INTERMITTENT... THICK DRIZZLE	CONTINUOUS THICK DRIZZLE	DRIZZLE AND FOG	SLIGHT OR MODERATE DRIZZLE AND RAIN	THICK DRIZZLE AND RAIN
RAIN	INTERMITTENT SLIGHT RAIN	CONTINUOUS SLIGHT RAIN	INTERMITTENT MODERATE RAIN	CONTINUOUS MODERATE RAIN	INTERMITTENT HEAVY RAIN	CONTINUOUS HEAVY RAIN	RAIN AND FOG	SLIGHT OR MODERATE RAIN AND SNOW, MIXED	HEAVY RAIN AND SNOW MIXED
SNOW (OR SNOW AND RAIN, MIXED).	INTERMITTENT SLIGHT SNOW IN FLAKES	CONTINUOUS SLIGHT SNOW IN FLAKES	INTERMITTENT MODERATE SNOW IN FLAKES	CONTINUOUS MODERATE SNOW IN FLAKES	INTERMITTENT HEAVY SNOW IN FLAKES	CONTINUOUS HEAVY SNOW IN FLAKES	SNOW AND FOG	GRAINS OF SNOW (FROZEN DRIZZLE)	ICE CRYSTALS (OR FROZEN RAIN DROPS) (SLEET)
SHOWERS	SHOWERS OF SLIGHT OR MODERATE RAIN	SHOWERS OF HEAVY RAIN	SHOWERS OF SLIGHT OR MODERATE SNOW	SHOWERS OF HEAVY SNOW	SHOWERS OF SLIGHT OR MODERATE RAIN AND SNOW	SHOWERS OF HEAVY RAIN AND SNOW	SHOWERS OF SNOW PELLETS (SOFT HAIL)	SHOWERS OF SLIGHT OR MODERATE HAIL OR RAIN AND HAIL	SHOWERS OF HEAVY HAIL, OR RAIN AND HAIL.
THUNDERSTORM	RAIN AT TIME THUNDERSTORM DURING LAST HOUR	SNOW or RAIN AND SNOW MIXED, AT TIME, THUNDERSTORM DURING LAST HOUR	THUNDERSTORM SLIGHT WITHOUT HAIL, BUT WITH RAIN (OR SNOW)	THUNDERSTORM, SLIGHT WITH HAIL, AT TIME OF OBSERVATION	THUNDERSTORM MODERATE WITHOUT HAIL, BUT WITH RAIN (OR SNOW)	THUNDERSTORM MODERATE WITH HAIL	THUNDERSTORM HEAVY WITHOUT HAIL, BUT WITH RAIN (OR SNOW)	THUNDERSTORM COMBINED WITH DUST STORM	THUNDERSTORM HEAVY WITH HAIL

GENERAL WEATHER SYMBOLS

All of the other information shown on the station model is self-explanatory. Knowing the meaning of the symbols anyone can look at a weather map and get a pretty good idea of what the weather is like at that particular place.

LOWER CLOUDS	MIDDLE CLOUDS	HIGH CLOUDS	CLOUDS IN SKY	PRESSURE TENDENCY
NO LOWER CLOUDS	NO MIDDLE CLOUDS	NO HIGH CLOUDS	ABSOLUTELY NO CLOUDS IN SKY	RISING, THEN FALLING.
CUMULUS OF FINE WEATHER	TYPICAL ALTOSTRATUS, THIN	CIRRUS, DELICATE	LESS THAN ONE TENTH	RISING, THEN STEADY; OR RISING, THEN RISING MORE SLOWLY.
CUMULUS HEAVY AND SWELLING, WITHOUT ANVIL TOP	TYPICAL ALTOSTRATUS, THICK (OR NIMBOSTRATUS)	CIRRUS, DELICATE, NOT INCREASING, ABUNDANT BUT NOT FORMING A CONTINUOUS LAYER	ONE TENTH	UNSTEADY
CUMULONIMBUS	ALTOCUMULUS, OR HIGH STRATOCUMULUS, SHEET AT ONE LEVEL ONLY	CIRRUS OF ANVIL CLOUDS, USUALLY DENSE	TWO OR THREE TENTHS	STEADY OR RISING
STRATOCUMULUS FORMED BY THE FLATTENING OF CUMULUS CLOUDS	ALTOCUMULUS IN SMALL ISOLATED PATCHES	CIRRUS INCREASING	FOUR, FIVE, OR SIX TENTHS	FALLING THEN RISING
LAYER OF STRATUS OR STRATOCUMULUS	ALTOCUMULUS ARRANGED IN MORE OR LESS PARALLEL BANDS	CIRRUS OR CIRROSTRATUS ADVANCING OVER THE SKY BUT NOT MORE THAN 45° ABOVE THE HORISON	SEVEN OR EIGHT TENTHS	FALLING, THEN RISING
LOW BROKEN UP CLOUDS OF BAD WEATHER	ALTOCUMULUS FORMED BY A SPREADING OUT OF THE TOPS OF CUMULUS	CIRRUS OR CIRROSTRATUS ADVANCING OVER THE SKY AND MORE THAN 45° ABOVE THE GROUND	NINE TENTHS	FALLING, THEN STEADY
CUMULUS OF FINE WEATHER AND STRATOCUMULUS	ALTOCUMULUS ASSOCIATED WITH ALTOSTRATUS	VEIL OF CIRROSTRATUS COVERING THE WHOLE SKY	MORE THAN NINE TENTH BUT WITH OPENINGS	UNSTEADY
HEAVY OR SWELLING CUMULUS AND STRATOCUMULUS	ALTOCUMULUS CASTELLATUS, OR SCATTERED CUMULIFORM TUFTS	CIRROSTRATUS NOT INCREASING AND NOT COVERING THE WHOLE SKY	SKY COMPLETLY COVERED WITH CLOUDS	FALLING
CUMULONIMBUS AND LOW RAGGED CLOUDS OF BAD WEATHER	ALTOCUMULUS IN SEVERAL SHEETS AT DIFFERENT LEVELS	CIRROCUMULUS ASSOCIATED WITH CIRRUS	SKY OBSCURED BY FOG, DUSTSTORM, OR OTHER PHENOMENON	RISING, THEN FALLING

WEATHER MAP SYMBOLS

After each local situation has been entered, additional symbols can be drawn to show the relationship to the general picture. Isobars—lines connecting areas of equal pressure—are drawn in with a black lead pencil. These are drawn for every two, three, or four millibars, according to the scale of the map. The isobars are labeled at the ends, or, when they are closed, in some other appropriate place. The area within the

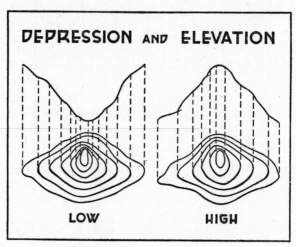

isobar having the lowest pressure is marked "Low" or "L." The area within the isobar having the highest pressure is marked "High" or "H." Thus the anticyclones and cyclones are located.

Isobars indicate the contour of pressure. It will be easier to understand if one thinks of a "high" as a hill of pressure, and a "low" as a valley.

Isotherms are not usually drawn in at airport offices. When entered they are drawn in light blue and usually for 10 degree intervals.

From the characteristics of weather existing at the various stations the trained meteorologist can easily locate and identify various frontal formations. These are entered on the airport

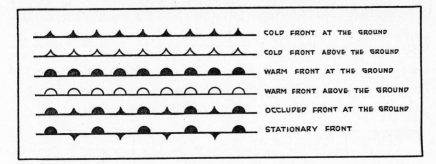

▲▲▲▲▲▲▲▲	COLD FRONT AT THE GROUND
△△△△△△△△	COLD FRONT ABOVE THE GROUND
●●●●●●●●	WARM FRONT AT THE GROUND
⌒⌒⌒⌒⌒⌒⌒⌒	WARM FRONT ABOVE THE GROUND
●▲●▲●▲●▲	OCCLUDED FRONT AT THE GROUND
●▽●▽●▽	STATIONARY FRONT

charts by means of colored lines. For surface fronts, heavy solid colored lines are used, blue for cold fronts, red for warm fronts, and purple for occluded fronts. For upper fronts broken lines of the same color are used. Stationary fronts are shown by a continuous red and blue line. When fronts are shown in printed charts the international symbols are used.

The air masses are located on the airport charts by colored symbols. Blue is used for air masses of polar origin and red for those of tropical origin. The symbols used are the abbreviated names of the various air masses.

Precipitation, when great enough to be recorded, is shown by green symbols on the airport charts. Intermittent precipitation is denoted by wide diagonals known as hatching. An area of continuous precipitation is indicated by close diagonals known as shading. Drizzle areas are represented by a series of commas, and showers, including snow flurries and sprinkles, are shown by a series of inverted triangles.

While the same basic weather system is used by the various services, slight variations do occur and changes in symbols are made from time to time. It is not difficult, however, to keep pace with these if the method is understood.

INTERMITTENT PRECIPITATION	CONTINUOUS PRECIPITATION	SHOWERS	DRIZZLE
/////	▓▓	▽ ▽ ▽ ▽ ▽ ▽ ▽ ▽	，，， ，， ，，，

PRECIPITATION SYMBOLS

Another chart of great importance to the pilot is the winds-aloft chart. These charts are made up four times a day at about one hundred stations and show the direction and velocity of the wind at 2000-foot intervals up to 14,000 feet. By reference to this chart the pilot can select the altitude with the most favorable wind for a cross-country flight.

WINTER... AIR MASS	CLOUDS	CEILINGS	VISIBILITIES	TURBULENCE	SURFACE TEMPERATURE °F.
cP (NEAR SOURCE REGION)	NONE	UNLIMITED	EXCELLENT (EXCEPT NEAR INDUSTRIAL AREAS, THEN 1-4 MILES).	SMOOTH EXCEPT WITH HIGH WIND VELOCITIES.	10-TO-60
cP (SOUTHEAST OF GREAT LAKES)	STRATOCUMULUS AND CUMULUS TOPS 7,000-10,000 FEET.	500-1,000 FEET, 0 OVER MOUNTAINS.	1-5 MILES, 0 IN SNOW FLURRIES.	MODERATE TURBULENCE UP TO 10,000 FEET.	0-TO-20
mP (ON PACIFIC COAST)	CUMULUS TOPS ABOVE 20,000 FEET.	1,000-3,000 FEET, 0 OVER MOUNTAINS.	GOOD EXCEPT 0 OVER MOUNTAINS AND IN SHOWERS.	MODERATE TO STRONG TURBULENCE.	45-TO-55
mP (EAST OF ROCKIES)	NONE	UNLIMITED	EXCELLENT EXCEPT NEAR INDUSTRIAL AREAS, THEN 1-4 MILES.	SMOOTH EXCEPT IN LOWER LEVELS WITH HIGH WINDS.	30-TO-40
mP (EAST COAST)	STRATOCUMULUS AND STRATUS TOPS 6,000-8,000 FEET.	0-1,000 FEET	FAIR EXCEPT 0 IN PRECIPITATION AREA.	ROUGH IN LOWER LEVELS	30-TO-40
mT (PACIFIC COAST)	STRATUS OR STRATOCUMULUS.	500-1,500 FEET	GOOD	SMOOTH	55-TO-60
mT (EAST OF ROCKIES)	DO	100-1,500 FEET	DO	DO	60-TO-70
SUMMER					
cP (NEAR SOURCE REGION)	SCATTERED CUMULUS	UNLIMITED	GOOD	MODERATE TURBULENCE UP TO 10,000 FEET.	55-60
mP (PACIFIC COAST)	STRATUS 2,000-5,000 FEET.	100 FEET 2,500 FEET, UNLIMITED DURING DAY OVER LAND.	½-10 MILES	SLIGHTLY ROUGH IN CLOUDS SMOOTH ABOVE.	50-60
mP (EAST OF PACIFIC COASTAL AREA)	NONE EXCEPT SCATTERED CUMULUS NEAR MOUNTAINS.	UNLIMITED	EXCELLENT	GENERALLY SMOOTH EXCEPT OVER DESERT REGIONS IN AFTERNOON.	60-70
S (MISSISSIPPI VALLEY)	NONE	DO	DO	SLIGHTLY ROUGH UP TO 15,000 FEET.	75-85
mT (EAST OF ROCKIES)	STRATOCUMULUS EARLY MORNING CUMULONIMBUS AFTERNOON.	500-1,500 FEET A.M.; 3,000-4,000 FEET P.M.	DO	SMOOTH EXCEPT IN THUNDERSTORMS THEN STRONG TURBULENCE.	75-85
PROPERTIES OF AIR MASSES					

It is neither necessary nor possible for every pilot to be able to forecast weather. But all pilots should know enough about weather principles to be able to make intelligent use of the weather map. No flight should be attempted without reference to the weather map or checking with the meteorologist. Weather Bureau personnel are trained to work with pilots. They are courteous and eager to be of assistance. Con-

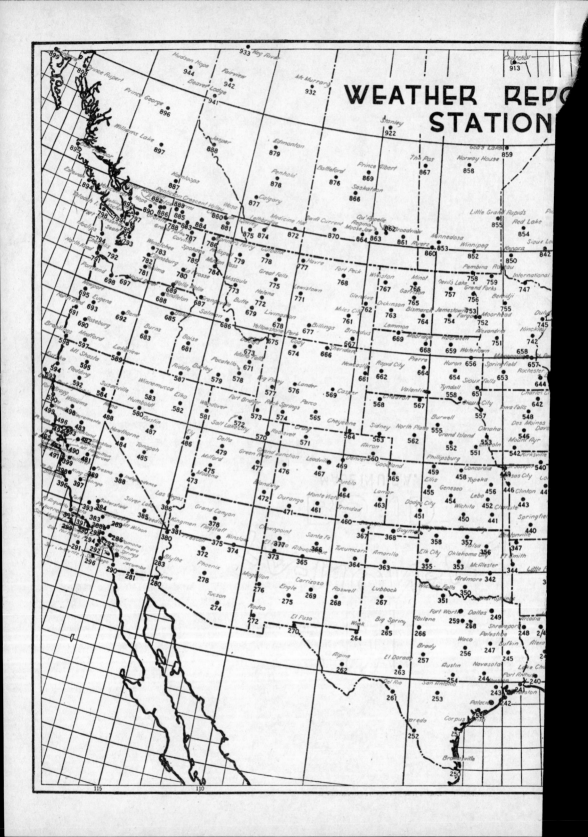

WEATHER REPORT STATIONS

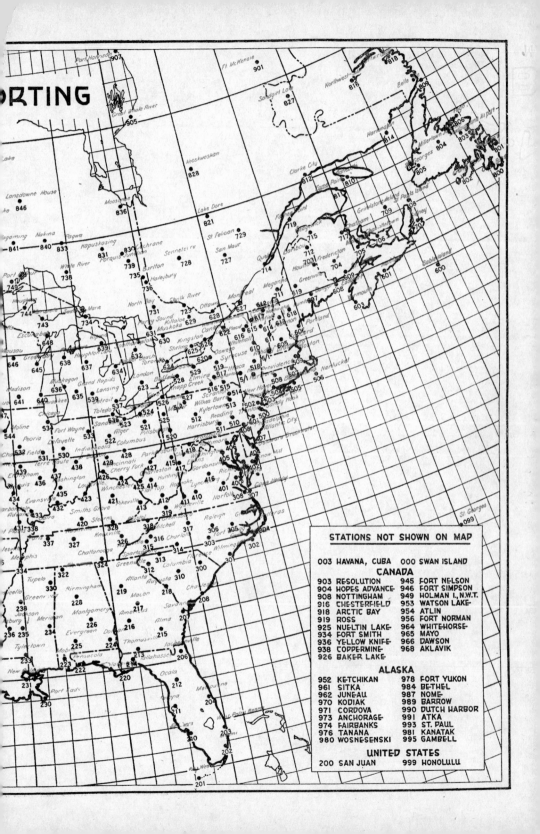

RTING

STATIONS NOT SHOWN ON MAP

003 HAVANA, CUBA   000 SWAN ISLAND

CANADA

903	RESOLUTION	945	FORT NELSON
904	HOPES ADVANCE	946	FORT SIMPSON
908	NOTTINGHAM	949	HOLMAN I., N.W.T.
916	CHESTERFIELD	953	WATSON LAKE
918	ARCTIC BAY	954	ATLIN
919	ROSS	956	FORT NORMAN
925	NUELTIN LAKE	964	WHITEHORSE
934	FORT SMITH	965	MAYO
936	YELLOW KNIFE	966	DAWSON
938	COPPERMINE	968	AKLAVIK
926	BAKER LAKE		

ALASKA

952	KETCHIKAN	978	FORT YUKON
961	SITKA	984	BETHEL
962	JUNEAU	987	NOME
970	KODIAK	989	BARROW
971	CORDOVA	990	DUTCH HARBOR
973	ANCHORAGE	991	ATKA
974	FAIRBANKS	993	ST. PAUL
976	TANANA	981	KANATAK
980	WOSNESENSKI	995	GAMBELL

UNITED STATES

200 SAN JUAN   999 HONOLULU

ditions may be such that they look perfectly satisfactory yet a change for the worse may be just about to occur which could easily get a pilot into plenty of trouble. This impending hazard will be recognized by an experienced man and here the meteorologist may prevent unpleasant experiences. On the other hand bad weather is always replaced by good, and this

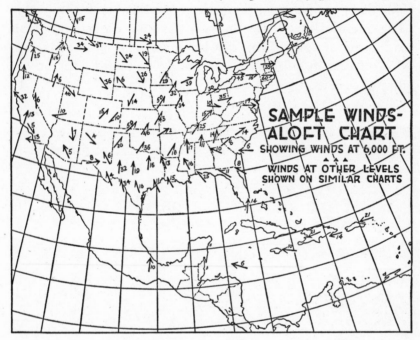

will also be indicated to the trained eye by the weather map. Thus a flight that is impracticable at the moment may be perfectly safe a few hours later.

The way to read a weather map is to try to look at the map so that you will see the actual weather itself. As a pilot you will be interested in the ceilings, clouds at various levels, visibility, wind direction and velocities, icing conditions, thunderstorms, trend of later weather along the route, etc. With a little practice one is soon able to read the symbols

on the map and to visualize the actual conditions. This comes only with practice, but the ability to take advantage of the great service offered by the weather map is worth the trouble of mastering the simple technique involved. The excellent record of safety of the airlines has been made possible only by a thorough knowledge of the weather and the use of this knowledge together with modern methods and equipment. The identical facilities that the airlines use are available to the private pilot. The weather map is the most important single factor in safe flying, and should be used by the private flyer as it is used by the military and airline pilot.

15

AIRWAY WEATHER REPORTS

ANOTHER tremendously valuable service rendered by the Weather Bureau is the hourly weather service. As explained in the previous chapter, weather observations are taken every hour at most of the weather stations in the country. Stations along airways are arranged in sequence as they appear, and other stations near the airways are selected so that their reports will give a picture of the weather along and near the airways.

An illustration of a chart showing the stations making hourly reports is on page 142. Also shown are stations off the airways that make observations, and the larger airports where the synoptic chart is made up every six hours. This chart is available in all airway Weather Bureau stations. When a pilot wishes to make a trip he consults the chart to determine the reporting stations along the route. He can then check the weather at these stations and determine the weather within an hour at any point.

For the convenient transmission of the weather data and to aid the pilot, stations are arranged in sequences corresponding with established airways. By consulting with the meteorologist, and with a little practice, a pilot can soon become

AIRWAY METEORO

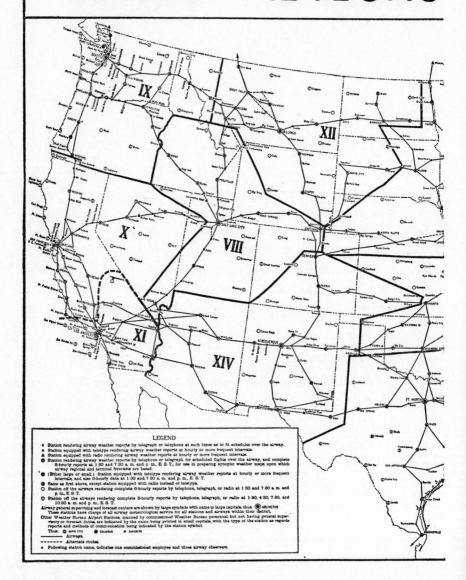

LEGEND

○ Station rendering airway weather reports by telegraph or telephone at such times as to fit schedules over the airway.
● Station equipped with teletype rendering airway weather reports at hourly or more frequent intervals.
▲ Station equipped with radio rendering airway weather reports at hourly or more frequent intervals.
◉ Station rendering airway weather reports by telephone or telegraph for scheduled flights over the airway, and complete 6-hourly reports at 1:30 and 7:30 a. m. and p. m., E. S. T., for use in preparing synoptic weather maps upon which airway regional and terminal forecasts are based.
⦿ (Either large or small.) Station equipped with teletype rendering airway weather reports at hourly or more frequent intervals, and also 6-hourly data at 1:30 and 7:30 a. m. and p. m., E. S. T.
⦿ Same as first above, except station equipped with radio instead of teletype.
◐ Station off the airways rendering complete 6-hourly reports by telephone, telegraph, or radio at 1:30 and 7:30 a. m. and p. m., E. S. T.
⬤ Station off the airways rendering complete 3-hourly reports by telephone, telegraph, or radio at 1:30, 4:30, 7:30, and 10:30 a. m. and p. m., E. S. T.

Airway general supervising and forecast centers are shown by large symbols with name in large capitals, thus ⦿ ARLINGTON. These stations have charge of all airway meteorological service for all stations and airways within their district.

Other Weather Bureau Airport Stations, manned by commissioned Weather Bureau personnel, but not having general supervisory or forecast duties, are indicated by the name being printed in small capitals, with the type of the station as regards reports and methods of communication being indicated by the station symbol.

Thus: ◉ RAPID CITY   ● COLUMBUS   ● SANDUSKY

———— Airways.
------- Alternate routes.
• Following station name, indicates one commissioned employee and three airway observers.

142

LOGICAL SERVICE

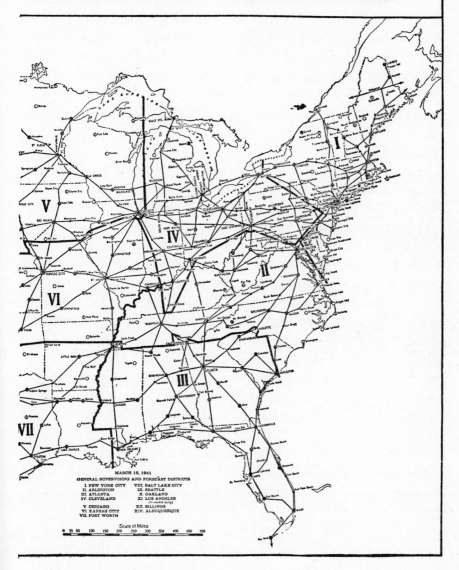

MARCH 15, 1941
GENERAL SUPERVISING AND FORECAST DISTRICTS

I. NEW YORK CITY   VIII. SALT LAKE CITY
II. ARLINGTON   IX. SEATTLE
III. ATLANTA   X. OAKLAND
IV. CLEVELAND   XI. LOS ANGELES
       (forward only)
V. CHICAGO   XII. BILLINGS
VI. KANSAS CITY   XIV. ALBUQUERQUE
VII. FORT WORTH

Scale of Miles
0 25 50   100   150   200   250   300   350   400   450   500

familiar with the sequences most frequently used and know where to find the stations he wants quickly.

For instance if we were making a flight from New Orleans to Pensacola we would obtain the weather within the last hour at New Orleans, Biloxi, Mobile and Pensacola. Nearby are Crestview, Evergreen and Dothan which would tell us what the weather was a short distance away from our course. The stations are identified on the reports by letters, usually quite descriptive. New Orleans is NO, Biloxi is OX, Mobile is MS, etc. The illustration on page 338 shows an actual weather sequence of this section.

Each Weather Bureau station has these reports arranged a little differently, depending upon the areas that it covers. Each station has complete reports for distances about five hundred miles each way. In addition reports for major airways at much greater distances are available. The illustration shows the convenient arrangement of teletype sequences at the New Orleans Airport Weather Station.

The reports for the stations along the flight path for several hours back should be examined to get an idea of the trend of the weather. These reports should be studied in connection with the weather map in the Weather Bureau Office. These handy reports together with the six-hour weather map will give the pilot who understands how to use these facilities an accurate picture of weather conditions prevailing anywhere in the country.

Sometimes the trend of the weather is more important than the current weather. Many flights are rendered possible by an examination of the reports showing that bad weather exists, but containing indications of clear weather to come. On the other hand prevailing good weather is no guarantee that conditions will remain good. Many a pilot's life, and the lives of his passengers, have been safeguarded because reports of bad weather ahead have impelled the pilot to note alternate airports that he could get into in case of an emergency.

The teletype reports are partly in code and partly in plain language. The reports themselves always appear in sequence and the information given is also in a definite order. The information given and the order of each hourly report is as follows:

1. Station identification symbol.
2. Classification of report.
3. Type of report.
4. Time of report.
5. Ceiling.
6. Sky cover.
7. Visibility.
8. General weather.
9. Obstructions to vision.
10. Barometric pressure in millibars.
11. Temperature.
12. Dew point.
13. Wind direction and velocity.
14. Altimeter setting in inches.
15. Remarks.

It is not difficult to interpret these reports, but they require a little study and understanding. Let's take each element and consider it separately.

The first item is the station identification or call letters. This is usually given in two and occasionally three letters. Lists of station names and call letters are posted at Weather Bureau airport bulletin boards. The pilot should familiarize himself with the letters of the stations and sequences used most frequently.

Following the call letters is the classification of the report.

The letters C, N, or X are shown on the reports of control airports. Control airports are large main airports at which the Civil Aeronautics Administration controls traffic on the airways. If none of the classification letters appears the airport is not a control airport. If the letter C appears it means that the airport is open for contact flight. Contact flights are those that can be made when the ground or water can be seen. There are minimum ceilings and visibilities for contact flight under various conditions and localities. Usually the ceiling required is at least 1000 feet and the minimum visibility one mile. These vary with circumstances and the regulations may be obtained from the Civil Aeronautics Administration. When the letter N appears it means that the airport is under instrument flight rules and only pilots and airplanes properly trained and equipped can fly. The airport is closed to all flying when the letter X is given.

Next appears the type of report. This item appears only if important changes in the weather have occurred since the last report or if a special request has been made for the weather at that station. It will then be marked SPL, indicating a special report. LCL, or local reports, are local extra observations and appear only on reports sent over local circuits. These are valuable in that they are made every 15 minutes during periods of low ceiling and poor visibility.

The time of the report follows. This is given on the 24-hour clock and with the standard zone time used. Thus, 1335 E is 1:35 P M Eastern Standard Time and 0925 M is 9:25 A M Mountain Standard Time. Reports appearing in sequence do not carry the time in each station report. This is given for the whole group at the beginning of the sequence. These first four items serve as identifying items.

The group of weather elements now appear. The first is the ceiling. If no ceiling report is given the ceiling is above 9750 feet and is considered unlimited. This report, by dropping the last two digits, is given in hundreds of feet. Therefore 45 means a ceiling of 4500 feet, and 4 indicates a 400-foot ceiling. The ceiling is considered as zero when it is below 51 feet. This condition is shown in the sequence report by a zero. When the letter E precedes the ceiling figures it means that they are estimated. A plus sign ahead of the ceiling figures indicates that the balloon was blown from sight at that level and before reaching the clouds. The letter V following the ceiling indicates that it is variable. This variation is up to 200 feet when the ceiling is between 1000 and 2000 feet and 100 feet when the ceiling is below a thousand. In general the ceiling is the most important individual item on the report to the pilot.

After the ceiling will come the symbol for the condition of the sky. It is omitted when the ceiling is zero or the visibility is one-fifth mile or less. The symbols depict the state of the sky. There are four general conditions of state of the sky, *clear* when less than one-tenth of the sky is covered by clouds, *scattered clouds,* when from one-tenth to five-tenths, *broken clouds,* when from six- to nine-tenths, and it is *overcast*

SKY TELETYPE SYMBOLS

◯	CLEAR
◐	SCATTERED CLOUDS
◑	BROKEN CLOUDS
⊕	OVERCAST
◐/	HIGH SCATTERED
◑/	HIGH BROKEN
⊕/	HIGH OVERCAST
⊕ ◑	OVERCAST, LOWER BROKEN
⊕ ◐	OVERCAST, LOWER SCATTERED
◑ ◑	BROKEN, LOWER BROKEN
◑ ◐	BROKEN, LOWER SCATTERED
◐ ◑	SCATTERED, LOWER BROKEN
◐ ◐	SCATTERED, LOWER SCATTERED
⊕/◑	HIGH OVERCAST, LOWER BROKEN
⊕/◐	HIGH OVERCAST, LOWER SCATTERED
◑/◑	HIGH BROKEN, LOWER BROKEN
◑/◐	HIGH BROKEN, LOWER SCATTERED
◐/◑	HIGH SCATTERED, LOWER BROKEN
◐/◐	HIGH SCATTERED, LOWER SCATTERED

when more than nine-tenths of the sky is covered by clouds.

The height of lower scattered clouds is given in hundreds of feet ahead of the scattered clouds symbol. A plus or minus sign preceding the cloudiness symbol indicates "dark" or "thin" respectively.

The most important item to the pilot in the weather report, next to the ceiling, is the visibility. This is shown in miles. When no visibility is shown, it is over 10 miles. The letter V following the visibility figures indicates that it is variable by as much as one-quarter mile either way.

The following letters indicate the "weather" element of the report:

R—Rain	AP—Small hail
S—Snow	SP—Snow pellets
ZR—Freezing rain	SQ—Snow squall
L—Drizzle	RQ—Rain squall
ZL—Freezing drizzle	T—Thunderstorm
E—Sleet	SW—Snow showers
A—Hail	RW—Rain showers

Tornado—Always written out in full

The above elements are reported in three degrees. If the symbol has a minus after it, a light degree is indicated. An unaccompanied symbol stands for a moderate degree and a heavy degree is shown by a plus sign after the symbol.

The next element is obstructions to vision. This item indicates anything in the atmosphere acting to reduce visibility. It is shown in the reports in accordance with the following list:

F—Damp haze   D—Dust
F—Fog   BS—Blowing snow
GF—Ground fog   GS—Drifting snow
IF—Ice fog   BD—Blowing dust
K—Smoke   BN—Blowing sand
              H—Hazy

With the exception of the symbols for damp haze or hazy, when a minus sign is added after the symbol, a light intensity is indicated. The unaccompanied symbol here also means a moderate degree, while the addition of a plus sign depicts a high degree of obstruction to vision. An additional F is added to the thick fog symbols when a *dense* thick fog exists.

The barometric pressure is indicated next. It is given in 3 figures, tens, units, and tenths of millibars. A pressure of 998.9 is given as 989, 1016.3 as 163, and 1023.6 as 236, etc.

The temperature is given to the nearest whole degree Fahrenheit. A minus sign is placed preceding the temperature when it is below zero.

The dew point follows and also is given to the nearest degree Fahrenheit. Since it is located right next to the temperature a comparison can quickly be made to determine the tendency toward precipitation.

WIND DIRECTIONS	
↓	NORTH
↓ ↙	NORTH - NORTHEAST
↙	NORTHEAST
← ↙	EAST - NORTHEAST
←	EAST
← ↖	EAST - SOUTHEAST
↖	SOUTHEAST
↑ ↖	SOUTH - SOUTHEAST
↑	SOUTH
↑ ↗	SOUTH - SOUTHWEST
↗	SOUTHWEST
→ ↗	WEST - SOUTHWEST
→	WEST
→ ↘	WEST - NORTHWEST
↘	NORTHWEST
↓ ↘	NORTH - NORTHWEST

Arrows show the wind direction and are very easy to interpret.

The velocity is given in miles per hour after the direction symbol. For "calm" the letter "C" is used in place of the velocity figure. A letter "E" after the velocity figure denotes that it is estimated.

When the wind is gusty it is shown by the addition of a plus or minus sign after the velocity. A minus sign means "fresh gusts," and a plus sign means "strong gusts." If no sign is given the wind is steady.

Another feature of the wind that often will indicate the trend of weather is the shift in direction, also shown when appropriate. When the wind has shifted owing to a wind shift line, this is shown after the other wind data by an arrow indicating the former wind direction. The time of the change follows, together with the intensity of the shift. A minus sign indicates a mild shift, the absence of a sign means a moderate shift and a plus sign denotes a severe shift.

The altimeter setting is the final datum given in the sequence reports. This is given in three figures representing the inch and hundredths of an inch of pressure. Thus, 30.10 would be written as 010, and 29.87 would be shown as 987. Altimeter setting is vital to the pilot flying on instruments. Each sensitive altimeter has a window which contains an adjustable pressure scale. When this scale is adjusted to the altimeter setting of a station the altimeter will indicate the height of the aircraft above sea level. The pilot knows the elevation of the airport, so he can easily tell the height of his airplane over the station. If the instrument is working properly and is free from error the pointers will indicate the elevation of the field above sea level upon landing.

Special conditions are disclosed at the end of the report. These are transmitted in authorized abbreviations that are easy to understand. A list of abbreviations is available for inspection at all Weather Bureau Airport Stations.

It must now be clear that this system gives a wealth of weather information to the pilot. The limitations of space have necessitated the condensed system of transmission. Many of the data that are left out are as significant as some which are included. The only way to obtain adequate knowledge of how to use the reports is by using them. Let us interpret the reports of the illustration on the next page, which is a copy of an actual sequence.

TIME—1430   Eastern Standard Time

REGULAR REPORT

1. *Houston*—Control Airport, closed—ceiling 200 feet—overcast—visibility 1½ miles—light drizzle, moderate smoke, light fog—pressure 1024.7 mb.—temperature 40 degrees—dew point 39 degrees—north wind 12 miles per hour—altimeter setting 30.24 inches.

2. *Beaumont*—ceiling 500 feet—overcast—visibility ¾ mile—moderate drizzle—light fog—pressure 1025.1 mb.—temperature 37 degrees—dew point 37 degrees—north, northeast wind 12 miles per hour—altimeter setting 30.26 inches.

3. *Lake Charles*—Control Airport, closed—ceiling 500 feet—overcast—visibility ¾ mile—light drizzle—light fog—pressure 1024.9 mb.—temperature 37 degrees—dew point 36 degrees—north, northeast wind 9 miles per hour—altimeter setting 30.25 inches.

4. *Camp Beauregard*—ceiling estimated 5000 feet—overcast—visibility 10 miles or more—(not equipped with barometers)—temperature 38 degrees—dew point 22 degrees—northeast wind 11 miles per hour.

```
1430E
HU X 2⊕11/2L-KF- 247/40/39↓12/024
JU 5⊕3/4LF- 251/37/37↓↙12/026
LC X 5⊕3/4L-F- 249/37/36↓↙9/025
WCB E50⊕ · 38/22↙11
TZL E8⊕⊕3F- 240/38/36↙17/024
JR C E35⊕7 247/41/35↓10/025/HIER CLDS VSBL
NO C E45⊕8 237/43/30↓17/022
MS E20⊕7L- 247/33/31↓↙13/024/L INTMT
NC E30⊕6K-237/40/28↓15/022
HW SPL E30⊕3L-K- 240/37/30↓↘9/023/PCPN VERY LGT
NI E45⊕7 234/45/30↓3/021
TEN E30⊕8. 244/36/23C/023
XW E35⊕3K- 247/33/24→3/024
TUG C E32⊕3K- 247/33/22→↘3/025/2K- S
VL E35⊕ 234/43/22↑2/022
AG C ⊕/60⊕8 237/41/16→↗11/019
UN ⊕/5K- 240/43/24→↗10/021
GY -⊕/4K- 220/50/32↘2/017
AJ -⊕/ 227/53/33→↘8/018
JX C E40⊕ 213/64/39↖4/015
DB 50⊕ 213/65/51←2/015
OR C ⊕30⊕ 69/53↘3
OU -⊕/30⊕ 207/73/60←7/013/⊕V⊕
TVB E50⊕30⊕ 203/75/61↖8/012
TWZ C E35⊕⊕7L- 196/70/62←↙4/010/VSBY 4 E
MM C E60⊕/⊕ 190/74/65←↖9/008/35⊕
KW ⊕/25⊕ 176/70/65↙15/004
FM E40⊕/⊕ 193/70/60↓5↙009
TLL-⊕/50⊕ 67/47↓↙7
TM E60⊕ 220/66/48↓↙6/017/BINOVC
FC O 227/60/40↙2/019
TJ C -⊕/8 227/55/32↓10/018
+
```

ACTUAL   TELETYPE   REPORT

5. *Lafayette*—ceiling estimated 800 feet—overcast, lower broken clouds—visibility 3 miles—light fog—pressure 1024.0 mb.—temperature 38 degrees—dew point 36 degrees—northeast wind 17 miles per hour—altimeter setting 30.24 inches.

6. *Baton Rouge*—Control Airport, contact—ceiling estimated 3500 feet—overcast—visibility 7 miles—pressure 1024.7 mb.—temperature 41 degrees—dew point 35 degrees—north wind 10 miles per hour—altimeter setting 30.25 inches—higher clouds visible.

7. *New Orleans*—Control Airport, contact—ceiling estimated 4500 feet—overcast—visibility 8 miles—pressure 1023.7 mb.—temperature 43 degrees—dew point 30 degrees—north wind 17 miles per hour—altimeter setting 30.22 inches.

8. *Mobile*—ceiling estimated 2000 feet—overcast—visibility 7 miles—light drizzle—pressure 1024.7 mb.—temperature 33 degrees—dew point 31 degrees—north, northeast wind 13 miles per hour—altimeter setting 30.24 inches—moderate drizzle intermittent.

9. *Pensacola*—ceiling estimated 3000 feet—overcast—visibility 6 miles—light smoke—pressure 1023.7 mb.—temperature 40 degrees—dew point 28 degrees—north wind 28 miles per hour—altimeter setting 30.22.

10. *Crestview*—Special report—ceiling estimated 3000 feet—overcast—visibility 3 miles—light drizzle—light smoke—pressure 1024.0—temperature 37 degrees—dew point 30 degrees—north, northwest wind 9 miles per hour—altimeter setting 30.23 inches—precipitation very light.

Try working out the rest yourself for the practice.

16

PROVERBS, PORTENTS AND PREDICTIONS

S_{OME} people seem to be endowed with a highly developed weather sense. They have an uncanny knack of being able to predict changes in the weather by what seems to be instinct. This ability is neither instinct nor accident, but rather the result of a great deal of observation and interest in the weather. This knack can be developed by anyone with practice and when it is developed by the aviator it will be of extreme value to him in his work.

A great deal of the science of meteorology is contained in the weather lore that has accumulated for nearly six thousand years. There is a wealth of signs, sayings, jingles and proverbs that in many instances prove remarkably accurate because they are based on observation and scientific fact.

In itself weather lore is of course not consistently dependable, but it proves of great help when considered in connection with scientific information. Many sayings about the weather are local and apply only to certain places and for specified seasons. Very often when accurate weather data are not available, however, surprisingly accurate guesses can be made by the amateur who trains himself to become weatherwise.

It is very interesting to explore some of the more popular sayings and portents to determine the scientific reason behind them. Let us look into some of the better-known sayings.

PROVERBS

"Evening red and morning gray,
Come on, boy—let's be on our way.
But evening gray and morning red,
No flying today, stay home in bed."

The dust of the atmosphere permits the passing of the red rays of sunlight much better than the blue ones. When sunlight passes through a considerable thickness of atmosphere the blue rays are filtered out, leaving a predominance of red color. When the sun sets in a blaze of red light it means that the rays are coming horizontally through a long stretch of atmosphere near the earth, indicating that there are few or no clouds to the west and that good weather prevails there. As weather comes generally from the west it should be good the following day. When the evening is gray it indicates the presence of clouds obscuring the sun and therefore the possibility of poor weather moving in.

When the morning is gray, clouds are in the east indicating that any bad weather is in that direction. This has already come and gone and will continue to retreat. On the other hand if the sun rises and meets no obstruction other than clear air we again have the phenomenon of the red coloration. This means that good weather prevails in the east and bad weather lies off to the west and should move in soon.

"When the hair turns damp in the scalp-
house it will bring rain."

This gruesome American Indian proverb is based on sound principles for when the hair of the captured scalps turned damp, the excessive moisture in the air presaged rain. Without realizing it the Indians were using the principle of one of the important instruments of the weather, the hair hygrometer.

> *"Rainbow in the morning, sailors take warning.*
> *Rainbow at night, sailors delight."*

Long a popular jingle, this also has a sound reason for its existence. When a rainbow appears in the morning it will be projected by the sun from the east on the clouds in the west. This shows the presence of storm clouds in the west, making it highly probable that poor weather is heading toward you. But the rainbow at sunset will appear on the shower clouds in the east, and the very fact that it gets through to reach the clouds to form the rainbow indicates that there is clear weather off in the west.

> *"Long foretold, long last,*
> *Short notice, soon past."*

A well-known characteristic of the weather is given here. Thunderstorms usually build up quickly, are violent for a time but do not last long. Cold front formations come up quickly, are normally of short duration, and move on. The first warning of a warm front, however, is the cirrus clouds that appear many hours before the appearance of the bad weather itself. The bad weather may be a whole day's time or more away, but when it does come it covers a wide area and requires considerable time to pass over. Fortunately, while of longer duration it is usually of milder nature.

> *"Rain before seven, shine before eleven."*

This proverb is true often enough to have earned recognition. This holds true particularly with rain that appears as a result of nocturnal cooling. The rain stops when the sun comes out and warms the air evaporating the clouds that caused the rain. This proverb is usually correct because local rain normally does not last long. In order for the saying to be true the rain must come before seven, which allows four hours for it to clear. It does not hold true for the transient rain storms of warm front formations that come and remain for sometimes as long as several days.

> *"Mackerel sky and mare's tails*
> *Make lofty ships carry low sails."*

The mackerel sky is the sky with cirrocumulus clouds. Mare's tails are cirrus clouds. Both of these clouds indicate the coming of a warm front which brings increasing wind as it approaches. With the increase in wind velocity the sailors have to lower their sails to keep from capsizing the ships or damaging the masts.

PORTENTS

Because we have to make no preparation for good weather nor take any precautions to guard against or avoid it, predictions of bad weather become more important than those of good weather. True, if we know that good weather is coming trips can be planned and projects started. But bad weather requires protection to life and property, whether it be the elaborate precautions against a hurricane or merely carrying an umbrella to keep dry under a local shower.

There is much that tells us of impending bad weather. We can observe the clouds, the sky and the wind and we can also learn from animals, birds, insects and inanimate objects. If you have not thought about it before, try to associate everyday things like the following with the weather. You'll be surprised!

Drains, swamps, and ditches smell worse before a rain. The lower pressure before a rain permits more of the heavier gases to escape, thus making the odor more noticeable.

Flowers smell sweeter. More of the minute droplets that carry the smell are released because of the lowered pressure.

Sensitive flowers contract their blossoms. To protect themselves from the increased humidity.

Swallows fly lower. To catch insects, which also fly lower because the increased moisture makes their wings heavier or harder to keep in motion.

Corns and joints ache. Because of the lowered pressure on the body.

Smoke falls to the ground. The dust particles that make up the smoke become heavier in the damp air before a storm.

Flies hang on and bite. Their wings are heavier from the increased moisture in the air and they hang on longer, which gives them more time to bite.

Bees swarm before a storm. The increased moisture (or increased viscosity) burdens their wings and warns them of the coming rain.

Steady southeast wind. The moisture content of the southeast wind is greater than that of the others because it blows off water, except in the Rocky Mountain section. Coming from the warmth of the south heavily laden with moisture it needs but slight cooling to discharge its burden of rain.

Halo around the moon or sun. A halo around the moon or sun is caused by refraction of the light by the ice crystals of cirro type clouds. These clouds will eventually thicken and lower to bring rain.

Clouds lowering on hills. The lowering of clouds always indicates an increase in humidity which is a sure sign of rain and poor visibility to the pilot.

A backing wind. A backing wind is a wind changing steadily in a counterclockwise direction. This change in direction indicates that a "low" is approaching whose center will pass nearby, bringing rain and poor visibility.

When clouds float at different levels and in nearly opposite directions, expect heavy rains. Such an unsettled condition of the atmosphere indicates separate bodies of air with different temperatures. This is bound to result in the warmer air being cooled to its dew point to bring rain.

When cirrus clouds merge into cirrostratus. As previously explained, this is a sure sign that a warm front is approaching with its inevitable lowering of clouds and rain.

Perhaps the most famous bit of weather lore is the poem usually credited to Dr. Edward Jenner, the discoverer of vaccination. It contains a wealth of weather wisdom and is quoted here in full:

> The hollow winds begin to blow,
> The clouds look black, the glass is low,
> The soot falls down, the spaniels sleep,
> And spiders from their cobwebs creep;
> Last night the Sun went pale to bed,
> The Moon in halos hid her head,
> The boding shepherd heaves a sigh,
> For see! a rainbow spans the sky;
> The walls are damp, the ditches smell,
> Closed is the pink-eyed pimpernel;
> Hark how the chairs and tables crack!
> Old Betty's joints are on the rack;
> Her corns with shooting pains torment her
> And to her bed untimely sent her;
> Loud quack the ducks, the peacocks cry,
> The distant hills are looking nigh;
> How restless are the snorting swine!
> The busy flies disturb the kine,
> Low o'er the grass the swallow wings;
> The cricket, too, how sharp he sings!

Puss on the hearth, with velvet paws,
Sits wiping o'er her whiskered jaws;
The smoke from chimneys right ascends,
Then spreading back to earth it bends;
The wind unsteady veers around,
Or setting in the South is found;
Through the clear stream the fishes rise,
And nimbly catch th' incautious flies;
The glowworms, num'rous, clear, and bright,   .
Illumed the dewy dell last night;
At dusk the squatty toad was seen
Hopping and crawling o'er the green;
The whirling dust the wind obeys,
And in the rapid eddy plays;
The frog has changed his yellow vest,
And in a russet coat is dressed;
The sky is green, the air is still,
The merry blackbird's voice is shrill,
The dog, so altered is his taste,
Quits mutton bones on grass to feast;
And see yon rooks, how odd their flight!
They imitate the gliding kite,
And seem precipitate to fall,
As if they felt the piercing ball.
The tender colts on back do lie,
Nor heed the traveler passing by.
In fiery red the Sun doth rise,
Then wades through clouds to mount the skies.
'Twill surely rain,—I see with sorrow
Our jaunt must be put off tomorrow.

FAIR WEATHER PREDICTIONS

Not all weather signs indicate poor weather. There are numerous ways in which the wary aviator can tell whether he should go out to the airport or go to the movies instead. Many a pilot has gone to bed secure in the knowledge that he could go ahead with his plans for a flight the following day, because he had read the signs.

Spiders build webs. These insects are able to tell when good weather is coming, by dryness of the air and the changes in pressure, and then they build their webs fearlessly. They seem to know that rain and moisture are far off and will not destroy the results of their labor.

Dew or frost. Frost and dew form only on still cloudless nights. Even if there are no clouds in the sky a stratum of warm moist air would prevent heat radiation from the earth and no dew or frost could form. Hence either dew or frost in the morning is a pretty good sign of fair weather for the new day.

Wide difference between temperature and dew point. The wider the difference between the temperature and dew point the better the weather. Until the dew point and temperature approach one another no condensation or precipitation is possible. Without condensation there can be no clouds, fog, rain, etc., to restrict flying.

A veering wind. Veering winds are those changing direction in a clockwise direction. They show that the low pressure area is passing away and good weather is coming.

Westerly winds. With the exception of the Pacific Coast and western Florida, west winds have been blowing over dry land and therefore are not heavily moisture laden. Consequently they are an almost universal guarantee of good weather, with the exception of the places noted.

Cirrus clouds dissolving. When clouds of any type dissolve it is a sign that the air is dry and is absorbing the moisture of the clouds. If cirrus clouds dissolve they are not the true cirrus that warns of the coming of a warm front and bad weather. When clouds of any kind diminish it is a sign of good weather.

High clouds. When clouds are high there is relatively little moisture in the air. As long as clouds remain high the weather and visibility will remain good.

This chapter could go on indefinitely telling about air that is rough when there are cumulus clouds because of the upward and downward currents of convection; how bluish clouds bring high wind; to beware of hot thin air—and gusty air on takeoffs and landings, and so on. It should be pointed out, however, that there is no truth to proverbs which seek to correlate weather with the phases of the moon, etc. Long range forecasts such as squirrels gathering nuts portending a hard winter, or a thin coat on a fox pointing to an early summer, are of course pure superstition.

The first part of this book has explained how anyone interested in aviation can tell WHEN it is safe to fly. The next step is navigation, or HOW to get where you want to go.

17

PRINCIPLES OF NAVIGATION

IT is commonly believed that the study of navigation is very difficult and that it calls for a high degree of technical or mathematical knowledge. Unquestionably such knowledge is helpful in this as in all other applied sciences, but it is a fact that anyone who can read and write and is able to do simple arithmetic can become a competent navigator. All that is necessary to become proficient in air navigation, or avigation, is earnest effort, practice and common sense.

In its original sense navigation had to do with ships and the art of sailing, but we use the same principles in the act of moving from one place to another by any means whatsoever. When you want to go from one room to another in your home you merely walk in the right direction and in a short time, when you have covered the distance, you are where you wanted to go. You determine the direction of the other room by visual observation, which in such a simple case is scarcely conscious, and you get there by following a certain path in reference to other parts of the house.

When you go to your office in the morning or return at night you use the same method. You start out, go straight, bear right, turn left, pass corners, turn at the traffic signal or the car track, noting as you go the gas station, the river, or any other of the reference points that tell you that you are on the right path. Traveling from one city to another you follow a known highway constituting a continuous reference line along which appear all sorts of signs and landmarks to keep you on the right track.

All of this is a simple form of navigation. It comprises the chief elements of navigation, namely, position, direction, distance and time. You want to go to some place that is a certain distance from your present position in a definite direction, and it will take time to get there. These are the primary elements of navigation, whether by sea, land or air. The same principles apply whether the case is the simple act of going from one room to another in your house or moving in relation to the heavenly bodies as in celestial navigation.

The first factor to be considered is that of position, which is the location of a place in relation to other places. Direction is the position of one point as observed or determined from another. But before we can establish direction we must accept some one point as a standard. Once we have established such a point we can readily describe the location of all other points by their relationship to the standard reference point. This relationship of one position to a standard position, or of one point to a standard point, is called the *bearing*.

The best way to understand bearing is by means of the geometric figure we know as a circle. The Babylonian scientists divided the circle into 360 parts, called degrees, to correspond with the number of days in their year. If these divisions are marked out progressively on a circle's circumference and we stand in the center of that circle, in any direction we look we shall see some number. The number that we would see will be the bearing, or direction, in degrees from us in relation to the zero point. The zero point, in other words, becomes our standard reference point. Now, if this zero point is called north, the 90 degree point east, the 180 degree point south, and the 270 degree point west, we have an excellent system of indicating direction.

HOUSE BEARS 42°
AIRPORT BEARS 140°

To find the bearing of any point, or the direction or angle it is from you, you only have to imagine where your gaze will cross the circle when you look at the point in question. Thus if you see your office from your home, over the 90th point on the circle, you know that the office is east of your home, or that its bearing is 90 degrees.

Now we come to distance, which may be defined as the length of the path between two points. Distance is commonly measured on the earth in terms of miles. Our statute mile is merely an arbitrary unit taken from the English furlong.

One mile equals 8 furlongs of 660 feet or 5280 feet. The distance between any two points can be indicated in terms of miles.

Having the principles of position, direction, and distance established, we merely have to take into account the amount of time it takes to travel from one point to another. This will give us the rate of speed and we then have a working basis for all of our problems of navigation.

In aerial navigation we still want to go from one point on the earth's surface to another. However, we travel not along the earth's surface but above it, through an entirely different medium. Aerial navigation, in addition to the basic problems, has special problems that must be solved in a special manner.

Before we can begin to solve these problems of aerial navigation, an elementary understanding of the earth as a physical object is not only desirable, but necessary.

18

THE EARTH

THE earth is commonly spoken of as a sphere. For all practical purposes this is true, although actually the earth is not a true sphere. It has already been shown that the earth has a steady rotating motion and we have noted that gyroscopic action keeps it approximately in one plane. We have referred to the North and South poles—the points where the imaginary axis of the earth intersects the surface. These are the two places where theoretically no motion exists. With the points that we know as North and South definitely located, it becomes possible to cover the earth with an orderly pattern of imaginary lines which may be used for reference.

Circling the earth lengthwise, or longitudinally, are lines running through and connecting both poles. These lines are called *merid-*

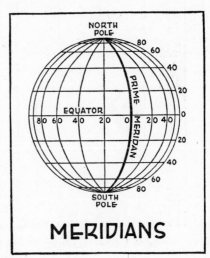

MERIDIANS

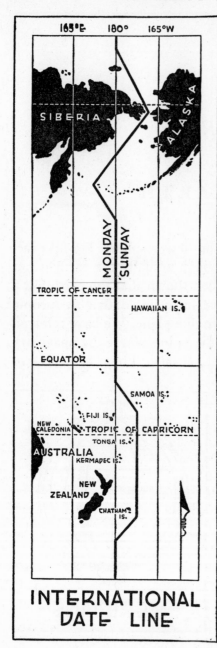

165°E   180°   165°W

SIBERIA

ALASKA

MONDAY   SUNDAY

TROPIC OF CANCER

HAWAIIAN IS.

EQUATOR

SAMOA IS.

FIJI IS.

NEW CALEDONIA   TROPIC OF CAPRICORN

TONGA IS.

AUSTRALIA

KERMADEC IS.

NEW ZEALAND

CHATHAM IS.

INTERNATIONAL DATE LINE

ians and we use them to measure *longitude*. In order to distinguish between different meridians one has been established as the *zero* or *prime meridian*. This is sometimes called the *Greenwich Meridian* because it passes through Greenwich, a part of the City of London, England. At each degree going east and west of the prime meridian are other meridians similarly circling the earth north and south. On the opposite side of the earth from the prime meridian is the 180th meridian, known as the *International Date Line*.

Degrees are units too large for the precise location of places. Consequently each degree is divided into 60 minutes and each minute is further divided into 60 seconds. It must be noted that in this connection minutes and seconds are not units of time, but of angle or bearing. Any point east or west of the prime meridian may therefore be located in degrees, minutes and seconds. The position of a place east or west of the prime meridian is called the longitude of that place.

Crossing the meridians east and west are parallel circles appropriately called parallels. These parallels cross the meridians at right angles and are similarly divided into degrees, minutes and seconds. They define *latitude*. The *prime* or *zero parallel* is called the *equator*. The parallels are numbered starting at zero at the equator to 90 degrees at each pole. Latitude, therefore, is the position of a place North or South of the equator.

It may be seen that any point on the earth's surface may be definitely located by means of latitude and longitude. For instance, the location of the observatory of the Smithsonian Institution in Washington, D. C., is 38 degrees, 53 minutes and 17 seconds north of the equator and 77 degrees, 1 minute

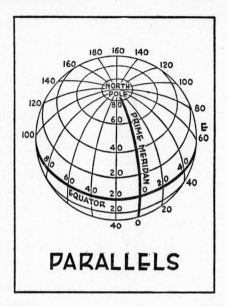

PARALLELS

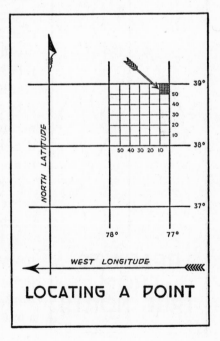

LOCATING A POINT

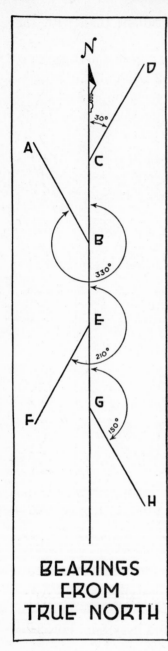

BEARINGS
FROM
TRUE NORTH

and 34 seconds west of the Greenwich Meridian. This point would be written lat. 38° 53' 17" N. long. 77° 1' 34" W.

We have seen that the meridians run north and south and the parallels run east and west. The meridians establish longitude and the parallels latitude. Knowing the latitude and longitude of each of two points, we can establish the direction or bearing of one with respect to the other. This is most conveniently done by regarding true north as the standard reference direction, and locating all other points with reference thereto. The meridians give us the direction of north itself and we can define the relationship of other points to one another by the manner in which they "bear" on true north. In this manner direction is established. In the illustration on this page, D bears 30 degrees from C, A bears 330 degrees from B, F bears 210 degrees from E and H bears 150 degrees from G.

While the numbered meridians have a definite location, for purposes of navigation any line running north and south may be called a meridian. In our navigating we will be more concerned with the meridians than with the parallels.

On a flat surface the shortest distance between two points is a straight line. On a sphere this is still true but the straight line between two points would have to go *through* the sphere. On the surface the shortest distance between two points is along the *arc* of a *great circle*.

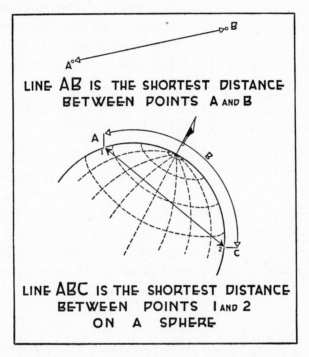

LINE AB IS THE SHORTEST DISTANCE BETWEEN POINTS A AND B

LINE ABC IS THE SHORTEST DISTANCE BETWEEN POINTS 1 AND 2 ON A SPHERE

A great circle is any circle on the earth which divides the globe into two equal parts or hemispheres. The meridians and the equator are all great circles, but the parallels are not. Obviously a parallel like the 40th, for example, which runs across the United States in the approximate latitude of New York, does not divide the earth into two equal parts. The northern part is smaller than the southern. It is not necessary, however,

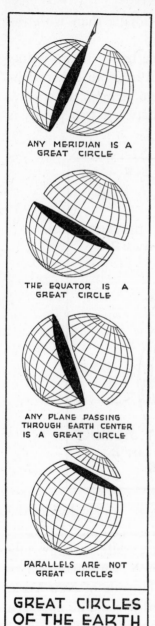

ANY MERIDIAN IS A
GREAT CIRCLE

THE EQUATOR IS A
GREAT CIRCLE

ANY PLANE PASSING
THROUGH EARTH CENTER
IS A GREAT CIRCLE

PARALLELS ARE NOT
GREAT CIRCLES

**GREAT CIRCLES
OF THE EARTH**

for a great circle to run north and south like the meridians or east and west like the equator. Any plane intersecting the earth's surface and passing through the center of the earth forms a great circle. A great circle can run in any direction as long as its plane passes through the center of the earth, and its arc is always the shortest distance along the surface between the two points which it connects.

Because of its dependable regularity the amount of time that it takes for the globe to make one complete rotation has been established as the unit of time that we know as a day. The day is said to start when the sun is directly over the meridian on the opposite side of the earth. The middle of the day is the instant that the sun is directly overhead or crossing the meridian on which we are standing.

This instant is known as M, noon, or 12 o'clock. But instead of letting every meridian have its own noon, the earth is divided in an east-west direction into 24 zones or divisions of 15 degrees each (24 × 15 degrees = 360 degrees or the complete circle). This gives us 24 noons as the earth makes one complete revolution. These 24 divisions correspond to the 24 hours of the day. The Greenwich Meridian

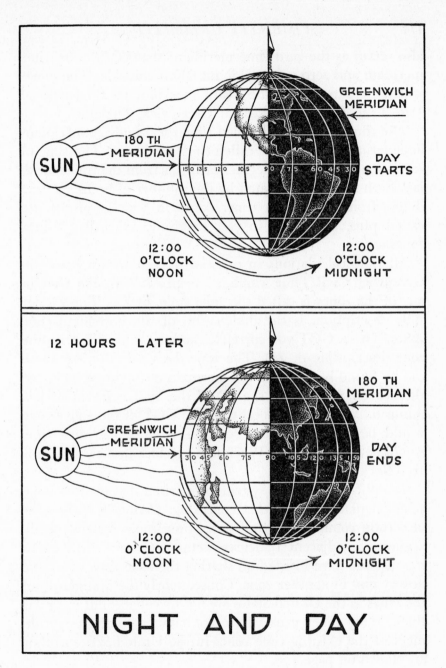

GREENWICH
MERIDIAN

180 TH
MERIDIAN

SUN

DAY
STARTS

150 135 120 105 90 75 60 45 30

12:00
O'CLOCK
NOON

12:00
O'CLOCK
MIDNIGHT

12 HOURS LATER

180 TH
MERIDIAN

GREENWICH
MERIDIAN

SUN

DAY
ENDS

30 45 60 75 90 105 120 135 150

12:00
O'CLOCK
NOON

12:00
O'CLOCK
MIDNIGHT

NIGHT AND DAY

also serves as the zero time meridian; that is, the zero time meridian and zero geographic meridian coincide. Therefore, when the sun crosses the 180th meridian or International Date Line, a new day starts at Greenwich, England.

The time divisions are called *time zones* and the meridians designating the zones are called *time meridians*. The time of each zone is set for 7½ degrees each way from the time meridian. Each zone is designated by the number of hours its time differs from Greenwich time. Zones in west longitude are called plus, and zones in east longitude are called minus zones.

All time calculations in celestial navigation are based on Greenwich Civil Time which is known as GCT. The time in any of the zones is called the zone time, or ZT. The ZD, or zone description, is the designation of the individual time zones. To get GCT you correlate the zone time, ZT, with the zone description, or ZD. The zone description of any place can be found by dividing the meridian of the place by 15, to the nearest 10th. Thus the ZD of the 87th E meridian is a minus 6. At 10 o'clock local time the GCT of the above zone would be 4 o'clock. New York, in W 75th meridian time would be in plus 5 zone. When it is 5 o'clock in New York it is 10 o'clock in London.

Complications in this system have arisen that tend to make time calculations somewhat confusing. Owing to the wishes of certain communities and states time zones are not neatly arranged in adjacent 15-degree sections. Certain small towns in one zone have insisted on sharing the zone time of a large nearby city in another zone. Consequently the boundaries of the zones in the United States are not meridians, but irregular lines. Many other causes have contributed to the establishment of the existing time zones in the United States as they are shown on page 176.

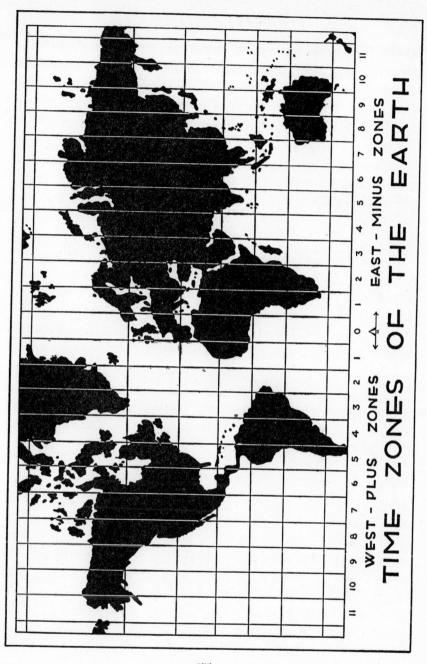

TIME ZONES OF THE EARTH

WEST - PLUS ZONES ←→ EAST - MINUS ZONES

Another cause of confusion is that although one day consists of 24 hours, our clocks and watches have faces showing only 12 hours. This means that our clocks and watches must go around twice for one day's time. Thus the hours of the day from midnight until noon have come to be known as the

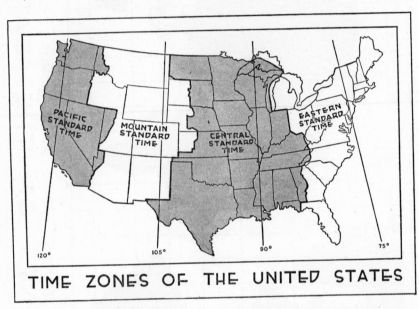

TIME ZONES OF THE UNITED STATES

A M hours from the Latin *ante meridian,* meaning before the meridian, while P M is derived from the Latin *post meridian,* or after meridian. In the Navy and in navigation practice generally the A M and P M system is not used. The time is kept from 0 to 24 in 4 digits. Thus 9:00 A M becomes 0900, and 2:37 P M is 1437, and so on. This is confusing at first but becomes easy with practice. The hours before noon are easy enough to understand, and the hours after noon become clear when it is realized that subtracting 1200 will give the P M hours as we know them in everyday life.

In making reports to airway traffic control centers, when

time zones are to be crossed it is best to report in the time of one's watch, stating which zone time that is. This will prevent confusion resulting from not knowing whether to add or subtract an hour.

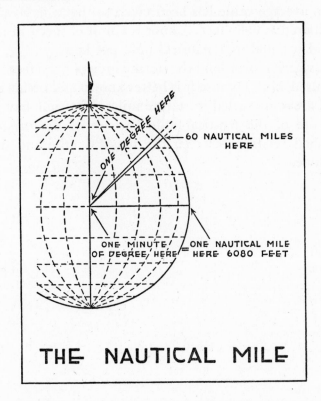

THE NAUTICAL MILE

To return for a moment to our explanation of a great circle, it will be remembered that a great circle is one whose center is the center of the earth itself, and the circumference of which lies upon the earth's surface. The length of arc on a great circle subtended by one minute of angle at the earth's center has been established as a nautical mile. Another way of putting this is to say that one minute of latitude is a nautical mile. There being 60 minutes in a degree, it follows that one degree of arc on the earth's surface is 60 nautical miles in length.

Since the earth is not quite a true sphere, the length of one minute of arc on a great circle will vary slightly. However, an average value has been taken so that a nautical mile is considered as 6080 feet. A knot is a unit of speed in navigation and is equal to 1 nautical mile per hour.

In navigation over land the statute mile of 5280 feet is commonly used, both because it is better known and because maps of land areas are scaled in statute miles. Maritime navigation makes use of the nautical mile because of the convenient established relation between the nautical mile and degrees of latitude.

19

MAPS AND CHARTS

If it were possible to look off into the distance and see the places you want to fly to, aerial navigation would be a simple matter. All you would have to do would be to take off, look for the city you wanted to go to, and then head toward it. You would fly in the direction of your destination, passing over the rivers, lakes, railroads and other ground features automatically. It would be as simple as crossing the street.

But because of limitations of visibility, curvature of the earth, distance, etc., this is not possible. So we must have some sort of device that represents the earth over which we travel. To be of any value this device must be accurate and it must be of large enough scale to show the common terrain features of the earth. Thus equipped, a pilot can check the features on this device against the actual features on the ground, as he flies over them, and thus fly a straight course. This is essentially the principle of piloting, the simplest type of navigation.

The most realistic way of showing the earth is as a globe. Of course the use of a globe in an airplane is not practicable, not only because of its shape, but because the scale would necessarily be so small that not much detail could be shown.

Nor would an enlarged portion of a globe be much more convenient. The best representation of the earth for use with aircraft is the plane-surface map. Such a map is merely a representation on paper of the earth or a portion of the earth's surface.

The map is the most important tool of the navigator. This is true regardless of what method of navigation he uses. A chart is the same as a map except that a chart is usually thought of as a map showing water areas rather than land areas. Correctly speaking, a chart is a projection of the earth's surface made especially for navigational uses. Therefore the maps used in aerial navigation are referred to as charts.

With a suitable map or chart we have gone far in solving

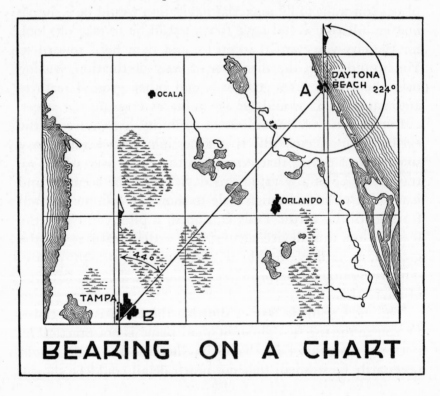

BEARING ON A CHART

our navigational problems. From charts we can determine location, bearing and distance. Points are located on a chart in relation to the meridians and parallels. The bearing between them can be determined by connecting the points with a straight line and then measuring the angle this line makes with the meridian.

The distance between the points can be determined from the scale of the map. Scale is nothing more than the proportionate size of the map compared to the part of the earth it represents. Thus a scale of 1 to 1000 would mean that each unit on the map would be equal to 1000 such units on the earth. This method of indicating scale is called *representative fraction.*

Other ways of indicating the scale of a map are by words and figures, and graphically. Words and figures may be used in the form of a statement such as, 1 inch equals 8 miles. The graphic method employs a graduated rule on the map, divided into equal parts, each representing a certain distance on the ground. Most maps carry more than one scale indication for convenience.

A variety of map types are in common use, each serving a special purpose. As aerial navigators, we need a special type of map. We want one made especially for aviation. There are various types of aeronautical maps published, each designed for a particular type of flight.

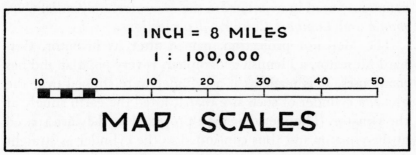

1 INCH = 8 MILES

1 : 100,000

MAP SCALES

The ideal aeronautical chart would show areas in their true shape, their true proportion, the great circles as straight lines and the meridians and parallels crossing each other at right angles. But as the earth is a spherical object and is necessarily portrayed as a flat surface on charts, certain of these features must be sacrificed to more important features. It

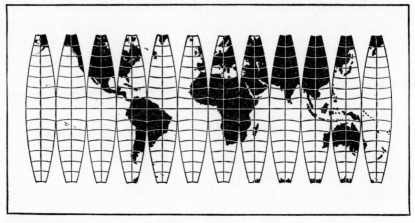

is therefore necessary to understand the basic principles of map-making, and in what qualities each method surpasses, in order to know which map is best for any particular type of flight.

The system of lines, symbols and curves used to represent the earth on a flat surface is called a *projection*. There are many different kinds and variations of projections. Those most commonly used in aviation are the *Mercator, Polyconic, Gnomonic* and *Lambert Conformal* projections.

The Mercator projection, named after its inventor, Gerhard Mercator, a Flemish geographer, is very popular and has many uses. It is made as if a cylinder were slipped over the globe, a cylinder of such size that it fitted the earth snugly at the equator. The meridians are projected as they are spaced at the equator and thus continued to the cylinder as straight lines, parallel and equally spaced. The parallels of latitude are carried to the cylinder as they would be seen from the center of the earth. They also are represented as straight parallel lines, crossing the meridians at right angles. However the spacing of the parallels is not equal. As the distance toward the poles increases the spacing becomes greater. Owing to the increased spacing of the parallels and the fact that the

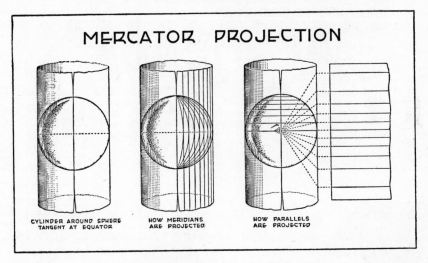

MERCATOR PROJECTION

CYLINDER AROUND SPHERE
TANGENT AT EQUATOR

HOW MERIDIANS
ARE PROJECTED

HOW PARALLELS
ARE PROJECTED

meridians do not converge at the poles as they do on the earth, great distortion results in the higher latitudes. Because of the varying latitude spacing it is not possible to use a uniform scale of distances which will apply to all portions of the chart.

However, the Mercator has definite advantages which for many purposes outweigh the undesirable features. A straight line connecting two points is a true bearing. This is the path an airplane would fly and is known as the *track*. It is not a great circle but a *rhumb line* or *loxodromic curve*—a line that cuts all meridians it crosses at the same angle. The Mercator is an easy map to plot upon as latitudes and longitudes may be

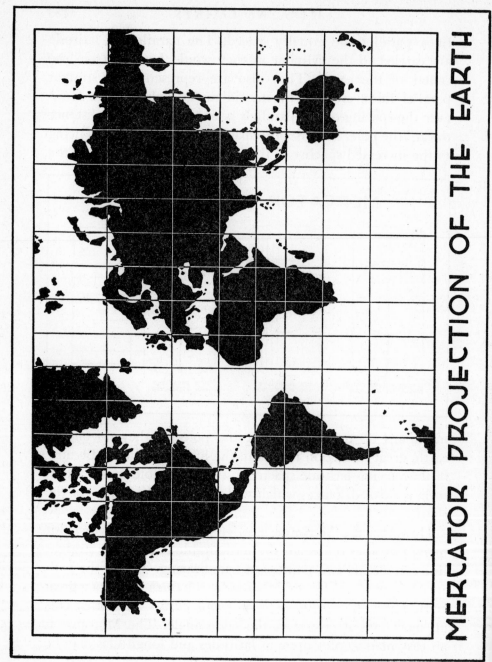

MERCATOR PROJECTION OF THE EARTH

laid down easily and accurately. Finally, the latitude scale is in nautical miles, each minute of arc of latitude being equal to one mile at the same latitude.

This type of chart has not come into universal use in aviation, but could very easily be adapted to aerial navigation if there were not better types available. It is used in maritime navigation and by Navy pilots whose work must be consistent with methods and charts of the fleet.

In the polyconic projection (polyconic means "many cones")

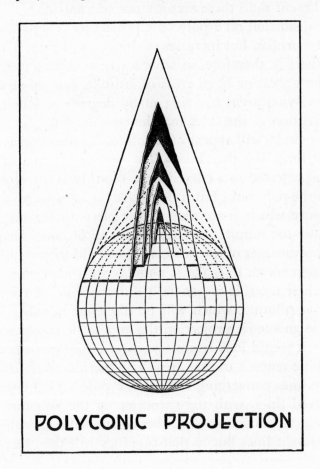

POLYCONIC PROJECTION

the central meridian of the area to be represented is shown as a straight line. Along this line the parallels of the area are spaced as they are on the sphere. Then each parallel is projected separately upon a cone tangent to the earth at that parallel. On the finished chart, while the central meridian appears as a straight line, all others are curves converging to a center in the extended central meridian. The parallels of latitude are arcs of circles, whose centers also lie in the extension of the central meridian. Since they have different centers and different radii these arcs are not concentric.

The distortion on a polyconic projection is zero along the central meridian but increases to the east and west. The polyconic chart is, therefore, suitable for representing long north and south areas or large areas of latitude, but unsatisfactory for portraying areas covering many degrees of longitude as the distortion at the sides may be considerable.

Great circles will appear on a polyconic projection as almost straight lines, but the rhumb line, or line of equal bearing, will be projected as a curved line. Plotting is therefore difficult on the polyconic, but it does have the advantage of a scale of distance which is accurate at any place on the map. This is because the minutes of latitude are all of equal length.

The advantages of the polyconic as an aid to navigation are not great enough to make it popular with navigators generally. When used, it is generally for the type of navigation known as piloting, which will be discussed shortly.

In the gnomonic projection the area to be represented appears as it would look from the center of the earth projected on a plane tangent to that area. The meridians are shown as straight lines converging toward the pole and the parallels are curved lines, with the exception of the equator. When the point of tangency is at the equator the meridians remain straight lines but in that case they will then be parallel

POLYCONIC PROJECTION
OF
NORTH AMERICA

to one another as they are in the Mercator projection.

Since the observer is supposed to be at the center of the earth, he is in the plane of all great circles. Therefore, all great circles appear as straight lines on the projection. It follows that any straight line on the gnomonic projection is a portion of a great circle.

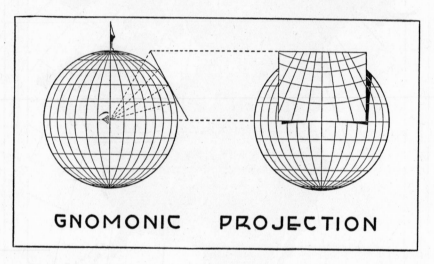

GNOMONIC   PROJECTION

Since a great circle is the shortest distance between two points on a sphere, and is represented on a gnomonic projection as a straight line, this projection is very valuable in plotting long courses.

In actual practice when a long course is to be flown it is laid down on the gnomonic projection. The latitude co-ordinates are noted where this course crosses the various meridians. These co-ordinates are then transferred to a Mercator projection and connected by straight lines, which results in a large arc composed of short lines or cords. This will be an approximate great circle course on a Mercator projection.

In the discussion of the Mercator projection it was brought out that a straight line on a Mercator is not a great circle but

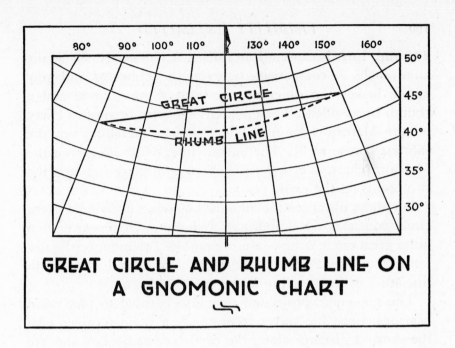

GREAT CIRCLE AND RHUMB LINE ON A GNOMONIC CHART

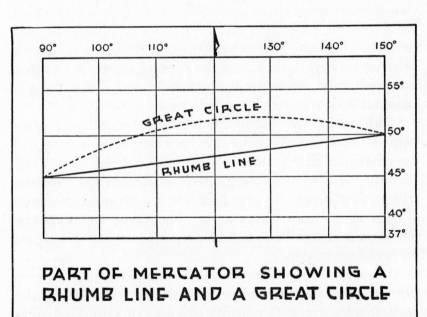

PART OF MERCATOR SHOWING A RHUMB LINE AND A GREAT CIRCLE

a rhumb line, because all meridians it crosses are cut at the same angle. A comparison between the Mercator and gnomonic makes the difference between a great circle and a rhumb line evident. The great circle course becomes a curve on the Mercator. Rhumb line flying is, therefore, not the shortest course to fly. The curved line, while longer on the Mercator chart, is actually the shortest distance between the two points on the earth.

For short distances the amount of saving in flying a great circle course is not important. Usually on flights over 600 miles great circle courses are preferable. For instance the distance from New York to Paris is 3088 nautical miles by rhumb line and 2976 nautical miles by great circle course.

The gnomonic projection may also be used to plot radio bearings, since the waves received by a radio receiver take the shortest distance along the earth and radio bearings are consequently great circle tracks. About the only use to which the gnomonic projection can be put in aviation is to plot radio bearings and great circle courses, since the distortion becomes very great away from the point of tangency. Another reason why the gnomonic is not widely used is that the distance scales are extremely complicated.

While maps, other than those made especially for aeronautical work, may be helpful in an emergency, it is best to use charts designed primarily for avigational purposes. Until recently there were no such charts available. But with the tremendous increase in popular flying a great need for standardized aeronautical maps arose. The Coast and Geodetic Survey was assigned the task of preparing satisfactory charts for aerial navigation.

After considerable thought and investigation the Lambert Conformal projection was selected as the one offering the greatest advantages. It portrays extensive longitudinal areas accurately, which makes it particularly suitable for representing the wide east-west area of the United States. Because of its acceptance and general use it will be treated in greater detail than other types.

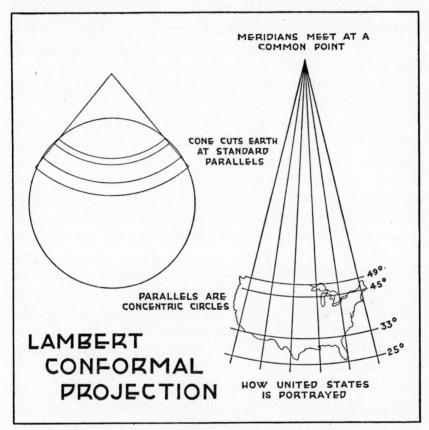

MERIDIANS MEET AT A COMMON POINT

CONE CUTS EARTH AT STANDARD PARALLELS

PARALLELS ARE CONCENTRIC CIRCLES

LAMBERT CONFORMAL PROJECTION

HOW UNITED STATES IS PORTRAYED

49°
45°
33°
25°

This projection was perfected in 1772 by Johann Heinrich Lambert, a physicist, mathematician, and astronomer. Little was known about it until the first World War, when it was adopted by the Allies because of its accurate representation of the topography of the warring countries of central Europe.

The Lambert Conformal is a conic projection, but it is

projected on the area of one cone, which is not tangent to the earth but cuts it at two selected parallels within the area to be represented. The parallels selected to represent the United States are the 45th and the 33rd, which are known as standard parallels. Along these parallels the scale is exact. The area between is projected inward and the scale is slightly smaller. The area shown outside of the parallels is slightly larger in scale than on the earth. This error is very slight, however. The illustration on page 191 shows the method of construction of the Lambert projection.

On the finished chart the meridians appear as straight lines converging at a point beyond the limits of the chart. The parallels of latitude are concentric circles whose common center is the intersection of the meridians. Meridians and parallels intersect at right angles, and the angles formed by any two lines on the earth's surface are correctly represented.

On the Lambert a straight line is practically a great circle course and for all practical purposes represents the shortest distance between two points. All terrain features such as lakes, rivers, etc., are represented in their true form, as indicated by the word "conformal" in the name. One scale can be used anywhere on the chart and in addition the latitude scale is in nautical miles. Different sections can be joined accurately. The Lambert is an easy chart to plot upon. In general it is the most satisfactory of all projections for aerial navigation, combining practically all of the desired qualities and having a minimum of unfavorable features.

20

ESPECIALLY FOR AVIATION

THERE are several types of Lambert charts of the United States available to pilots. These may be obtained direct from the Coast and Goedetic Survey or from dealers throughout the country. An index, price list and list of dealers can be had by writing to the Coast and Geodetic Survey, Washington, D. C.

The Aeronautical Planning Chart covers the entire United States on a scale of 1 to 5,000,000 or about 80 miles to the inch. It is useful in planning long flights.

There are six charts overlapping one another covering the United States that are made especially for plotting radio bearings. These are called Radio Direction Finding charts and are developed on a scale of 1 to 2,000,000 or about 32 miles to the inch. The illustration on page 322 shows the coverage of these charts.

The most generally used charts, however, are the sectional and regional charts. The sectional charts, of which there are eighty-seven covering the United States, are on a scale of 1 to 500,000 or about 8 miles to the inch. These are suitable for all forms of navigation, but because of their large scale, fidelity, and wealth of information are particularly adapted

CHARTS OF THE UNITED STATES

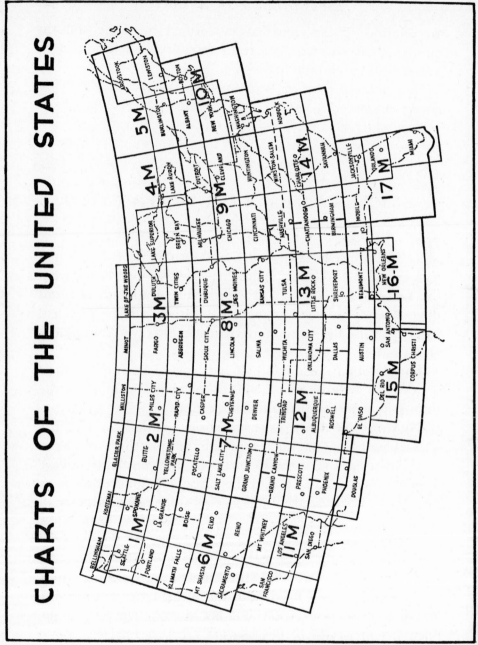

to piloting. These charts are identified by name and the proper chart covering a certain territory is determined by reference to a graphic index.

The regional charts are on a smaller scale covering the same area represented by two or more sectional charts. They are on a scale of 1 to 1,000,000 or about 16 miles to the inch and are made up in 17 sheets to cover the whole country. They are identified by number and are shown on the graphic index sheet of the illustration on page 194. Since they represent a larger area than the sectional chart they are more convenient on longer flights, obviating the necessity of changing charts frequently. They show all essential information, but the detail and landmark information shown on the sectional chart is not included on the regional chart.

Being designed primarily for aviation use, these charts include only information helpful to the air navigator. Features found on general maps, if of no help to the navigator, are omitted. On the other hand, details of importance to the pilot are often stressed because of their landmark or reference value.

Intelligent use of any chart requires an understanding of its features. All maps have information on the boundaries to show how to use them to the best advantage. The air navigation maps show the representative fraction scale in the upper right corner, and the name and index of adjoining sheets in the lower right corner. This index is helpful in quickly determining adjoining charts when a course runs off the one in use. Other aids to the use of the charts are the scale of miles, in graphic form at the bottom, minutes of latitude or nautical mile scale on the left side and minutes of longitude, also on the bottom. A short description of the construction features in the lower left corner is very helpful to those who want to take full advantage of the data offered.

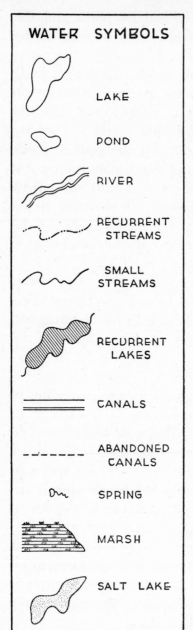

WATER SYMBOLS

LAKE

POND

RIVER

RECURRENT STREAMS

SMALL STREAMS

RECURRENT LAKES

CANALS

ABANDONED CANALS

SPRING

MARSH

SALT LAKE

Of great importance and interest to the pilot are the symbols representing topographical and aeronautical landmarks. Most of these symbols have been standard on United States Government maps for years and are commonly known. Others, such as the aeronautical symbols, being comparatively new, and of a specialized nature, are not so well known.

The more familiar a pilot becomes with these signs and the other features of the charts, the better success he will have in navigating.

Perhaps the easiest topographical features to distinguish are the water landmarks. These are shown in blue, the lakes and large rivers outlined and the smaller streams and canals as blue lines. While all of the features such as dry lakes, salt basins, canals and recurrent streams are not important all over the country, there are certain areas where these are conspicuous and distinctive guides.

Small towns with a population of 1000 or less are shown by a black circle. Larger towns with a population of between 1000 and 5000 are shown by a yellow square, and cities are shown in their actual shape. Railroads, called the "iron compass" by old-time pilots, are excellent landmarks. Crossties at 5-mile intervals, indicate whether the railroad is one track or more. Tracks are shown in black while prominent highways are drawn as purple lines.

Telegraph and power lines are represented by a red line broken with the letter T. These are particularly good references because they are plainly visible. Where they pass through forests there is usually a clearing alongside the line so that they are very plain. High-tension towers are painted silver and are very easy to see.

Lookout towers, quarries, oil derricks, etc., represented by appropriate symbols, are selected and placed on the chart because of their visibility from the air. Where a particularly good landmark cannot be spotted on the

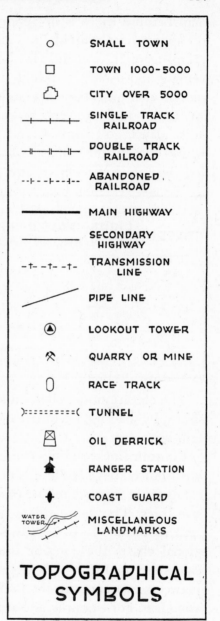

TOPOGRAPHICAL SYMBOLS

map because there is not enough room, or because there is no appropriate symbol, it is shown by a dot with an arrow pointing to it, and described verbally. These are very convenient and usually strikingly visible landmarks. Some examples of such miscellaneous landmarks found on various charts are tanks, radio towers, power stations, saw mills, lumber mills, dams, golf courses, and resorts. Others of interest are white domes and towers, silos, tall stacks, church steeples, logging camps, refineries, and prisons.

0	1000	2000	3000	5000	7000	9000	MAX.
GREEN	LIGHT GREEN	PALE BROWN	LIGHT BROWN	MEDIUM BROWN	DEEP BROWN	DARK BROWN	

KING MT. 3100

DEPRESSIONS

SAND DUNES

The elevation, or relief, on a sectional and regional chart is shown by shading, hachures, contour lines, and figures for certain locations.

Contour lines are lines connecting points of equal elevation or distance above sea level. The contour interval is the vertical distance represented by the difference between two successive lines. The datum plane is the point taken to represent zero elevation. It is usually sea level. On sectional and regional charts the contour interval is 1000 feet. Distinctive colors are used to represent certain elevations. Thus any area between two contour intervals may vary in altitude within 1000 feet. For example, the areas between the 1000- and 2000-foot interval, colored light green, have an elevation that will run anywhere between 1000 and 2000 feet above sea level.

At higher elevations one color may represent more than 1000 feet. The colors are given on each chart, with the elevation that they represent. The contour intervals are well labeled so that it is very simple to determine the elevation of any point to within 1000 feet. This is accurate enough for most purposes.

With a little thought and map study a fairly good mental picture of the elevation may be obtained from the contour lines and colors. When the lines are far apart they represent a

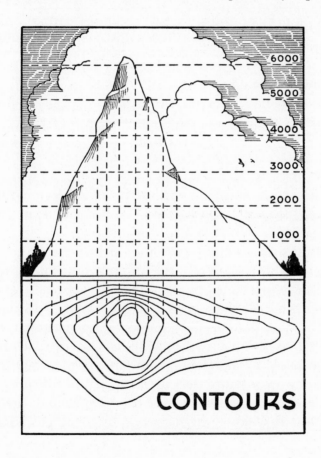

gradual slope; when they are close together the slope is steep. Contours that run together indicate a vertical slope or cliff, and where the rock overhangs the contour lines cross.

Where there is an abrupt rise, such as a mountain peak, it is represented by short radiating lines, together with the elevation in figures. Occasionally depressions in the ground make excellent reference points and these are shown by hachures on the inside of the outline of the depression.

To the above topographical features is added additional aeronautical information of special value to the aviator. This information is given on the charts in red.

The different kinds of airports with their elevation above sea level are shown by distinctive symbols. The letters LF near an airport symbol indicate that it is equipped with lighting facilities for night flying. The various airway beacons appear, spotted about every 10 miles along the various airways. The airways themselves connect important cities.

Beacons, which are to airmen what lighthouses are to seamen, have various features. Used principally as reference and identification points for night flying, they fill the need caused by objects not being visible in darkness.

The rotating beacon, indicated by a star with a white center, is a powerful light rotating six times a minute and sending out its beams of light about horizontally. Each beacon is numbered for each ten-mile distance from the terminus of the airway it is located upon.

Certain rotating beacons have course lights, shown on the chart by arrows pointed in the direction of the lights. These course lights are in color, green when near a lighted field, yellow near an unlighted field, and red when no field is nearby. These course lights flash an identifying signal, in code, which is indicated on the chart near the beacon symbol.

Some rotating beacons have an auxiliary beacon that also

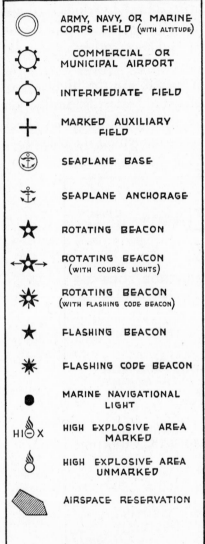

○	ARMY, NAVY, OR MARINE CORPS FIELD (WITH ALTITUDE)
✪	COMMERCIAL OR MUNICIPAL AIRPORT
✪	INTERMEDIATE FIELD
✛	MARKED AUXILIARY FIELD
⚓	SEAPLANE BASE
⚓	SEAPLANE ANCHORAGE
★	ROTATING BEACON
←★→	ROTATING BEACON (WITH COURSE LIGHTS)
✴	ROTATING BEACON (WITH FLASHING CODE BEACON)
★	FLASHING BEACON
✳	FLASHING CODE BEACON
●	MARINE NAVIGATIONAL LIGHT
HI⊖X	HIGH EXPLOSIVE AREA MARKED
⊙	HIGH EXPLOSIVE AREA UNMARKED
◣	AIRSPACE RESERVATION

AIRWAY INFORMATION

flashes a signal in code. These are identified by rays added to the symbol.

A plain star, smaller than the rotating beacon star, indicates the location of a non-rotating flashing beacon. When this type flashes a code signal, rays are added to the star symbol.

Beacons located at airports are placed in combination with the airport symbol so that the beacon appears in the center of the airport.

Air space reservations are spaces designated by executive order and may not be flown over at any altitude. These are shown by crossruling. Danger and high explosive areas, over which flight is restricted, are appropriately marked.

Unusual obstructions are indicated by a towerlike design and the height of the object is given in figures.

Placed conveniently in various places on the chart are compass roses, or circles graduated in degrees and quarter points, which can be used to measure courses and bearings quickly.

Lines of equal magnetic variation and the various civil air-ways are shown in red. The civil airways are 20 miles wide and terminate in control zones, and meet other airways at control zones of intersection.

The radio ranges, also shown in red, are the highways of the air. Their operation will be covered later. Radio marker beacons are aural reference points by which a pilot may check his position by radio. The "M" type, shown on the chart by a

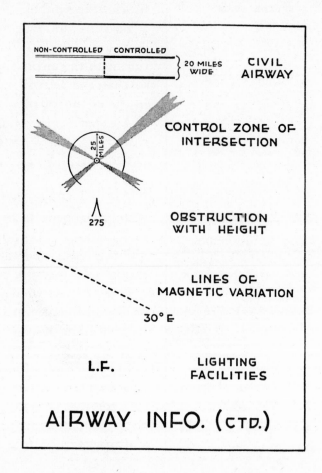

SENTINELS OF TWO AGES. Guarding against invasion of the Mississippi Valley, Fort Pike on Pass Rigolets ..
along the Old Spanish Trail kept vigil a century ago over the Mississippi Sound. And now the airway beacon along
the Buccaneer Route of the National Airlines offers silent protection to the flyers of our day.

dotted circle, is a low-power transmitter with a range of about ten miles. It operates on the same frequency as the radio range on which it is located. Often placed at the junction of two beams, it serves as notice to the pilot that it is time to

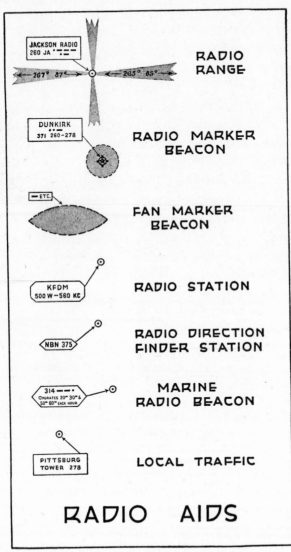

RADIO AIDS

retune his receiver to the new beam. "FM" type markers emit an ultra-high-frequency signal in a fan-shaped pattern. These are located on airways, usually near large airports. With proper equipment their signals can be received by radio. They also emit signals that can be received as light. Selected broadcasting stations with their frequencies are given for radio-compass use or for broadcast reception. Radio direction finder stations and marine radiobeacon stations are shown with their frequencies.

The data supplied on these charts are constantly changing with new developments. This is particularly true of the aeronautical and radio data. While this is not so important for the pilot flying by piloting or dead reckoning, it is vital that charts used in instrument flight be kept up to date. Changes on these charts are noted on the *Weekly Notices to Airmen* sent to airports and to those who request them by the Civil Aeronautics Administration. Charts are revised from time to time, but it is up to the owner to keep them up to date once they have been published. These *Notices* have been discontinued to the general public for the duration but will be resumed after the war is over.

21

METHODS OF NAVIGATING

THERE are four basic methods of aerial navigation, namely, piloting, sometimes called pilotage, dead reckoning, celestial navigation, and radio navigation.

Of these four methods *piloting* is by far the simplest and probably the one most commonly used by private pilots. It is accomplished by flying in relation to landmarks and ground features, such as lakes, rivers, railroads, mountains, power lines, etc. It is extremely simple when the pilot knows and can see the country over which he is flying. With a good knowledge of chart reading, and with the appropriate chart, it can be done safely without instruments, even over strange country. Piloting is used on short cross-country flights, in good weather, when the ground is visible.

Dead reckoning is that method of air navigation whereby a pilot can determine his course and position by calculation from flight data. It is twofold in scope. The course is planned before taking off. Later, during flight, positions are determined by the course and time flown, the speed of the aircraft, etc., and checked by any other methods available. Dead reckoning comes from the original expression "deduced reckoning," which implies planned preparation. It is very effective and accurate, and combined with piloting as a check becomes very dependable. A good knowledge of dead-reckoning principles will enable a pilot to fly cross country safely even under unfavorable conditions.

Celestial navigation is the system of determining position on the earth by reference to the celestial bodies. This is done by observation of the sun, moon, stars, and planets. This type of navigation is seldom used on flights under 1000 miles, except as a hobby. Its practical value lies in its use on long flights. A knowledge of celestial navigation is not only practical but is necessary to the transoceanic pilot. It is also a necessity to the military bombing pilot, who must make long flights over hostile country and return without landing, usually at night.

Long flights are made at high altitudes and great distances are covered above the overcast. When one is out of sight of the ground for long periods of time, celestial navigation becomes an important supplement to radio navigation. In case of poor radio reception, or total radio failure, celestial navigation can be depended upon. This type of avigation is not practicable for the average private pilot, and an understanding of it is not required for a pilot's certificate.

The importance of *radio navigation* is steadily increasing. It is particularly valuable in bad weather. Radio used in conjunction with the proper instruments provides a means of maintaining flight that otherwise would be impossible. The most important radio method is that of the Civil Aeronautics Administration. In this system a pilot is guided by means of radio beams directed to and from airports. The pilot follows these beams by the intensity, tone, and character of the radio signals. The use of radio will soon become universal. Many airports today will not permit airplanes to land unless they are equipped with two-way radio.

With the exception of celestial navigation, which is generally reserved for long non-stop flights, we shall discuss in detail the other methods of avigation, beginning with the simplest—piloting.

By this time, after the study of the sectional and regional charts and the repeated mention of landmarks and reference points, the principle of piloting probably has become clear. But because it is such an important and widely practiced method of avigating, a little further discussion is indicated.

To fly a course by piloting it is only necessary to have, as navigation materials, a chart of the area, a pencil and a straightedge. To begin, a straight line is drawn on the chart connecting the starting point and the destination. The area along this line should then be studied to determine if there are any terrain features along the route such as mountains, forests, wide swamps, etc., which might make flying over a direct course hazardous. If there are advisable detours, they should be planned at this point, otherwise the direct line will represent the route to be followed. Prominent and distinctive landmarks and their relative position along the line of flight should be noted. All that remains then is to take off, head in the general direction of the destination, and follow the line by referring to the selected landmarks. Actually there is a little more to it than that.

Let us take a practical example of a flight to be navigated by piloting, and analyze the various factors that must be considered so that we may proceed safely and intelligently. In order that the discussion may be thoroughly practical certain matters other than those pertaining solely to navigation will be considered.

Let's suppose we want to fly from Buffalo, N. Y., to Erie, Pa. The first step is to get the Detroit sectional chart upon which the whole flight can be traced. Upon looking at the chart it becomes apparent that if we were to take off, head for Lake Erie, and follow its south shore, we would eventually come to Erie, and then to the airport on the other side of the city. The basic principle of piloting, that of flying in relation to known landmarks—Lake Erie, in this instance—would thus have been followed. This is all that a great many pilots would do.

But let us, for the sake of efficiency, be a little more systematic and lay our ruler on the chart connecting the Buffalo and Erie airports. It is evident that following this course would take us quite far out over the water. In case of motor failure it would be doubtful if land could be reached safely. Therefore, it would be good judgment to break this up into two flights, Buffalo to Dunkirk, then Dunkirk to Erie. We then draw lines connecting these points and the lines become the course, or track, of the airplane over the ground.

From the scale, the airline distance is found to be 42 miles

from Buffalo to Dunkirk and 54 miles from Dunkirk to Erie
or a total of 96 miles for our trip. The ship we will use cruises
at 85 miles per hour and carries enough gas for three hours,
so we will not have to stop for fuel. The flight will be made
in the middle of the day so we will not be concerned with
lights. Although the flight will be along the airways, it will
be a contact flight, which is one made when the ground can
be seen. Therefore, over open country, any altitude between
500 and 3500 feet will be permissible within the altitude requirements of the air traffic rules. The ground elevation, along
the course, is less than 1000 feet so no consideration need be
given to providing for extra altitude.

At this point it is advisable to fold the chart so that it
can be handled conveniently in the plane. This is important
because there is little space, even in a closed plane, to handle
an unruly chart. In an open plane, with the wind blowing
around the cockpit, it is next to impossible to control an
unfolded map, and very often maps are lost when badly
needed.

A chart can be folded in any manner that makes it easy to
handle, and every pilot has his individual way. I prefer
to fold the edges back so that the course is displayed, then
make up the map in eight folds, after which the whole thing
is clipped together, with the starting point on top. This makes
a very handy and compact job and as the plane moves along
the course, the chart can be progressively opened and clipped
together again with the desired area on the outside.

The next step in preparing for our flight is to get a weather
report.

This being a contact flight, we are not greatly concerned
with wind direction and velocity except that it must not be
too gusty or too strong. But we do want to know what the
general weather is at our destination and along the route. So,

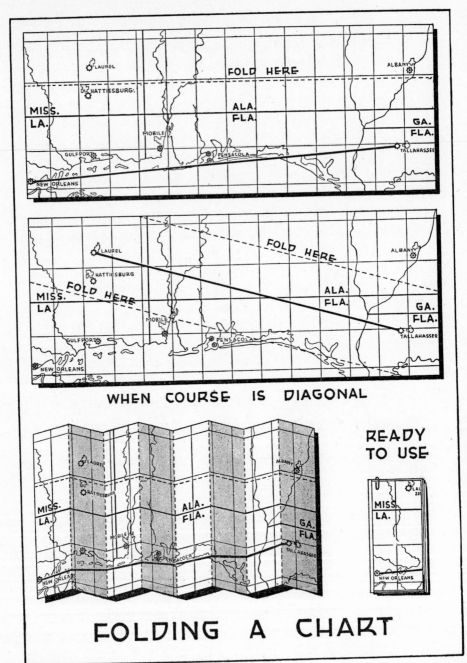

WHEN COURSE IS DIAGONAL

READY TO USE

FOLDING A CHART

we call at the airport office of the Weather Bureau, produce our credentials, and investigate the weather.

We find that the weather is fine at Erie and along the course, as it is at Buffalo. The ceiling and *visibility* are *unlimited,* the winds are moderate and the temperature is typical of a summer day. Looking at the chart we see nothing that indicates a change for the worse. After checking the weather we make up our flight plan and file this with the authorities.

Confident that we have been careful and methodical, we make a final check of the gas supply and of our ship, start the engine, warm it up, and then use our radio to request permission to take off. Permission being given, we taxi to the end of the right runway, head into the wind and "give it the gun."

After circling the field to get a safe altitude we head southwest and are soon at the lake. As our straight course takes us out a short distance from land, we climb high enough so we can reach shore in case of motor trouble.

All that remains now is to continue following the black line by checking against the terrain features. This would be very simple even if the lake were not below us. There are main highways, railroads, a power line, airway beacons, and streams to go by. The course is checked against these periodically to note progress and ascertain position.

As we move along several conspicuous objects lying on the track ahead are selected. If these are kept aligned as one sights a gun on a target, the course can be flown straight. As the nearest object is approached another farther on is selected, always keeping two or more on a line with the aircraft. This procedure is known as following ranges, and since it automatically allows for any sideward wind, permits us to fly a more direct and accurate course.

In about a half hour we should pass over the Dunkirk Airport where our course is changed by bearing slightly to the right. After 35 minutes we shall be over Erie, which is easily recognizable by its harbor. The airport is about 7 miles dead ahead from the center of the city. The wind very likely will

FLYING RANGES

affect the time, making it a little more or a little less, depending upon its force and direction.

We land, taxi up to the line, and so complete our first practical cross-country flight. The airport manager will assist us in making out the proper arrival reports.

Piloting is just as simple as that. While all piloting problems will not have such convenient and prominent landmarks, the principle will still be the same.

Dead reckoning, on the other hand, is somewhat more complicated. Before we can make a flight similar to the one above, using the principles of dead reckoning, it will be necessary to have some knowledge of the compass, its variation and deviation, and the part the wind plays in our computations.

22

THE MAN-MADE LODESTONE

IN an earlier section it was shown that the north pole, or true north, is the standard reference point for all other places on the earth. In dead reckoning, instead of using many landmarks, as in piloting, true north itself is the reference used. To go from one point to another on the earth it is only necessary to determine the bearing of the destination to the starting point and then proceed, keeping this bearing constant. The problem is to know just where true north is so that our bearing can be determined and then maintained. If we could see true north there would be no difficulty, but of course we cannot.

Man's ingenuity has developed several types of instruments for indicating true north and for determining direction. These are called compasses. One is the sun compass, which operates on a basis somewhat similar to that of the sun dial. Direction is determined by the relative position of the sun on the horizon. It is employed in polar regions, but is not practical for application to airplanes. The sun must be shining or it cannot be used, and it is cumbersome to mount and to handle.

The gyro compass, correctly known as the directional gyro,

is an instrument that depends upon the action of a gyroscope for its operation. It indicates a selected direction rather than north. It has many advantages and, used in conjunction with the magnetic compass, is a very valuable navigation instrument. It will be discussed at greater length later.

The radiocompass is rapidly becoming a popular aid to navigation. It takes advantage of the directional qualities of a loop aerial. A radio station, commercial or airway, is selected in or near the city to which one wants to go. The radiocompass is tuned to this station and as long as the airplane is headed for the station the indicator hand registers zero. When the airplane gets off the heading the indicator hand points to the left or right. It is only necessary to keep the indicator on zero and the airplane will be guided directly to the radio station.

Undoubtedly the most valuable instrument in navigation is the magnetic compass. This instrument is comparatively light and inexpensive. It is reliable, simple, and easy to maintain, and it has a long life. It can withstand the shocks of landings and takeoffs and remains accurate after being subjected to violent maneuvers in aerobatics. When its limitations are understood, in the hands of a capable pilot it is a highly dependable instrument.

The magnetic compass is a very old device and has been in constant use for many hundreds of years. Nearly 3000 years ago the Chinese discovered that if a

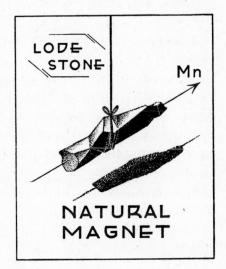

piece of a certain kind of stone were suspended so that it could turn freely, it would always come to rest pointing in a certain direction. In the West this mineral came to be called the lodestone, or leading stone, because it would lead mariners in a certain direction. It was soon noticed that the lodestone always pointed toward a bright star. This star was named the lodestar, which we know as Polaris, or the North Star.

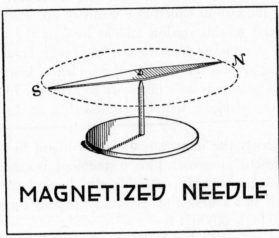

MAGNETIZED NEEDLE

Lodestone is a yellow-colored substance, now known to be one of the oxides of iron. It was first found in the province of Magnesia in Asia Minor, from which the name magnetite, or magnet, is derived. This ore was later found in other places, particularly in Spain, Sweden and the United States.

It was discovered that the properties of the lodestone could be transmitted to iron and steel. Thus a long thin piece of steel that had been in contact with this natural magnet for a time will assume magnetic properties of its own. In effect it becomes an artificial magnet.

Magnets have the peculiar property of attracting or repelling one another. The force of attraction or repulsion is exhibited most conspicuously at the ends or poles, which are distinguished by marking one red and the other blue.

If two magnets are brought together so that the two blue poles or the two red poles are adjacent the magnets will repel each other. On the contrary, when opposite poles are brought

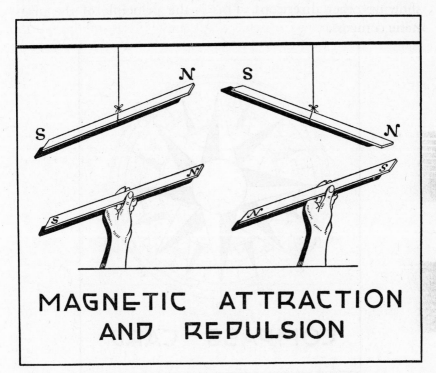

MAGNETIC ATTRACTION
AND REPULSION

together the magnets are mutually attracted and cling to one another. This phenomenon is known as the law of magnetic attraction and repulsion.

The fact that a magnet, when freely suspended, always comes to rest pointing in one direction, gave rise to the belief that the earth itself is a huge magnet. This has been scientifically confirmed, and because a magnet always comes to rest in a generally north-south direction the poles are designated as north and south, respectively. Thus our red pole becomes the north, or north-seeking pole of the magnet and the blue is the south or south-seeking pole.

Once we have a needle or bar that always points to magnetic north, it is a simple matter to attach a card to the needle showing other directions. This is the principle of the magnetic compass.

COMPASS CARD

The modern compass is the result of the work of Lord Kelvin, who perfected it in the latter part of the last century. He replaced the long heavy needle of earlier compasses with the short compact needle in present use. The magnetic element of the compass consists of from two to twelve small flat or cylindrical needles or rods, highly magnetized. To these the compass card is fastened, and the whole assembly is secured in a carrier case.

AIRCRAFT
COMPASS

In the actual aircraft compass, the card itself does not indicate the headings. These are inscribed on a scale, either vertical or beveled, attached to the circumference of the card.

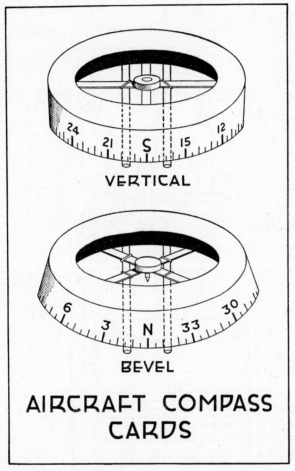

VERTICAL

BEVEL

AIRCRAFT COMPASS CARDS

The headings are shown on the outside of the scale so the compass can be read from the rear. In other words, when the card, scale, and pivot assembly are set in the container case, you see the scale through a small opening with the north of the scale on the south end of the magnet. All other headings

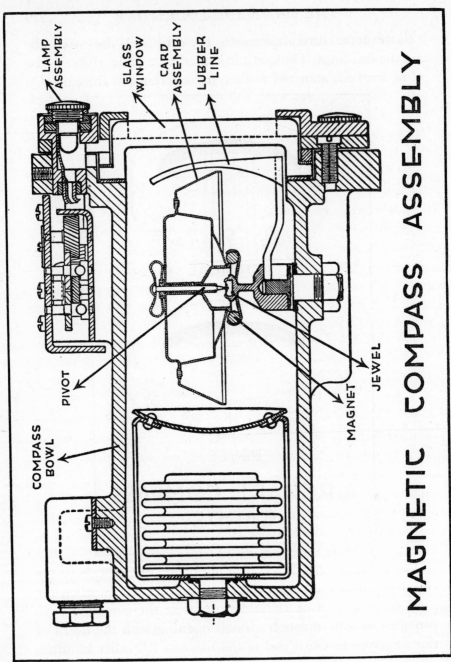

LAMP ASSEMBLY

GLASS WINDOW

CARD ASSEMBLY

LUBBER LINE

PIVOT

COMPASS BOWL

JEWEL

MAGNET

MAGNETIC COMPASS ASSEMBLY

220

are likewise reversed, affording a correct reading when the instrument is mounted on the panel directly in front of the pilot's eye. For ease of reading the last zero is omitted from scale readings. Thus 3 means 30 degrees, 12 is 120 degrees, 24 is 240 degrees, and so on.

The bowl, besides acting as a carrier for the scale, holds the damping fluid. The magnetic element, being very delicately balanced, would swing uncontrollably with turning movements of the aircraft unless means were taken to retard it. Accordingly most compass bowls are practically filled with some liquid such as kerosene, or a mixture of alcohol and water, to slow up and damp out the oscillations of the compass card. The time rate at which a compass card swings is called its *period*. On certain types of compasses the oscillations are almost entirely damped out. This type, not being subject to oscillation, is termed an *aperiodic compass*.

Directly in the center of the observation window of the compass is a vertical line called the lubber line. It is used as a reference mark. The point on the compass card directly behind this line is the heading of the airplane.

Before a magnetic compass can serve dependably its characteristics must be clearly understood. This instrument has very definite limitations and is subject to certain errors. These are so important in dead reckoning that they must be considered in detail.

First, the magnetic compass *does not indicate true north*. It indicates, or points to, magnetic north. This is a point in northern Canada located at Latitude 71 degrees N and Longitude 96 degrees W. Inasmuch as charts are projected with true north as a reference point, it is obvious that the magnetic compass is not in exact conformity with printed charts. In order to use the magnetic compass with charts some correction must be made.

The illustration shows just how this divergence occurs. Pn is the north pole, or true north, upon which all charts are based. Mn is magnetic north toward which the compass points. It is obvious that a magnetic compass at point A heads to the west of true north. The difference is shown by angle PAM

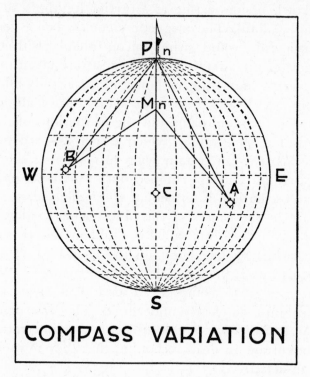

COMPASS VARIATION

and is expressed in degrees. This difference is called *compass variation, magnetic variation,* or just plain *variation.* Thus a magnetic compass at A, pointing let's say 12 degrees west of north, is said to have 12 degrees west variation. In other words the compass, as far as the chart is concerned, is 12 degrees off at point A.

At B a compass would point, let's say, 16 degrees east of true north. This is shown by angle PBM. The compass at

point B is then 16 degrees different from the chart and is said
to have 16 degrees east variation.

A compass at C, or anywhere along the line PC, would
point to both true north and magnetic north. The variation
along this line would be zero. This line of zero variation is

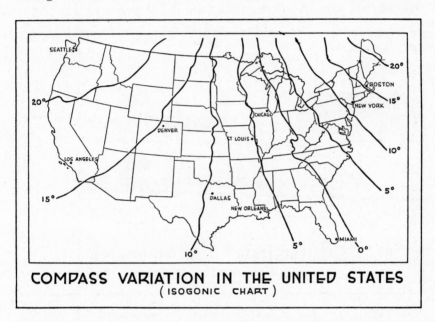

COMPASS VARIATION IN THE UNITED STATES
(ISOGONIC CHART)

called the agonic line. It can be seen that any location east
of this agonic line has west variation and any location west of
the agonic line has east variation. This line is printed on a
magnetic chart called the isogonic chart. Each way from the
agonic line are other lines called isogonic lines which connect
areas of the same magnetic variation. By referring to this
chart the magnetic variation of any locality can be easily
determined.

The reader should note that *variation* is the angle which
the magnetic needle makes with the geographical meridian,
and that it is the same for every compass in a given location.

It must not be confused with *deviation,* which is the individual error of a particular compass in a particular ship or aircraft. Variation is also known as declination in engineering and scientific work. Declination, however, is a term used in celestial navigation and to prevent confusion in navigation declination should not be substituted for variation.

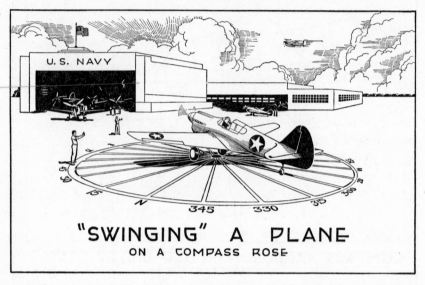

"SWINGING" A PLANE
ON A COMPASS ROSE

When a compass is first installed in an airplane it usually shows a marked individual error or deviation, caused by the magnetic field of the iron and steel of the aircraft itself. Ferrous parts of airplanes tend to become magnetized by hammering and riveting during manufacture. Most of the iron and steel in and around the engine becomes magnetized by induction from the electrical system. Moreover, the compass is generally near radios, generators, ammeters, etc., all of which have magnetic fields varying in intensity and direction. By a process called *compensating,* the deviation error at the various headings is determined and greatly reduced.

To compensate the compass the aircraft is placed on a compass rose, which is a pattern of radiating lines at an airport to represent the various magnetic headings. With the plane in flying position, engine running, lights and radio on, and all flying conditions simulated as closely as possible, the compass is calibrated. This is done by adjusting the compensating magnets with the aircraft on the 90, 180, 270 and zero headings.

The aircraft is then put through a process called *swinging the compass,* or *swinging ship.* The ship is again placed on the compass rose on successive 30-degree headings and the compass error at these headings is noted. When greater accuracy is desired the compass is swung on every 15-degree reading. The error that cannot be removed is called the *deviation.* This error usually can be controlled to within 4 degrees. The remaining error is noted on a

COMPASS	DEV.
N	2 W
30	1 W
60	1 W
E	2 W
120	1 W
150	2 E
S	2 E
200	2 E
240	0
W	0
300	1 E
330	3 W

DEVIATION TABLE

deviation card, which is placed on the instrument panel near the compass, where it can be referred to quickly. It will be shown later how deviation corrections are made in navigating.

The compass is subject to all sorts of shocks and adverse influences, so it should be calibrated at regular intervals. Special calibrations should be carried out after the airplane has been damaged, overhauled, or modified, and after new equipment has been added. Calibration is also called for if the aircraft has been moved from one locality to another. The degree of dependability that can be expected from a compass depends upon the care it receives.

Another error of the compass which it is very important for the pilot to understand is the eccentricity called *Northly turning error*. At the magnetic equator the compass needle is parallel to the surface of the earth. At the magnetic pole the needle would point vertically downward if its mounting permitted. This *inclination* or *dip* increases with the latitude, from zero at the equator to maximum or vertical at the magnetic poles. In the northern hemisphere, in order to keep the compass card horizontal, the rear or south end of the card is weighted slightly. As long as the airplane is level the effect of dip is counteracted and the compass heading is not affected. But on certain turns this dip component makes the compass erratic.

For instance, suppose the aircraft is heading north and it is desired to make a turn to the right or east. When the aircraft is banked to the right the compass is tilted and the north end of the card will be attracted downward or to the east by the dip force. The axis is no longer vertical and the north end of the needle tends to fall, which makes the compass indicate a *left* turn even though the airplane is turning right. When the airplane turns from north to the left, or west, the same principle applies so that the airplane, while turning left, appears to be turning right. The amount of this turning error depends upon the individual compass and the sharpness of the turn.

When turning away from the south the compass runs ahead so that it appears as if the airplane were turning faster than its actual movement. The compass is accurate when turning on easterly or westerly headings. It is only on northerly and southerly courses that this error need be considered. Because the effect is greatest when turning away from north it is called the *Northly turning error*. This characteristic is only of a temporary nature and the card will return to the correct heading sometime during the turn or shortly thereafter, depending upon the degree and amount of the turn.

Such deviations are of little consequence in clear weather when the ground is in sight. It is a different story, however, for the partially trained pilot who tries to fly in bad weather without full knowledge of instruments and their limitations. It is very difficult, and sometimes dangerous, to maintain a heading on northerly courses in gusty air. There have been many pilots who have come to grief through ignorance of this characteristic of the compass. I have flown ships with high quality, well-maintained compasses that showed an opposite turn of as much as 30 degrees before coming around to the correct heading.

A few minor errors to which a compass is subject may be mentioned. These, called *local attraction errors,* are caused by ore deposits in certain localities, power plants, metal buildings, generators, etc.

23

VARIATION AND DEVIATION

WHEN discussing the various methods of navigation it is difficult to state just where one method leaves off and another begins. After flying a while each pilot develops his individual methods, depending upon the equipment available, his experience, and his personal inclinations. Perhaps the average experienced pilot uses a combination of several methods. The important thing is to get there and get there safely.

Dead reckoning by its very nature is made up of a number of approximations and is therefore subject to error. In some cases errors tend to cancel one another and thus become negligible, while again they may accumulate and become serious. A truly remarkable job of navigation can be done by dead reckoning if careful methods are used.

The care which is used in preparation depends largely upon the job to be done. If the flight is to be a short one, over familiar country and under good weather conditions, less attention to detail is required than for a long complicated flight. Flights made under contact conditions when many landmarks are available for checking present no difficulty whatever. On the other hand long flights with fast airplanes, under conditions of bad weather and uncertain terrain, make the matter much more complicated. A little extra care in preparing for a flight may make the difference between a successful trip and an unsuccessful one.

But these things are relative. Careless methods, in navigation as in all things, are bound to produce indifferent results. It cannot be too strongly emphasized that whatever is done should be done carefully and methodically. Then if errors, instead of neutralizing one another, are found to be cumulative, the results will still be good enough to insure successful navigation.

In the following treatment of dead reckoning it is realized that the subject is not covered exhaustively. But the method described is logical, basic, and generally accepted. In practice, it will not be found difficult, and a good command of the technique more than repays the effort expended.

The materials and equipment necessary for a job of dead reckoning are a chart, or charts, of the area to be flown over, a pencil, straightedge, protractor, a drafting compass to describe circles, and a watch. In addition a magnetic compass and an altimeter are necessary on the instrument panel. These instruments are standard equipment on all aircraft today, and the other materials mentioned are easily obtainable. In addition an air speed indicator, a sensitive altimeter, spacing dividers, parallel rulers, a computer, drift indicator, and directional gyro are very helpful and make for greater accuracy. To begin with, however, we shall work with only the essential materials.

The first step is to connect the starting point and destination on the chart with a straight line, the same as for piloting. With the protractor the bearing that this line makes with the meridian is measured, as in the illustration on page 231. Texarkana is the starting point, Eldorado the destination, and the bearing is 103 degrees. This becomes our true course,

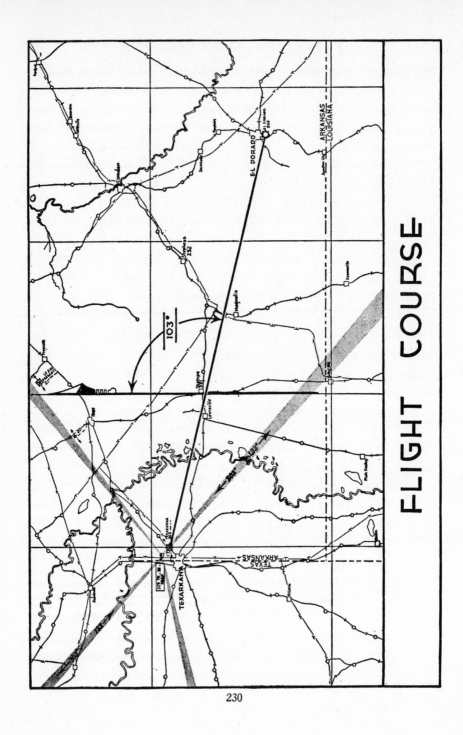

FLIGHT COURSE

or track. Now if the compass pointed true north all we should have to do would be take off, head the ship so that the compass read 103, and continue flying in the direction of our destination. The Jardur Flight Plotter used in the illustration

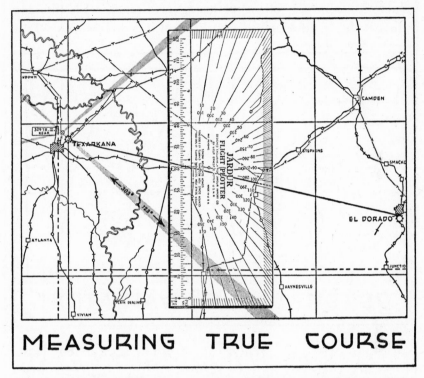

MEASURING   TRUE   COURSE

above to measure the true course is a handy pocket-size gadget with several convenient features. It is inexpensive and can be purchased at most airports. But it is obvious that a correction must be made in the compass heading because of the magnetic variation. Referring to our chart again, it is found that the course lies between the 7 and 8 east magnetic meridians. As the course is midway, either 7 or 8 can be used in making the correction to the true course. We shall use 7 as the correct figure.

This variation is added or subtracted from the true course, depending upon whether it is east or west. There are many little jingles intended to help the pilot to remember whether to add or subtract this correction. Many years ago my instructor taught me one that has always stuck with me. He called it the "Old Mariner's Rule" and it goes like this: "East

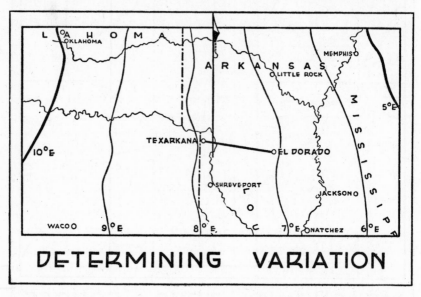

DETERMINING   VARIATION

is least, west is best." When the variation is east, it is least, or less, and therefore must be *subtracted* from the true course. When variation is west, it is best or more, and must be *added* to the true course. In our example the variation is 7 degrees east and according to the rule must be subtracted from the true course of 103 degrees, giving 96 degrees. This 96 degrees then becomes the magnetic course, which is the true course corrected for magnetic variation.

The next step is to correct for deviation, or the individual error of the compass in the particular plane we are flying. The same general rule will apply for correcting deviation as that used for variation. We look at the deviation card (shown below) to determine the deviation on our magnetic course of 96 degrees. There is no correction shown for 96, but it is easy to see that this comes between 90, or east, and 120. As 96 is slightly nearer the 90-degree point than the 120-degree point, and the deviation at both points is in the same direction, we shall consider the correction given on the 90-degree heading, which is 2 degrees west. Then, according to rule,

FOR	0	30	60	90	120	150
STEER	2	31	61	92	121	148
FOR	180	210	240	270	300	330
STEER	178	208	240	270	299	333

because the deviation is west, it must be *added* to the magnetic course of 96 degrees, giving us 98 degrees. This course of 98 degrees then becomes the compass course. The compass course is the magnetic course corrected for deviation, or the true course after both variation and deviation have been taken into account.

With the compass course determined, if there were no wind, or if the wind were directly on the nose or directly on the tail of the plane, it would only be necessary to take off, fly with the compass reading 98 and go directly to your destination.

A comparison of the card above and that on page 234 will reveal different methods of showing deviation. These cards save one step. Using the above card the magnetic course is determined as described. This is located in the "FOR" column. Then the compass course appears below in the corresponding "STEER" column.

When your airplane has a card like the one on this page you determine what your magnetic course happens to be, then refer to the deviation card to find the compass course to fly corresponding to this magnetic heading. If, as usually happens, your magnetic course does not come out exactly on any of the courses given, it is only necessary to interpolate. This merely means to strike an average of the deviation between the respective values for the two nearest given points.

MAGNETIC HEADING	0	30	60	90	120	150
COMPASS HEADING	359	30	59	88	118	147
MAGNETIC HEADING	180	210	240	270	300	330
COMPASS HEADING	180	209	238	269	300	329

The application of variation corrections in planning a course is largely a matter of common sense. For instance, on a flight from Fort Wayne to South Bend, Indiana, a distance of about 72 miles, the variation is first west and then east. This can be averaged and considered as 0 degrees for the whole flight, and the change in variation need not be considered. On north-south flights the change in variation is much less than on east-west flights. On a flight from New York to Chicago the variation changes from about 11 degrees west to 2 degrees east, or about 13 degrees over all. But a flight of this length probably would be broken up into several shorter flights, depending upon the speed and cruising range of the airplane. Long trips usually have to be broken up for food, gasoline, rest, and weather reports. On the shorter flights the average variation, that is, the variation at the midpoint of the course, is naturally used. This variation will generally not change more than 2 degrees in 100 miles on an east-west flight, so that it presents no great problem. Thus each section of the flight may be treated as a complete trip by itself, the course being changed at each successive intermediate destination.

There is another sound reason, other than change in variation, for breaking up a long flight into a series of shorter ones.

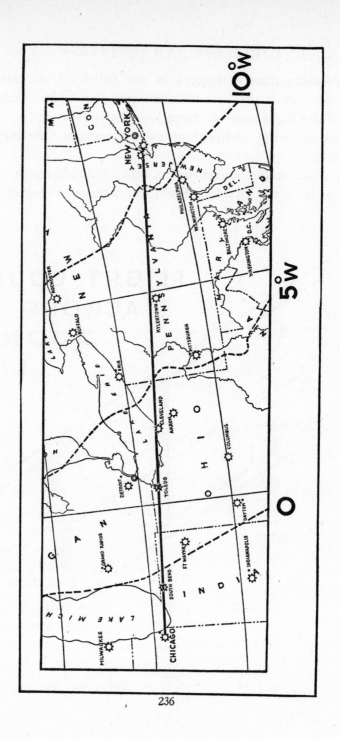

On the Lambert projection a straight line is an approximate great circle course. This being the case, when a course crosses meridians, the true bearing changes with each meridian crossed. Since the bearing is constantly changing, the compass course has to be corrected at regular intervals. On flights that

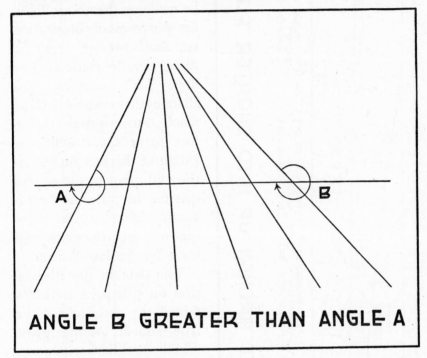

ANGLE B GREATER THAN ANGLE A

run north or south there is no such requirement. On flights that cross only 3 or 4 degrees of longitude, it is also relatively unimportant. The course in these cases is measured at the meridian in the middle of the track and the slight error in flying the course need not be considered. But where more than 3 or 4 degrees are crossed the flight should be broken up into shorter flights and the true courses of each measured at the middle meridian, as stated above. Thus a flight from New York to Chicago, of 725 miles and crossing about 14 degrees

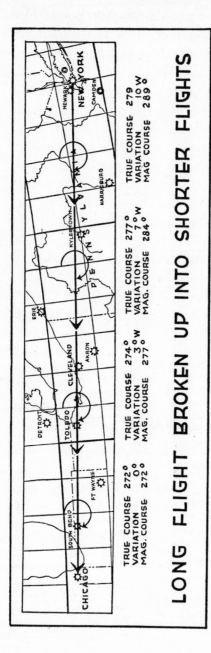

LONG FLIGHT BROKEN UP INTO SHORTER FLIGHTS

of longitude, should be broken up into about four shorter flights.

While stops at intermediate airports would normally be made on the above flight, for purposes of illustration we shall assume that the flight can be made in one hop. Let's examine the changes that occur when the whole course is divided into four parts. The middle meridian of the first quarter is the 76th, that of the second quarter the 79th, the 83rd is about right for the third quarter, and the 86th will serve for the last quarter.

The data in the illustration on this page were obtained by measuring the true course at the given middle meridians with a protractor. From the illustration it can be seen that the true bearing, or true course, of the first section of the flight is 279 degrees and that of the last section is 272 degrees. The difference is entirely due to the fact that the meridians of the Lambert Conformal projection converge to a common point. This change in bearing while crossing meridians is constant for any place on the chart and amounts to 2 degrees for every 3 meridians crossed. If the pilot so wishes he can adjust for this factor as he goes along. He merely adds 2 degrees to his course for every 3 degrees of longitude when flying east, and subtracts the same amount at the same intervals when flying west.

This would be fairly simple to do if it were the only correction to the course that is necessary. When wind corrections and variation corrections must be considered also it is hardly practical to do this as one flies along. The best way is to lay out the course, measure it with the protractor, make all corrections and plan as much as possible of the whole trip in advance before taking off. When that is done the change in course because of convergence of the meridians will automatically be taken care of and need not be considered.

The change in bearing because of convergence of the meridians should not be confused with variation. Change in variation is not constant and depends upon the area in which the course is located.

In the example of the New York to Chicago flight the change in variation together with the change in course due to convergence of the meridians totals 17 degrees for the whole trip, the magnetic course of the first section being 289 degrees and that of the last section 272 degrees.

The compass courses for the flight legs of the above example can be obtained by correcting the magnetic courses for deviation as previously explained.

So far we have talked about, and should understand true course, magnetic course and compass course. As yet we have not considered, in detail, the wind. We shall do so next and then we will be able to determine the compass heading. This is obtained by applying the wind correction to the compass course.

24

WIND AGAIN—A HELP OR A HINDRANCE

THE effect of wind on an aircraft is puzzling to the novice. Apparently it is difficult to understand that once the aircraft leaves the ground it operates in an altogether different medium. Speed over the ground is easy to understand because the average person is accustomed to traveling in trains, automobiles, and other vehicles. Also the ground can be seen and the sensation of objects whizzing past contributes to our comprehension of speed. But when it comes to flying high in the air in an invisible medium, speed is not so apparent. Because our earthbound vehicles go in the direction they are pointing it is not easy to realize how an airplane can point, or head, in one direction and yet proceed in another direction. This is because the air is an entity of its own, capable of self-movement relative to the earth. Our difficulty lies in adjusting movement through the air into terms of ground movement, which we understand. Our discussion of the movement of the atmosphere, in earlier chapters, must have given some idea of the effect of wind on an aircraft. Because wind exerts such an important effect on aircraft, and enters to such an extent into the determination of compass headings, it must be thoroughly understood.

In addition to the motion of the aircraft itself through the air, wind adds to or detracts from this speed. The easiest way to make this clear is to compare the airplane to a swimmer in water. Do you remember how slowly and laboriously you swam upstream against the current and how easy it was to swim downstream? When you swam across the stream you always had to head upstream, to allow for the current, in order to get directly across.

SPEED OVER GROUND
5 MPH

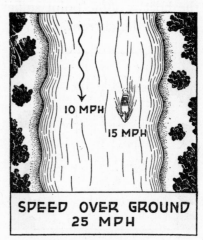

SPEED OVER GROUND
25 MPH

Suppose we had a motorboat whose speed we knew was 15 miles per hour. If the boat were headed upstream in a current of ten miles per hour it would go forward, relative to a fixed point on the shore at the rate of only 5 miles per hour. This would be called the *ground speed* in aircraft nomenclature, but the speed of the water flowing past the boat would still be 15 miles per hour. Now if this same boat were turned and headed downstream it would still only be going through the water at 15 miles per hour, but it would be moving past a fixed point on the shore at the combined speeds of the boat and the water, or 25 miles per hour. The ground speed then becomes 25 miles per hour.

If there is no current and it is desired to go from A to B, the boat is headed toward B and goes there directly without difficulty.

But when there is a current, the boat headed for B reaches the other shore at some point downstream at C. While the boat moves from A to C the water has moved from B to C. The water has made the boat drift to point C. Angle BAC is the drift angle. To reach point B, then, it is necessary to head the boat at some point sufficiently far upstream to offset the effect of the current.

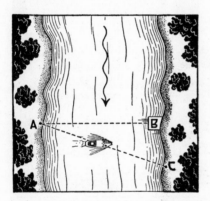 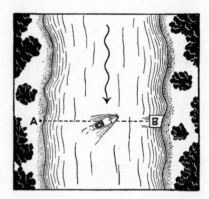

Now consider the similar effect of wind on an aircraft. If an airplane with a cruising speed of 100 miles per hour flies *into* a 20-mile-an-hour wind, while its air speed remains 100 miles per hour the ground speed is only 80 miles per hour. The same airplane going *down wind,* still holding its air speed of 100 miles per hour, would have a speed over the ground of 120 miles per hour. It's that simple, yet many people make hard work understanding it.

The effect of cross winds is no different. For instance, an airplane flying due east with a north wind will end up somewhere south of the place intended. The exact place which the airplane will reach can be determined when the speed of the

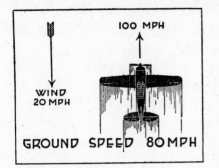

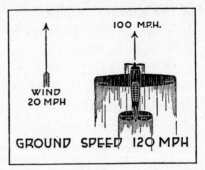

airplane and the velocity of the wind are known. For example, if the speed of the plane is 100 miles an hour, and the wind velocity is 20 miles per hour, the aircraft, at the end of an hour, will be 20 miles south of the intended point X or at P in the illustration below.

The same method of computation may be applied to aircraft flying in winds of any speed and angle with the course. Assume that we want to fly from airport E to airport X in the illustration on page 244 and that the speed of our airplane is 90 miles per hour. Using any convenient scale, such as 1 inch equals 40 miles, our aircraft would be somewhere on the circle B at the end of 1 hour if there were no wind blowing. But the wind is blowing 30 miles per hour from 42 degrees. Therefore the circle must be moved downwind in one hour

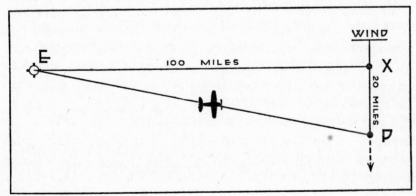

by the amount of EW. Then at the end of an hour's flying the plane would be somewhere on circle P. Where this circle intersects the course is where the airplane will be in one hour if the plane follows the true course. EP then represents the speed of the plane over the ground, or the very important ground speed. Measuring EP we find it is 1⅝ inches long, or 65 miles per hour ground speed.

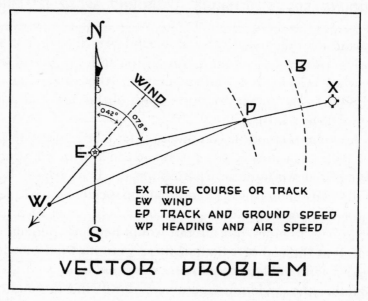

EX   TRUE COURSE OR TRACK
EW   WIND
EP   TRACK AND GROUND SPEED
WP   HEADING AND AIR SPEED

VECTOR   PROBLEM

By this procedure we have constructed what is called a *speed diagram* or *triangle of velocities*. This is also called a *vector* problem. It is the basic and fundamental motion diagram of all aerial navigation. Because it is so important let us consider it further. Knowing the ground speed, found in the above case to be 65 miles per hour, it is easy to measure EX and find out how long it will take to get to X. EX measures 2⅞ inches, corresponding to 115 miles, and at 65 miles per hour it would take one hour and 46 minutes to go from E to X.

Another important bit of information given by this diagram is the *wind correction angle* represented by angle EPW. This angle represents the amount we must head into the wind to correct for drift. This angle, measured with the protractor, is found to be 11 degrees.

In using the wind correction angle it is well to remember a simple rule, which is *add wind right*. Naturally we want to add the wind right; if, then, we add for a right wind, a left wind must be subtracted. This correction may be applied either to the magnetic course or to the true course. The only thing to remember is that the wind direction is given as true, therefore, *the speed diagram or triangle of velocities must be constructed on the true course,* to get the wind correction angle in the first place.

In our problem we have the wind coming from the left of the course, so the correction of 11 degrees must be subtracted. Thus far no variation or deviation has been given, so just assume that the variation is 11 degrees west and the deviation is 2 degrees east. To find what course to steer, or the compass heading, we measure EX and find this true course to be 78 degrees. By adding the 11 degrees west variation our magnetic course becomes 89 degrees. When the 2 degrees east variation is subtracted from the magnetic course we have the compass course of 87 degrees. Now we come to the final step, that of subtracting the 11 degrees wind correction, giving us the compass heading of 76 degrees. This is what the compass must read during the flight in order to make good the true course EX.

The compass heading thus can be seen to be the true course corrected for variation, deviation, and wind.

Before making the flight the true course on the chart should be marked off in mileage intervals. The interval used depends largely upon the inclination and experience of the pilot. It is suggested that, in the beginning of the course at least, an interval of ten miles be used. Further along the course, the interval may be increased to 20 miles if desired. Then, knowing the ground speed, the number of minutes it will take to fly from one mileage interval to the next should be figured. The time should be placed opposite each mileage interval on the chart. Better yet, this can be placed on a log prepared especially for this purpose. With this time information the pilot knows before taking off just where he should be at any given number of minutes from the time of departure.

In arriving at the compass heading and ground speed in the above problem we have assumed that our air speed will be steady and that the wind direction and velocity have been correctly reported and remain constant over the course. But actually these factors vary and proper consideration must be given to them. The air speed can be held fairly steady by maintaining a constant altitude and by careful use of the throttle once the desired altitude is reached. But while the plane is climbing or gliding this speed is substantially reduced and the overall ground speed will not be quite as great as expected. Actual wind conditions in flight may be considerably different from those reported because of differences in time and place, or on account of error in observation or reporting.

These variations, if they exist, should be discovered early in the flight in order that adjustments can be made in time to prevent the plane from getting too far off the right course. Accordingly the most important part of the flight is in the first few minutes after leaving the starting point. An error of a few degrees in the beginning of a flight is of little consequence, but the effect of the error increases with the distance traveled. An error of 1 degree amounts to 1 mile in 57. Accumulated errors can result in a pilot getting hopelessly lost. Just as soon as possible after taking off, therefore, the plane should be

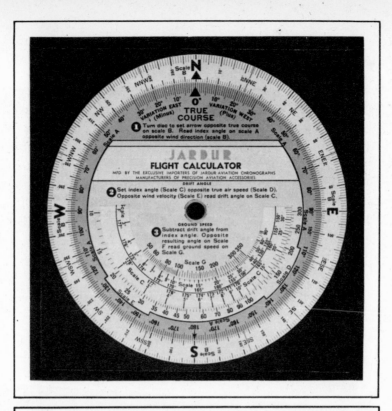

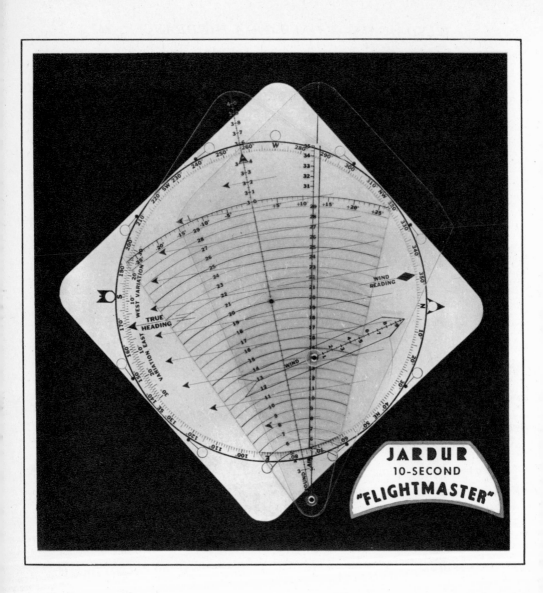

checked with some point, such as a bend in a river, known to be on the course. If the compass is on the calculated heading and the airplane points toward this known point it is a pretty good assurance that your calculations are correct. If the airplane heads to the right or left of the check point, it can be headed directly at the check point and the corresponding compass heading noted. This new heading can then be followed until later check points indicate whether it is correct or not.

Just as soon as possible after the compass heading is established as correct, or a substitute compass heading has been decided upon, the ground speed should be checked. This can be done very simply by noting the number of minutes it takes to fly between points where the distance has been predetermined. Good points to use are the first distance intervals marked on the chart. If the ground speed is found to be approximately as originally figured no adjustment need be made. If it is found that the ground speed is more or less than that determined on the speed diagram, it is an easy matter to revise the arrival time either mentally or with a computer.

Graphical solutions of navigation problems are accurate and dependable. There is no better way of illustrating principles in the classroom or in actual practice where time, room, and materials are not limited. But in an airplane where there is little space, or the pilot must do his own navigating, this is seldom practicable. The greater speeds of modern aircraft are making longer flights commonplace. A considerable amount of planning and calculating is required for a flight of any distance. There are many little devices such as *navigation computers, flight calculators,* and *plotting boards* on the market to make navigation easier.

The average individual is somewhat awed by a plotting

board or computer because it looks complicated. The service man and the airline pilot are taught to use these labor-saving devices and would not be deprived of them under any circumstances. A private pilot will make a few attempts at working problems and then lay a computer aside in disgust because he has not mastered it immediately.

A computer is of no value unless it can be used quickly and accurately. To become proficient in its use a pilot should read the directions and then study the device itself. He should work out various problems until the computer is so thoroughly understood that he can take full advantage of its possibilities.

Computers have a slide rule, usually circular, by which speed, time, and distance problems can be solved. Thus you can quickly determine how far an airplane will travel at a given speed in a certain time. Inversely, you can find the air speed of an airplane knowing the distance it has traveled in a certain time. Using the principle of the triangle of velocities, computers, calculators, and plotting boards have various ways of working to the same ends. These provide all of the information that a graphic triangle of velocities, with the same original information, will give.

These devices come in varied sizes and shapes. Some are large, easy to read, and have room on which to work. Others are small, but have the advantage that they can be carried around in the pocket. It is a matter of individual preference as to which type is used.

A popular calculator is the *Jardur* which may be purchased at most airports. It comes in a substantial cardboard material and is low-priced but durable. This is of a size that can be carried in the pocket yet contains facilities to work out any problems that a larger plotting board could handle.

On one side is the circular slide rule upon which problems

of time and distance can be computed. Fuel consumption and elapsed time are easily determined. As the reading of an air speed indicator is affected by temperature and altitude, some adjustment must be made to obtain the true air speed at the altitude being flown. A center scale, on the same side of the calculator, provides for these corrections.

The other side of the calculator has outer scales for determining the drift correction angle, compass heading, and ground speed. Knowing the wind direction and velocity and the air speed, the wind correction angle can be obtained with but two moves of the inner circle. Another move of the disc and a slight mental calculation gives the compass heading and ground speed. Many variations of the basic problem can be worked out with practice.

The illustration shows an elaborate and ingenious computer which will quickly solve any navigational problem. It is called the *Jardur 10-second Flightmaster* and will provide a great deal of fascination as one delves into its possibilities. Using this device one can work out the same kind of intricate navigation problems that the Navy pilot deals with. These involve radius of action problems from a moving base and interception problems with several changes in course. Over the ocean there are no landmarks and every wave looks just like another. Navigation must be accurate. Careless technique has no place in the services, nor should it be tolerated in civilian flying. A good computer will help you navigate quickly and safely.

When the correct compass heading and the ground speed are finally established in the air the pilot is not yet finished. He merely has a plan of action mapped out. He must continue to check regularly on the chart as he goes along to determine if the plan is being carried out. Otherwise, over unfamiliar country there is a good chance that he may become lost. Again it must be repeated that the important thing is that the flight be completed safely. Each pilot soon develops, with experience, his own style and refinements in technique. In discussing these methods with my associates I find that no two plan and execute a flight exactly the same in details, but the principles are fundamentally alike in all cases.

25

DEAD RECKONING

IN order to be as clear and practical as possible let's take an actual flight and trace the steps as we did in piloting. We want to fly from Philadelphia, Pa., to Rochester, N. Y., in a ship that cruises at 115 miles an hour. Reference to the chart index shows that this flight would appear entirely on the 10 M regional chart and this can be used for the flight. If only sectional charts are available the New York and Albany charts will be needed. Some pilots would prefer to use the two sectional charts because of the greater amount of detail given, thus lessening the possibility of getting lost over the mountains. This is optional; the advantage of greater detail in the sectionals is balanced by the bulkiness and awkwardness of the two charts. The lack of detail not available on the regional chart is offset by its compactness and ease of handling.

After we have selected the proper chart the true course is drawn on it and this course should be studied for special conditions. The most significant point to be considered is the fact that a portion of the flight is over relatively high terrain.

It is a clear day in June and to all appearances an excellent

251

day for a cross-country flight. At the weather office we determine from the charts of weather reporting stations that our flight would pass near Allentown, Park Place, Wilkes-Barre, Sunbury, Kylertown, Bellefonte, Woodward, Williamsport, Canton, Elmira, Dansville, Buffalo and Rochester. Some of these stations are well westerly of our proposed track, but they are checked because of the natural tendency of the weather to move easterly toward our course. A study of the weather reports, together with the current weather map, will give a mental picture of the weather prevailing in this area. If the weather man is not busy, he will give you his opinion of the weather. If he is broadcasting or busy with his necessary observations and reports, you can get the information for yourself from the teletype reports.

On this flight over mountainous country particular attention must be given the weather report. The contours on our navigation charts show that the flight crosses country with an elevation up to 3000 feet. The ceiling must therefore be sufficiently high to permit clearing the mountains. Orographic thunderstorm activity may be expected if the conditions are conducive. Also the visibility should be reasonably extensive so that you can see far enough to recognize check points. If there is any possibility that the weather may turn for the worse at any point in the flight, alternate airports should be selected and spotted along the track where a landing can be made in an emergency.

The weather for our flight turns out to be good all along the course. Upon consulting the winds-aloft report it is found that the wind at 5000 is the most favorable for our flight. Its velocity is 25 miles an hour and it blows from the 85-degree direction. While this is not a tail wind, such as we would like to have, neither is it a head wind to slow us up.

Returning to the chart, it is apparent that our entire

course lies within three degrees of longitude, between the 75th and 78th west meridians. Measuring the track at the mid meridian, the true course is found to be 331 degrees. The variation is clearly west and can be either 9 or 10 degrees.

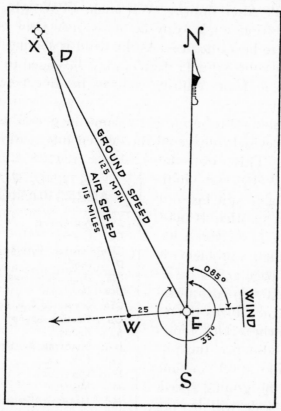

Upon selecting 9 degrees W as the correct variation we have the magnetic course of 340 degrees. Using the deviation card shown on page 234 the compass course becomes 339 degrees.

Now we are ready to construct the speed diagram. The first step is to draw a vertical line NS, on a separate sheet of paper, to represent the mid meridian. On this the true course of 331 degrees is drawn and marked EX. Then with a scale of, let's say, 1 inch equal to 40 miles, line EW is drawn downwind to represent one hour's wind. This wind line will be 1⅝ inches long. Next, with W as a center, take the air speed, which being 115 miles would be 2⅞ inches, and mark off point P. After drawing WP angle EPW, which is the wind correction angle, can be measured. Our protractor shows this to be 11 degrees. As the wind is coming from the right of the course this 11 degrees must be added to the compass course and the resulting compass heading becomes 350 degrees.

Before going further it is recommended that some sort of log be devised to have all the desired information readily

available. This can be worked up by each individual pilot to suit his own conception of what is most important. A suggested log of this flight problem is shown on page 255.

The next step is to measure EP which turns out to be 3⅛ inches. This represents the distance the airplane will travel in one hour, or the ground speed, which at scale will be 125 miles. Next, knowing the ground speed, we can measure the distance of the flight and determine the time it will take us to make it. The course from Philadelphia to Rochester measured with

STANDARD ABBREVIATIONS	
AS	Air Speed
CC	Compass Course
CH	Compass Heading
D	Drift
DR	Dead Reckoning
Dev	Deviation
ETA	Estimated Time of Arrival
GS	Ground Speed
h	Hours
IAS	Indicated Air Speed
Lat	Latitude
Long	Longitude
m	Minutes
MC	Magnetic Course
MH	Magnetic Heading
mph	Miles per Hour
PA	Pressure Altitude
TAS	True Air Speed
TC	True Course
TH	True Heading
Var	Variation
W	Wind
WC	Wind Correction Angle

LOG

TC	331°
VAR	9°W
MC	340°
WC	11°W
MH	351°
DEV	1°E
CH	350°
TAS	115
GS	125
MILEAGE	258
TIME	2h 04m
DEP	10 00
ETA	12 04

PHILADELPHIA ROCHESTER FLIGHT

CHECKPOINT	DISTANCE OUT	TIME OUT
CROSS SCHUYLKILL RIVER WEST OF BRIDGEPORT	19 MILES	10 09
BLUE MOUNTAIN RIDGE	65 MILES	10 31
SUMMERHILL	74 MILES	10 36
HAZLETON	84 MILES	10 40
BEND IN DELAWARE RIVER AT SHICKSHINNY	100 MILES	10 48
RANGER TOWER No 78	114 MILES	10 55
JOINING RAILROADS AT MILDRED	124 MILES	11 00
RAILROADS STREAMS AND HIGHWAYS IN VALLEY	140 MILES	11 07
HIGHWAY AND STREAM IN VALLEY	147 MILES	11 11
TOWN OF FASSETT – Sight SUSQUEHANNA R. on RIGHT	163 MILES	11 18
CHEMUNG RIVER AT ELMIRA	170 MILES	11 22
CROSS KEUKA LAKE	202 MILES	11 37
CROSS CANANDAIGUA LAKE	221 MILES	11 46
RAILROAD JUNCTION AT HONEOYE FALLS	240 MILES	11 55
CITY OF ROCHESTER ON RIGHT SIDE	258 MILES	12 04

the scale is 258 miles. At the speed of 125 miles per hour the flight should be made in 2 hours and 4 minutes.

The final step in preparation for the flight is to mark off either time or distance intervals along the track, or both. I prefer to mark off intervals of ten miles on the chart and then make note of outstanding landmarks along the track. These landmarks, with the approximate time of passing, are entered on the log. This is perhaps more work than the average experienced pilot will go to in making a flight of this kind. But the method is given here to provide for a thoroughly safe procedure, which can be modified to suit the individual and the conditions.

All that remains now is to taxi the ship out and request permission to take off. Just as soon as practical, after taking off, turn your plane until the compass is on the heading you have previously calculated—350 degrees. Then, while still climbing for your cruising altitude, start checking your course. There are almost always features, other than the prominent ones you have selected as check points, that can be identified so that you can check your heading to see if it appears correct. If your general track over these features appears to be correct, continue on until you reach your check points. If you meet the check points as planned you can relax a little in full confidence that your calculations were correct.

If you find, however, that the airplane is not passing over the track as it should, a correction is easy to make. When you are *sure* that you are not making your course good, you merely turn the plane to the right or the left, as the case requires, until you are *sure* that you *are* making the course good. Then when you have steadied down a reading can be taken on the compass. This then will be the new compass heading, to be followed unless proved incorrect by subsequent checks. In this manner you have automatically corrected for any errors in your original calculations caused by variations in wind or mistakes in figuring. If there is a marked discrepancy you should, of course, make every effort to find the cause so that your navigational technique will improve with experience.

Navigation is not complete, nor is the flight made, until the airplane is safely on the ground at its destination. As you can see from the above it is necessary that considerable checking be done in the early part of the flight to assure its being started correctly. Repeated checking is also necessary all along the course in order that the pilot may always know his position and be in full control of the situation. Once the compass heading is determined it should be held as long as the check points indicate its correctness. Difficulty is often encountered in holding a compass heading or when changing course in the air because of the apparent contrariness or indecision of the magnetic compass. On certain headings, owing to the dip and turning errors already mentioned, the compass seems unsteady and appears to oscillate so that it is difficult to find a heading and hold it. This will be overcome with experience, but a simple rule will help until that experience is gained. All you have to remember is that to get a higher number on your compass you have to turn toward the right. To get a lower reading you turn toward the left. If the air is rough it will swing a few times but will soon settle down nearer the desired heading. This rule of turning right for higher numbers is not literally true when you are flying due north, since there you jump from 360 degrees to 0. But the principle is correct. The rule will help until you no longer need it.

At this point it might be well to state that in trying to explain principles and at the same time be practical, I have described the methods normally employed in actual flying. In giving a genuine example of dead reckoning I have naturally combined it with piloting. This combining of methods is a check against error and is recommended as sound practice.

The preceding example covers only the first part of dead reckoning—that of planning a course by calculation before the flight. For relatively short flights where a pilot is his own navigator, this is sufficient. If the flight is planned correctly and flown carefully there is no need to plot the track or path of the airplane back onto the chart. But, there may be occasions when departures from the course are necessary and the actual path of the airplane should be plotted on the chart so that its location can be ascertained at any time. The data to be used in plotting come from the compass heading, the approximate ground speed, and the elapsed time. The necessity for this usually arises only on long flights, under unusual conditions and where a separate navigator is available with equipment and room to work.

In the first part of this discussion of dead reckoning we had a true course given and, in order to fly it, we had to find

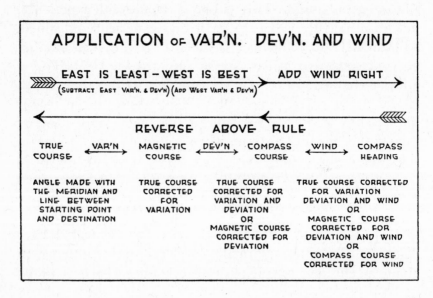

APPLICATION OF VAR'N. DEV'N. AND WIND

EAST IS LEAST – WEST IS BEST   ADD WIND RIGHT
(SUBTRACT EAST VAR'N. & DEV'N) (ADD WEST VAR'N & DEV'N)

REVERSE   ABOVE   RULE

TRUE COURSE	VAR'N	MAGNETIC COURSE	DEV'N	COMPASS COURSE	WIND	COMPASS HEADING
ANGLE MADE WITH THE MERIDIAN AND LINE BETWEEN STARTING POINT AND DESTINATION		TRUE COURSE CORRECTED FOR VARIATION		TRUE COURSE CORRECTED FOR VARIATION AND DEVIATION OR MAGNETIC COURSE CORRECTED FOR DEVIATION		TRUE COURSE CORRECTED FOR VARIATION DEVIATION AND WIND OR MAGNETIC COURSE CORRECTED FOR DEVIATION AND WIND OR COMPASS COURSE CORRECTED FOR WIND

the compass heading. The second phase is essentially the opposite. The compass heading is known and we must find the true course in order to plot it on the chart. Therefore, the simple rules given for applying variation, deviation, and drift angle are all reversed when working from compass heading to true course. It is consequently very important that a student understand clearly the various definitions and just what it is he is working for. In the past there has been considerable confusion because the various terms were not standardized and because of different methods of instruction. This is slowly being overcome by the general adoption of recognized methods and terms.

A careful study of the illustration on page 258 should clarify the standard terms and show how they are obtained.

In some methods and under certain circumstances the terms true heading and magnetic heading are used. This merely means that the wind correction has been applied to the true course or to the magnetic course, instead of to the compass course, as we applied it. It is sound practice to do this and, because it is preferred by many, the terms should be clearly understood. They will be used a little later and should be kept in mind.

26

PRACTICAL PROBLEMS

T HERE are times when it is desirable to know how far an
airplane may travel in a given direction and still have fuel
enough to return to the starting point. This has a very practical value to those who like to explore interesting new country from the air. Many times in my travels around the country I have made such flights. Very often commercial pilots
start on flights when the weather is questionable near their
destination. It is very valuable for them to know just how far
they can go and still get back safely if they have to.

The greatest distance an airplane may travel under given
wind conditions and still return to a predetermined point is
called its *radius of action*. The important thing to determine
in a radius of action problem is when to turn back. This can
be computed very easily by using the triangle of velocities
method just covered.

Let us take a practical example. We have heard that heavy
rains have resulted in wide areas being flooded in a region
bearing 322 degrees true from where we are. We should like
to survey this area for personal or business reasons, and want
to know just how far we can go. Our ship can remain in the
air safely for a little over 3½ hours and has a cruising speed

of 110 miles per hour. The wind is blowing 25 miles per hour from 195 degrees.

The first step is to draw the meridian MN and then the course of 322 degrees over which we wish to fly. This is shown worked out in the illustration on this page. At the same time we can extend E to P_2 because the return track will be the reciprocal of the track out. Next we draw one hour's wind

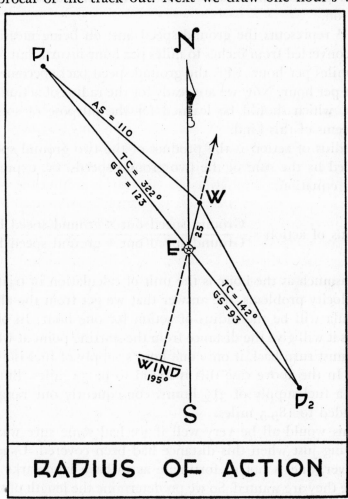

RADIUS OF ACTION

downwind from E to W, which at the scale of 20 miles equal to 1 inch will be 1¼ inches. With W as center and using the air speed as the radius, WP¹ and WP² are laid off. The air speed being 110 miles per hour, these lines at scale will be 5½ inches long. Now it is apparent that we have constructed a double velocity triangle or two problems in one. From this we have all the information we need for our radius of action solution.

EP¹ represents the ground speed out; on being measured and converted from inches to miles per hour it turns out to be 123 miles per hour. EP², the ground speed back, becomes 93 miles per hour. Now we are ready for the radius of action formula, which should be learned for the purpose of solving problems of this kind.

Radius of action is the product of the two ground speeds divided by the sum of the two ground speeds, or, expressed as an equation:

$$\text{Radius of action} = \frac{\text{Ground speed out} \times \text{ground speed back}}{\text{Ground speed out} + \text{ground speed back}}$$

Inasmuch as the hour is the unit of calculation in triangle of velocity problems, the answer that we get from the above formula will be the radius of action for one hour. In other words it will give the distance from the starting point at which you must turn back if only one hour's supply of fuel is available. In the above case this is found to be 53 miles. But we have a fuel supply of 3½ hours, consequently our range is extended to 185.5 miles.

This would all be very well if we had some sure way of knowing just when this distance had been covered. Usually, however, one is not so fortunate as to have landmarks just where they are wanted. So we predetermine the length of time it will take to travel this distance and the problem is solved. The time required to travel 185.5 miles at the outgoing ground speed of 123 miles per hour is 1 hour and 30 minutes.

This should allow us two hours in which to make the return trip. Let us check our calculations and see if this is verified. If we flew 185.5 miles away from our starting point this is also the distance of our return flight. According to our triangles of velocity the ground speed back is considerably less than the ground speed out. This is to be expected, since we had nearly a tail wind out and now have a head wind back. The ground speed back is 93 miles per hour, and it will take just two hours at this speed to travel the 185.5 miles back.

It is also possible to calculate radius of action problems in which the plane returns to another airport or to a moving base such as an aircraft carrier. The Navy pilot is often required to change course many times while out of sight of both land and his carrier. In the meantime the carrier might change course several times. This would seem to be a hopeless situation, but it is handled as a routine task. Of course the Navy pilot has elaborate equipment, and an intricate plotting board under his instrument panel that becomes as important to him as his right hand. The point is, however, that the navigation practices of service aviators and commercial and private pilots are alike based on the fundamental triangle of velocities.

The private pilot naturally will not be called upon to perform the precise navigation required in the services. There are several good plotting boards and computers available to save time in plotting courses and in navigating. Anything that can be done by these devices, however, can be done by hand, and that is the best way to learn principles and to become adept. There is no short cut—the only way to become skillful is through practice. The best practice is working out actual problems. Several examples are given here to help develop facility. They start out with simple exercises carefully selected to cover the basic principles and the various applications, and become more difficult as they progress.

After the following problems become clear by graphical solution, they can be solved with the computer.

Common abbreviations used in navigation are listed in the illustration on page 254.

PROBLEMS

(Answers will be found on page 266)

1. Given the true course of 27°, variation 13° east, what is the magnetic course?

2. The true course is 92°, variation is 10° west and deviation is 4° west. What is the compass course?

3. If the magnetic course is 217° and variation is 2° east, what is the true course?

4. The magnetic heading is 219°, variation is 7° west, deviation 3° east. Find the true heading and the compass heading.

5. Your compass course is 95°, the variation is 6° west and the deviation is 2° east. What is the true course?

6. If the true course is 4°, the variation 7° east and the deviation 3° east, what is the compass course?

7. The true course is 271°, variation 16° east, deviation 3° west and the wind correction angle is 9° with the wind on the right. What is the compass heading?

8. The compass heading is 327°, the variation is 5° west, deviation 3° east and the wind correction angle is 7° with the wind coming from the left. What is the true course?

9. The true course is 114°, the magnetic course is 121°, the compass course is 119°, and the compass heading is 127°. What is the variation and deviation, and on which side is the wind?

10. The compass heading is 71°, the compass course 60°, magnetic course 66° and the true course 64°. What is the variation, deviation, and wind?

11. The true course is 122°, variation is 9° west, deviation 2° east, ship cruises at 75 miles per hour and the wind is a 225° wind of 20 miles per hour. What is the compass heading?

12. The true course is 330° and the ship we are using cruises at 65 miles per hour. The weather man says the wind is blowing 15 miles per hour from 035. What will be our speed over the ground?

13. The distance between two cities is 315 miles over a course where the average variation is 12° east. The true course is 278° and the deviation of our compass at this reading is 3° west. The airplane has a cruising speed of 115 miles per hour and the wind is blowing 23 miles per hour from 315°. Compile a log of the flight.

14. There is some country bearing 27° from your airplane that you would like to fly over. Your airplane carries fuel for a little over 3 hours and cruises at 80 miles per hour. The wind is 18 miles per hour from 45° and the variation is 7° west. The deviation card of your ship is shown in the illustration on page 233. How far out can you fly before you must turn back? Show log of both legs.

ANSWERS TO PROBLEMS

1. 27° less 13°, gives a magnetic course of 14°.
2. 92° plus 10° plus 4° equals 106° compass course.
3. 217° plus 2° or 219° true course.
4. The magnetic heading of 219° less 7° gives a true heading of 212°. The magnetic heading of 219° less 3° gives a compass heading of 216°.
5. 95° minus 6° plus 2° equals 91° for the true course.
6. 4° minus 7° east variation would take us past 360° to 357°, minus the 3° deviation or 354° for the compass course.
7. 271° minus 16° east variation, plus 3° west deviation plus 9° wind equals 267° compass heading.
8. 327° plus 7° wind, plus 3° deviation, minus 5° variation makes the true course 332°.
9. The variation is 7° west, the deviation 2° east and the wind is on the right 8°.
10. The variation is 2° west, deviation 6° east and the wind is from the right 11.°

11. Draw meridian NS and at point E draw the true course of 122°. Put EW downwind. With W as center and a radius equal to the air speed mark off WP. Measure angle EPW which is 11°. Then 122° plus 9° minus 2° plus 15° equals 144° compass heading.

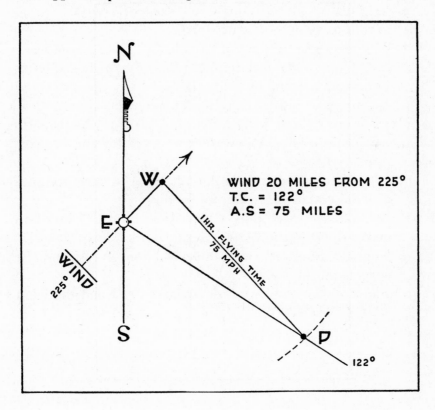

WIND 20 MILES FROM 225°
T.C. = 122°
A.S = 75 MILES

1 HR. FLYING TIME
75 MPH

WIND 225°

122°

12. Construct the triangle of velocities and then measure EP which represents the ground speed. Using the same scale used to construct the triangle of velocities, the ground speed will be found to be 56 miles per hour.

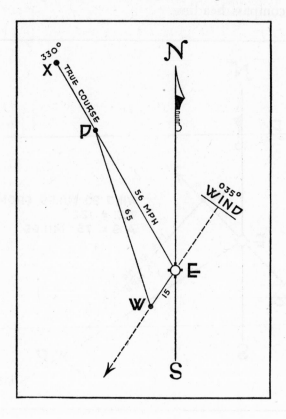

13. Answer to problem:

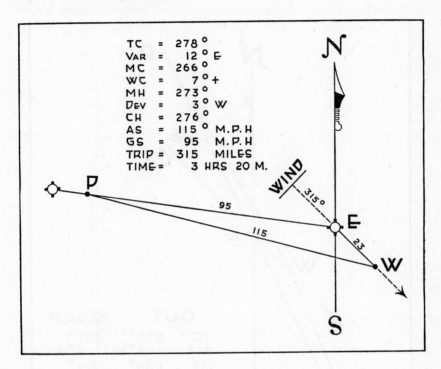

TC   =   278°
VAR =   12° E
MC   =   266°
WC   =   7° +
MH   =   273°
DEV =   3° W
CH   =   276°
AS   =   115° M.P.H
GS   =   95 M.P.H
TRIP =   315 MILES
TIME =   3 HRS 20 M.

14. Answer to problem:

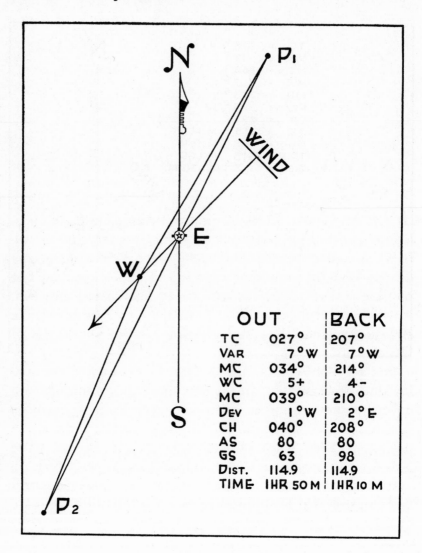

	OUT	BACK
TC	027°	207°
VAR	7°W	7°W
MC	034°	214°
WC	5+	4-
MC	039°	210°
DEV	1°W	2°E
CH	040°	208°
AS	80	80
GS	63	98
DIST.	114.9	114.9
TIME	1HR 50M	1HR 10M

27

NAVIGATION INSTRUMENTS

T HE Air Traffic Rules of the Civil Aeronautics Administration provide for two kinds of flying, *contact,* and *instrument.* A contact flight is one made under good weather conditions when the ground or water is continuously visible. The position of the airplane is controlled by reference to the earth. An instrument flight is made when the terrain is not visible and the airplane is flown by referring to various navigational instruments.

Contact flight conditions, or Class C, exist when the ceiling and the visibility are greater than the minimum laid down for the location in question by the Civil Aeronautics Administration. When the visibility becomes less and the ceiling lowers, Class N, or instrument conditions, prevail. Class X is when an airport is closed and no flying is permitted.

Instrument flying is a science all by itself and one which takes a great deal of study and practice. Only pilots who are qualified and have instrument ratings are permitted to fly under instrument conditions. However, most of the instruments used in instrument flying are called navigational instruments and can be very helpful in contact navigation. In addition to the magnetic compass, other basic instruments

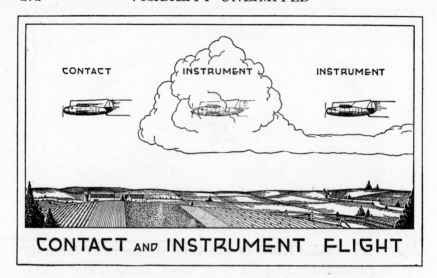

CONTACT AND INSTRUMENT FLIGHT

include the altimeter, air speed indicator, turn and bank indicator, rate of climb or vertical speed indicator and drift indicator. Although not usually thought of as a navigational instrument, a watch or clock is of cardinal importance.

Other instruments of extreme importance in instrument flying are the directional gyro, the artificial horizon and the gyropilot.

The *altimeter* is an instrument that indicates the approximate height of an aircraft over a given point. Set to read zero before taking off, it indicates the height above the airport, not the ground over which the plane is traveling. There are two kinds of altimeters, the *standard* and the *sensitive*. The principle of the altimeter is the same as that of the aneroid barometer. The only difference is that the dial of the altimeter is calibrated in feet instead of units of pressure.

The heart of the altimeter is an air-tight metal box called the diaphragm, or cell, from which the air has been removed. This cell is fastened to the inside of an air-tight case which is connected to the static line of the *pitot static tube*.

ALTIMETER

This pitot static tube is the tubelike projection that is seen on an airplane wing. Located at some point where the air is undisturbed by the wings or propeller, this device is a combination of two tubes, the pitot and the static. The end of the pitot tube is open to the air and receives the full impact of air stream pressure as the plane moves through the air. This pressure varies in proportion to the speed of the plane. The pitot tube obtains *dynamic pressure*.

The static tube is closed except for small openings back away from the end. This tube receives none of the air stream pressure. The static tube obtains static pressure, which is nothing more than the normal pressure of the atmosphere in a motionless condition.

The pressure inside the case of an altimeter, then, is that of the outside atmosphere at the same level. The case is connected to the static line to eliminate any variations of pressure inside the cockpit.

With the removal of the air from the cell the sides, owing to atmospheric pressure, will tend to draw together. This results in a delicately balanced device that is very sensitive to changes of static pressure.

Under normal pressure the natural strength of the sides of the diaphragm and the inward pressure of the atmosphere tend to balance. When the airplane climbs into areas of lower density the pressure on the vacuum cell lessens and the sides of the cell are pulled farther apart. As the airplane descends and the pressure increases, the walls of the diaphragm move closer together. The effect of these slight changes on the shape of the cell is magnified by a system of links and levers. This motion is then transmitted by a sector and pinion to a pointer on a dial. Thus change in altitude, through variation in pressure, causes proportionate changes in the shape of the diaphragm which when transmitted to the pointer and

INSTRUMENT PANEL

TWIN ENGINE INSTRUMENT PANEL

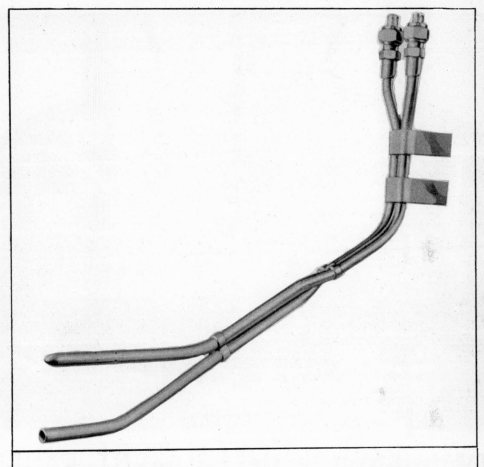

PITOT-STATIC TUBE

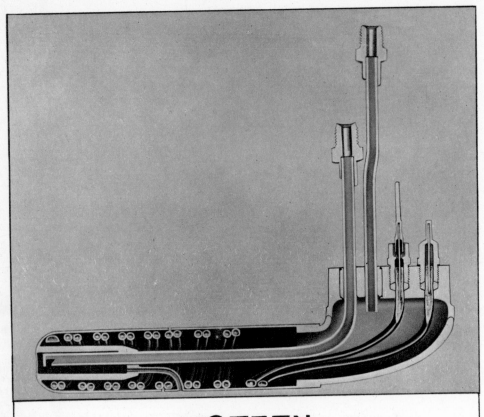

MODERN
PITOT STATIC TUBE

ALTIMETER

SENSITIVE
ALTIMETER

TURN AND BANK
INDICATOR

AIRSPEED
INDICATOR

PITOT STATIC TUBE

VENTURI TUBE

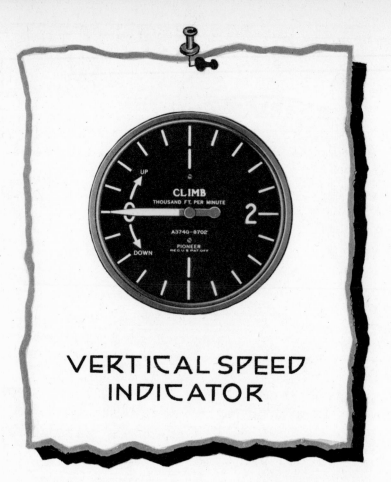

VERTICAL SPEED
INDICATOR

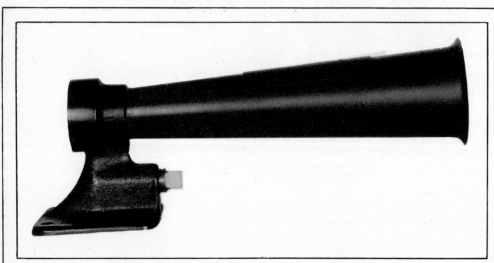

VENTURI TUBE

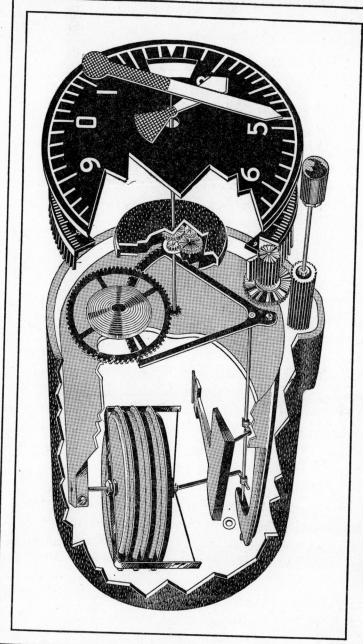

SENSITIVE ALTIMETER

dial indicate a change of altitude. A knob is provided which when turned will change the setting of the pointer. This knob should be turned before each flight so that the pointer is set at zero or on the setting desired by the pilot.

The *sensitive altimeter,* so called because of its response to slight changes in pressure, works on the same principle as the standard type. The sensitive type has two hands like a clock. One hand registers in thousands of feet and an additional hand indicates hundreds. The dial is graduated in units as low as 10 feet so that, with a little practice, very accurate altitude readings can be taken quickly.

The altimeter is subject to several errors. Perhaps the most important is that caused by temperature variations. This is because the altimeter, being a pressure measuring instrument, cannot discriminate between pressure changes due to change in altitude and pressure changes due to changes in temperature. Under instrument conditions this error is extremely important and external adjustments must be made with the knob so that the readings become dependable. For contact flying, however, it need not be considered unless the pilot wishes to familiarize himself with the details for practice.

The *air speed indicator* is an instrument that measures the speed of an aircraft passing through the air. It also depends upon variations in pressure for its readings, and is very similar in principle to the altimeter. Like the altimeter, the air speed indicator has a sensitive cell fastened to the inside of an airtight case. This case is connected to the static tube. The interior of the cell, however, is not evacuated, but is connected to the pitot tube.

As the air speed of the airplane increases, the pressure increases at the pitot tube and causes the cell to expand. This expansion is multiplied by gears and levers and transmitted to a pointer where it gives a reading of air speed in miles per hour. The air speed indicator merely measures the pressure difference between moving air and still air and translates this difference into a reading in miles per hour.

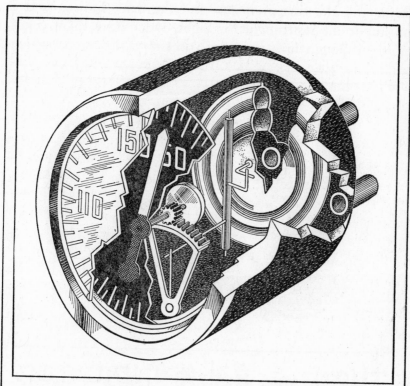

AIR SPEED INDICATOR

The air speed indicator is also subject to temperature and altitude errors which are taken into account by professional pilots. To estimate this error it is enough to remember that the indicated air speed runs about 2 per cent slow for every 1000 feet increase in altitude. Thus an airplane with an air speed indicator reading 100 miles per hour at 5000 feet actually has a true air speed of roughly 110 miles per hour. This can be figured with a computer as shown facing page 246.

The *turn and bank indicator* is a combination of two instruments, the turn indicator and the bank indicator. It is an important instrument for flight under instrument conditions. Although it is not at all necessary, nor even particu-

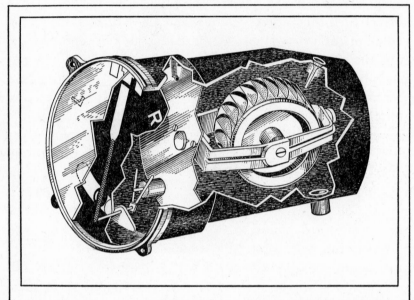

TURN AND BANK INDICATOR

larly helpful, for contact flight, it is explained briefly here because of its importance to aviation in general. If your ship has one, it may be used to check your flying technique, since the bank indicator will indicate slips and skids.

The *bank indicator* of the instrument is very simple in principle. It consists of a glass tube about two inches long and ½ inch in diameter curved upward on both ends. Inside is a steel ball free to roll in a liquid provided to prevent rapid swinging of the ball. When the airplane is in straight flight the ball is acted upon by gravity and remains in the lowest part of the tube, which in level flight is the center. If a wing goes down the ball rolls because of gravity to the side of the low wing. During a turn gravity continues to pull the ball toward its lowest point, but centrifugal force tends to make it roll toward the outside of the turn. In a correct turn these forces balance and the ball remains in the center of the tube. Hence if the ball is in the center of the tube the airplane either is in laterally level flight or in a correctly banked turn.

The *turn indicator* part of the instrument is slightly more complicated. It works on the gyroscopic principle and the essential part of this instrument is a small gyro. Almost every child at one time or another has had a gyroscopic top and knows how it will stand firmly when the inner wheel is rotating at a high speed. The precession factor, however, is not as well known and it is upon this phenomenon that the turn indicator depends.

Whenever a gyro, rotating about its own axis, is forced to turn about some other axis, it will attempt to align its axis of rotation with the axis about which it is forced to turn. The gyro of the turn indicator rotates about a lateral axis while an airplane, when turning, rotates about the vertical axis. Therefore when an airplane turns either to the left or right the gyro will try to place its axis in a vertical position. The shorter the turn of the airplane, the greater the force exerted by the gyro. The gyro is attached to a plate connected to a pointer on the instrument head. When the plane turns the gyro leans in proportion to the turn, exerting its force on the pointer, which indicates the rate of turn of the plane. When the plane returns to straight flight a spring pulls the gyro back to its former upright position.

As the operation of the turn indicator is dependent upon a spinning gyro, some means must be provided to keep the gyro rotating. This is done by directing a stream of air against the gyro wheel. There are several methods of producing this air stream, but the commonest is with the aid of a venturi tube.

A *venturi tube* is a trumpet-shaped tube with an opening in the narrowest part, called the throat. The venturi is placed on a strut of the airplane with the axis of the tube parallel to the line of flight and with the small end facing forward. When air passes through the tube the speed of the air in the throat is greater than the speed of the air outside. The speed of the air in the throat is also greater than in the front and rear parts of the tube. This is because a given amount of air entering the front part of the tube has to pass through a smaller opening at the throat. This extra speed causes a lower atmospheric pressure in the throat, and when a tube is inserted into the throat opening suction is produced.

The venturi tube is located in the propeller slipstream so that instruments depending upon this device for a reading will operate when the plane is on the ground. Thus, these instruments will give a reading during the takeoff.

This tube is connected to the case of the turn indicator which is airtight except for one opening called a *jet*. When the airplane flies through the air the suction of the venturi pulls the air from the case. Air then rushes into the case through the jet and strikes the edge of the gyro wheel. This gyro wheel has vanes like a water wheel and when impelled by the air rotates at a speed of about 10,000 revolutions per minute, according to the Pioneer Instrument Company.

When this instrument is working properly it is very dependable and accurate. With the needle in certain positions in a turn the airplane is known to be turning at a definite rate.

For instance, with the needle two widths off center the airplane, if not skidding, is turning at the rate of 3 degrees per second. At this rate a complete turn of 360 degrees will be made in 2 minutes. When on instruments a pilot can make a turn of any number of degrees by holding a standard turn for the required number of minutes or seconds.

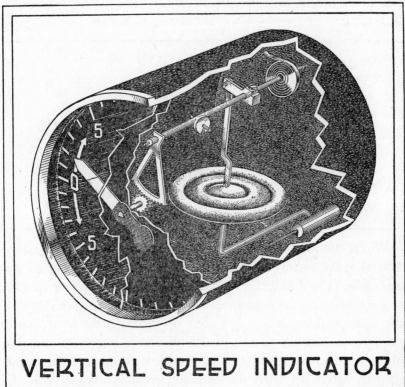

VERTICAL SPEED INDICATOR

The *climb indicator* is also known as a *rate of climb indicator* and a *vertical speed indicator*. It shows the rate in feet per minute at which an airplane is gaining or losing altitude. It does not, however, indicate the position of the nose in relation to the horizon.

Like the air speed indicator and the altimeter this instrument is essentially a pressure gauge having a diaphragm or cell in an airtight case. This cell is connected to the static line of the pitot static tube so that normal outside atmospheric pressure prevails inside. The interior of the instrument case is connected to the static tube also, but the entrance into the case is by means of a long, very small tube called a *capillary leak tube.*

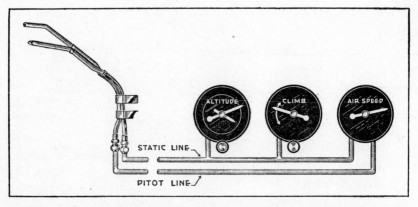

When the airplane climbs the decreasing pressure is transmitted immediately to the cell. Because the opening in the leak tube is so small the pressure in the case tends to remain at that of the previous level until it can leak out through the tube and equalize with that of the cell. As long as the airplane continues to climb the pressure inside of the diaphragm remains less than that of the case because it is unable to catch up with the outside pressure. When the airplane is in a dive or glide the pressures in the cell and in the case are reversed. These pressure differences, which are proportional to the vertical speed, cause expansion or contraction of the cell, which in turn is transmitted to a pointer on the dial.

The *Kollsman Direction Indicator* is a compass with a verti-

DRIFT INDICATOR

ADD TO COMPASS

SUBTRACT FROM COMPASS

AIRPLANE CLOCK

AVIATORS WATCH

DIRECTIONAL GYRO

cal dial representing the various cardinal and intercardinal points of the compass. The north position is at the top, east at the right, and all other points conform with the compass rose found on charts. A pointer on the dial indicates the direction in which the airplane is heading.

This is a very convenient instrument. It is provided with a double pointer to be used as a reference. The pointer is set on the desired heading by turning a knob at the bottom of the instrument. The pilot then only has to match up the pointers and the airplane will be on course. He does not have to remember the number of the compass heading. It is only necessary to keep the pointers together. An internal magnetic element actuates the pointer on the dial.

The instrument is easy to use and can be read accurately from any angle. The pointer in operation has a very short period so that it is nearly aperiodic.

Numerous devices have been evolved to determine the drift angle and the direction and velocity of the wind in flight. These are called bearing plates, grid plates, drift sights and drift indicators. Some of these are elaborate affairs from which the ground speed can also be determined. They are all dependent upon the ground being visible and their use is therefore limited to flight under contact conditions.

A simple *drift sight* consists of a circular scale and an inner ring which can be turned within the scale. On this inner grid ring are two or three parallel lines or wires which turn as a part of the ring. The center of the instrument is open or is covered with glass so that the ground below is visible when the instrument is mounted in the floor of the ship. It is so placed that when the reference lines are at zero on the scale they are parallel with the fore and aft axis of the plane. In operation the inner grid ring is rotated until objects on the ground appear to move along the grid lines. In this position the reference lines are parallel with the track of the airplane on the ground, and the angle they make with the fore and aft axis of the plane is the *drift angle*. This can be read directly from the scale.

If a drift sight is available it is not necessary to calculate the wind correction angle before flight. The compass course must be determined and then after taking off and reaching the desired cruising altitude, the airplane is headed on this compass course. The grid is turned as explained above and a drift reading is taken. The airplane is then headed *toward* the wind the number of degrees indicated on the scale. In a like manner if it is preferred to work out the triangle of velocities before flight the wind correction angle can be checked during flight and corrections made by use of the drift sight.

Clocks and watches are so generally used that their importance is taken for granted. It is obvious that an accurate timepiece is essential to navigation.

There are many timepieces made especially for navigation. Many excellent watches have appeared on the market in the past few years that give a variety of information in addition to time.

A very popular watch of this type among pilots is the *Jardur Chronograph*. It is available in a wide price range and with varied features, so that a pilot can select the watch that bests suits his needs. It is nonmagnetic, shockproof and waterproof—all very desirable characteristics for the active pilot. Serving as a stop watch or time-out watch it becomes handy in other fields as well as aviation. Special dials and scales permit many aeronautical calculations to be made quickly. These include ground speed, time consumed, gas used or still available, time turns under instrument conditions, and many other operations which make it an extremely valuable instrument for a pilot to have in his possession.

Aviation clocks must function under severe vibration and shock and be able to stand extremes of temperature. Since they are exposed to all kinds of weather they must have specially treated parts to prevent rust.

Luminous dials and pointers are necessary for night flight. The more elaborate clocks have extra dials to indicate elapsed time and sweep second hands for making time turns on instrument flight.

With all of this elaborate equipment for special conditions a cheap dollar watch comes in very handy and is quite dependable. Set at the time of takeoff at 12 o'clock, it serves to indicate time elapsed.

GYRO INSTRUMENTS

Of great interest and assistance to the navigator are the gyro instruments. These are not necessary for simple navigation, but when available they can be used to advantage. Found in practically all airline and military service planes, they are used most effectively as aids to instrument flying. They are becoming so well known in aviation, however, that they should have at least a brief mention even in a work devoted primarily to contact flight.

The directional gyro, previously referred to as the gyro compass, might be called a relative direction indicating instrument. It can be set on any compass heading and then used as a compass. It is much easier to use than a compass because it is free from magnetic disturbances; it does not lag, oscillate, or run ahead. Its reading is not made undependable by rough air, turning, banking, climbing or gliding.

The instrument contains a small gyro operated by air pressure from the venturi tube. This gyro, when operating, will maintain any direction to which it is set, for a short time.

In use, the airplane is put on the desired compass heading and held until the compass card settles down and becomes steady. The gyro knob is then turned until the card of the gyro reads the same as the compass. Then the caging knob is pulled out which frees the gyro unit and the course can then be flown by gyro. This is the procedure used under instrument conditions.

There is one characteristic of the directional gyro that must not be forgotten. Because of precession, the gyro changes direction by about 3 degrees every 15 minutes. This requires frequent resetting of the card with the compass for accurate navigation.

Some models of the directional gyro have an auxiliary bank indicator and are provided with suitable illumination.

The *gyro horizon* shows the position of the airplane in relation to the horizon. A gyroscope, air driven from the venturi tube, maintains a bar on the face of the instrument in a horizontal position. This bar, being always parallel with the horizon, serves as an artificial horizon and gives the instrument its name.

A miniature airplane is set into the center of the instrument case. Being in reality a part of the airplane itself, it moves as the airplane moves. As the airplane climbs, glides, or banks, the horizon bar seems to rise or fall the same way the natural horizon does. The miniature airplane assumes the same position relative to this bar that the real airplane does to the natural horizon. Thus a pilot using the instrument has the illusion of looking through a window in the instrument panel and seeing the airplane's relation to the horizon despite fog. The instrument also has a scale and an indicator that shows the degree of bank.

The *gyropilot* is an instrument which can actually fly an

GYRO-HORIZON

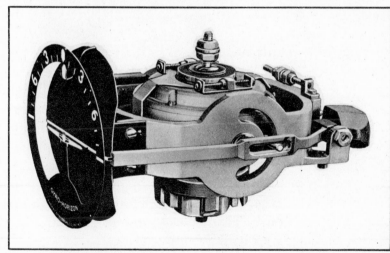

PARTS OF THE
GYRO HORIZON

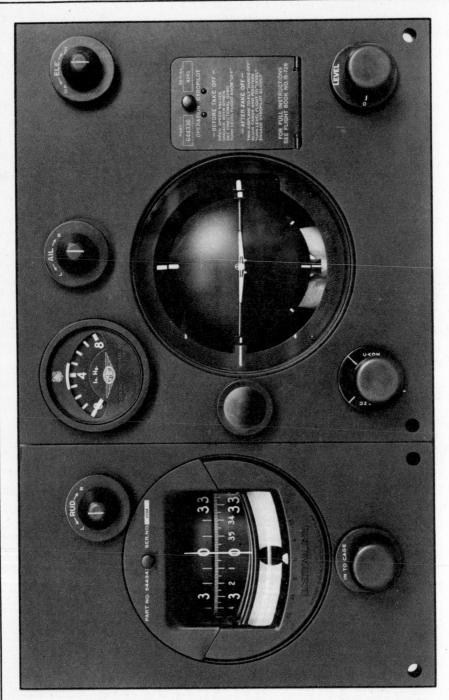

GYROPILOT

airplane, and on that account is sometimes called an automatic or robot pilot. It will fly the airplane straight at any level or will climb or glide the airplane as the human pilot directs. Fundamentally it is a combination of the directional gyro and the gyro horizon.

Although found on few private planes because of its weight and cost, the gyropilot is standard equipment on Navy Patrol planes and the larger airlines. As soon as the aircraft is clear of the airport and on its course, the human pilot rotates the adjusting knobs, turning complete control of the aircraft over to the gyropilot, and can then devote his attention to navigation, weather observations, reports, and radio.

28

AIRCRAFT RADIO

SPREADING over this country is a vast system of federal, state, and local highways that we take for granted. The growth of the automobile industry was entirely dependent upon the development of this highway system. The average person, however, does not realize that an almost identical system of aerial highways for the orderly control of air traffic also exists today. The same federal, state, and local governments have worked together so that aircraft can now fly over charted routes from coast to coast and from Canada to Mexico. Over these routes, linking cities to a vast airways network, travel the huge flying craft of commerce and national defense.

But these aerial thoroughfares differ from the land highways in that they are not made of asphalt or cement and stone. They are invisible and assume reality only when the key to their operation is in our possession. This magic key is radio, by means of which we find another kind of navigation at our disposal.

In the past few years radio has increased in importance until today it is no longer considered an accessory, but an essential part of an airplane. Airlines and military craft are furnished with complete radio apparatus as a matter of course.

The private pilot is also insisting that his personal airplane be fitted with adequate radio equipment. The airplane without radio today is excluded from the busier airports and the principal air lanes. Rightly so, for a pilot without radio is a nuisance in traffic, or even a menace to himself and others, particularly when visibility is poor.

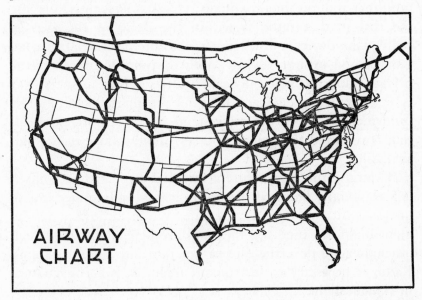

AIRWAY
CHART

Radio equipment ranges from a simple portable dry cell receiver to the elaborate and expensive combinations of radio compasses, multicoil receivers, direction finders, transmitters, etc., used by the airlines and the military services. New equipment and methods are continually appearing on the market but the underlying principles are basic and change but little.

The radio aids to navigation provided by the government are free to all those who care to use them and operate 24 hours a day. There are few regulations on the use of radio and these are simple and rational. There are no restrictions whatever on the ownership and operation of receiving apparatus. The rules that do exist apply to transmission and are designed to prevent cluttering up the air with unauthorized and indiscriminate communication.

Radio can no longer be considered expensive. With the many thousands of new pilots the demand for aviation radio has increased tremendously. Manufacturers have developed new lines and put them in quantity production, thus lowering the cost so that radio is within the reach of the average light plane owner and of course absolutely essential in commercial and military flying. With the portable receiver the private pilot can "ride the beam" just as well as airliners. Nor is it difficult to navigate by radio as many believe. The fundamentals are easy to understand. After that practice is all that is required for a pilot to take full advantage of the aids available.

Because radio is absolutely essential to instrument flight it is commonly believed that radio is used only under instrument conditions. This is not true. While radio and instrument flight are used together and are dependent upon each other they are nevertheless two separate and distinct systems. Radio is necessary to instrument flight. It is a convenience in contact flight.

Piloting and dead reckoning require constant attention to terrain. This is very interesting for a while, but can become tiresome when the novelty wears off. Radio navigation then becomes a blessing. With a little practice one becomes familiar with the system and obtains a good understanding for later training in instrument flight.

There is one great danger, however. Radio beam flying is so simple under good weather conditions that the inexperienced pilot is likely to be lulled into a false conception of his own capabilities. He may come to believe that if he can fly the beam in good weather he can also do so when the weather is not so good. When the weather is bad, do not fly except in case of absolute necessity. If you have to fly when the weather is bad, try to get an instrument rating which includes a thorough understanding of radio. This will be your assurance that you have at least an elementary knowledge of the rules and procedures, and, what is more important, the limitations of radio and instrument flight. It will also teach you your own limitations and thereby make you a safer pilot. There is a saying around airports that is so old that I hesitate to repeat it. It is an old-timer's advice to the fledgling: Don't try to be the best pilot, but try to be the oldest.

There are several methods of navigating by radio but the best known, and perhaps the simplest, is the radio range system of the Civil Aeronautics Administration. The larger cities of the country are connected by civil airways which are twenty miles wide and join airport to airport. Near these airports are beacons identifying the airport just as lighthouses mark certain locations for the seafarer. Instead of sending forth a beam of light, these airway beacons direct a "beam" of radio waves outward along the incoming airway. A pilot flying between cities on the airlines merely tunes his receiver to the right beam and then follows the signals into the airport.

Each beacon sends not one beam but four, and the spaces between beams also contain distinctive signals. This system of signals from a radio beacon is called a *radio range*.

The manner in which the beam is produced is very interesting. A transmitting station using a loop antenna or vertical tower radiating system sends signals out into an 8-shaped field as in the illustration on page 293. If another loop is placed so as to cross the first loop there will be two 8-shaped fields which overlap as shown by the illustration on page 294. If the two antennas were to send different signals there would be four areas in which clear signals could be heard and in the

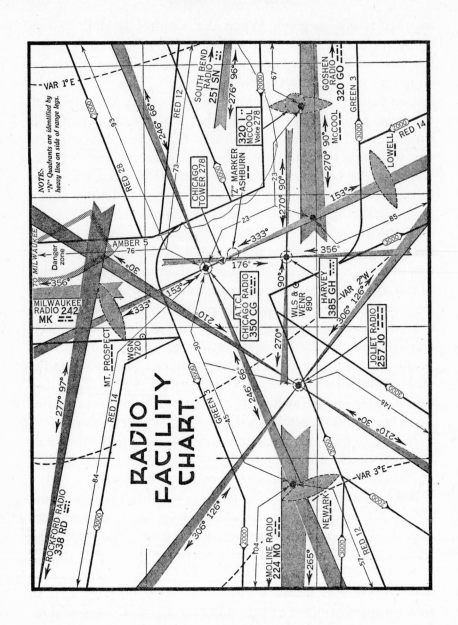

RADIO FACILITY CHART

NOTE:
"N" Quadrants are identified by
heavy line on side of range legs.

292

four areas where the fields overlap there would be mixed signals. Using this principle in the range system the first antenna sends forth a continuous series of N signals or "dah" "dits" of the Morse Code. The second antenna transmits a steady series of A's or "dit" "dahs." This results in four areas in which clear signals are heard, 2 A-areas and 2 N-areas. Dur-

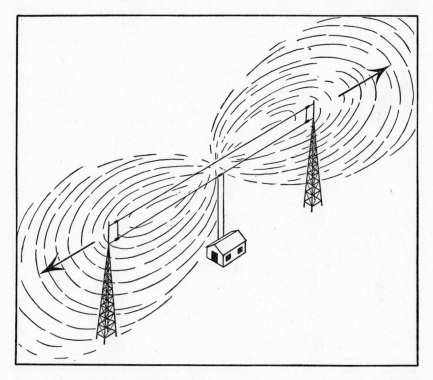

ing transmission the A's and N's are so timed that in the area where the fields overlap the A's and N's blend together, so that a steady tone is heard.

The manner in which this is accomplished is very interesting. The N or dah dit is the reverse of the A or dit dah. The spaces, or time intervals, between the dah dits fit exactly the sound of the dit dahs. Conversely the spaces between the

dit dahs are filled by the sound of the dah dits. The result
is a steady even tone that tells a pilot he is "on the beam."

Normally the areas of steady tone, called the *on-course,*
the *equisignal zone,* the *leg,* or the *beam,* are 90 degrees apart.
This does not always conform to existing airways at a range
station. Slight changes in pattern are sometimes possible to
direct all legs along the airways. The range station is usually

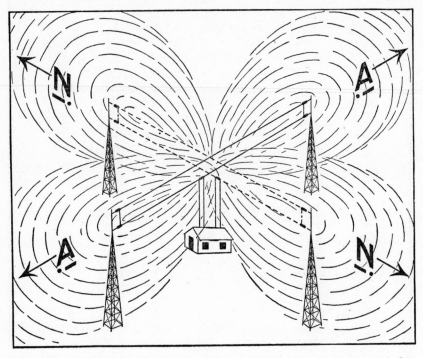

located so that one leg is directed over the best runway of the
nearby airport so that airplanes can be brought into this runway on instruments. In selecting the runway to use for instrument landings consideration is given to prevailing winds, obstructions, length of runways, nature of approach, etc. In
designating the quadrants a uniform system is used to aid in
orientation when on instruments. The quadrant through

which true north passes is assigned the letter N. If true north coincides with a beam the N is given to the quadrant on the west.

The beam is normally 3 degrees wide and between the off-course and on-course areas is another zone called the *bi-signal*

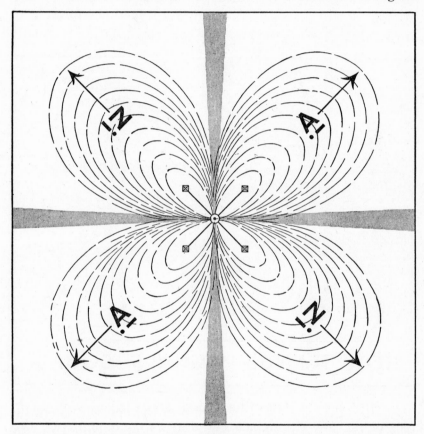

zone. In this zone upon approaching the beam the off-course signal begins to combine with the on-course signal so that both can be heard. In this zone either the N or the A is heard against a background of steady hum. On getting close to the beam the quadrant signal seems to fade as the background hum increases, until on reaching the beam the steady hum is all that is heard. This bi-signal zone is supposed to be 30 degrees wide on either side of the beam but the monotone background can rarely be heard more than a few degrees away

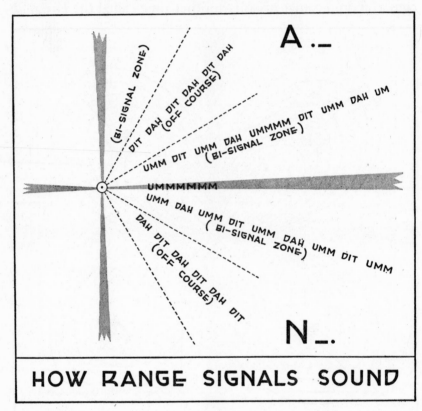

HOW RANGE SIGNALS SOUND

from the beam. The illustration above gives a graphic idea of the way the signals sound at different points on the range.

Twice each minute the range signals are interrupted and the station identification signal is broadcast. This consists of two letters in code and is the same as the symbol of the local airport Weather Bureau station. The identification signal is broadcast by both antennas, first by the N and then by the A antenna. These signals are subject to the same signal field and intensity as the A and N signals. Therefore, even though the beam is temporarily interrupted the relative signal strength tells a pilot his location relative to the beam. If he is on course he will hear both signals with equal strength. If

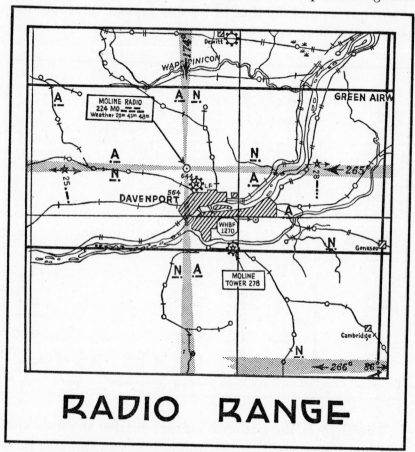

RADIO RANGE

the first of the two signals is weaker the pilot knows he is in the A-quadrant; if the first is stronger he is in the N-quadrant. With practice a pilot can estimate his approximate angular distance from the beam by the relative strength of the two identification signals.

The radio ranges are shown on the various aeronautical charts in pink and the bearings are given both toward and away from the range. These bearings are magnetic as measured at the range station. Reference to the charts will show the location of the ranges with a box giving the call letters, the frequency and the time of weather reports. This information is all that is required for radio navigation.

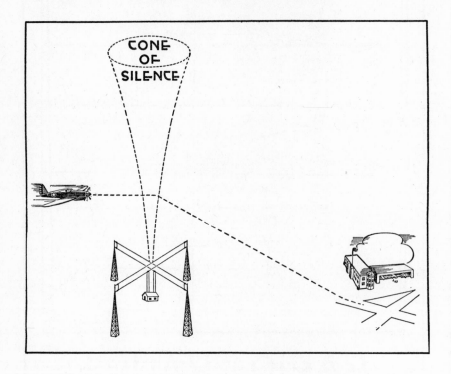

Directly over the station is an area narrow at the ground and growing gradually wider with altitude. In this area there is no signal and it is appropriately called the cone of silence. Just before this cone is reached the signal increases greatly in intensity and dies out as the cone is passed over. On the other side of the cone the signal surges again and quickly dies out.

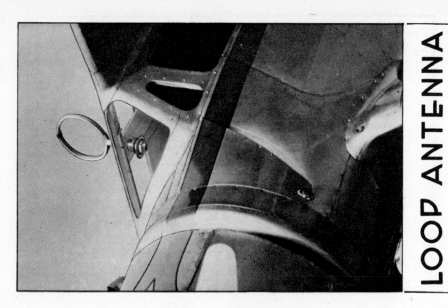

LOOP ANTENNA

PORTABLE RADIO

ANTENNAS ON AIRPLANE

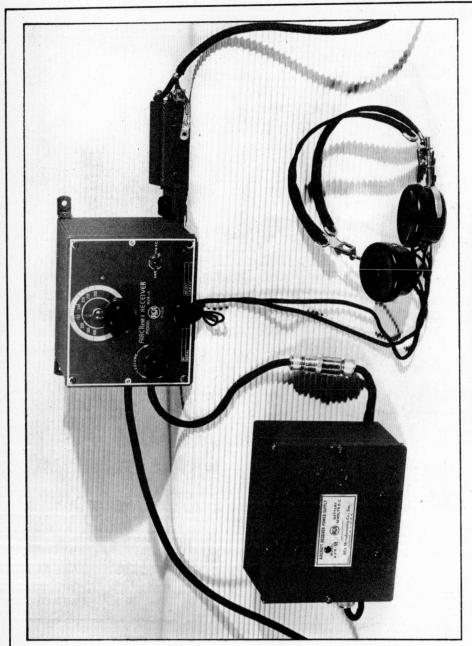

RADIO RECEIVER

This sequence tells the pilot flying on instruments when he has passed over the radio range station. There are other phenomena of the radio ranges such as bent, swinging and multiple beams, and an infinite number of variations on individual ranges. These will present no difficulties to the private pilot flying contact.

BENT BEAM

All he has to do is get on the beam and stay on it until he gets to the station. This automatically takes care of drift and any variations in the nature of the beam. Other aids to navigation are the Class-M, Class-Z and fan-markers, which are of great assistance to the pilot on instruments.

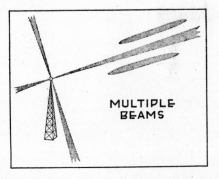

MULTIPLE BEAMS

The Class-M markers are placed at critical points along the radio ranges to serve as check points. They are of the same frequency as the range

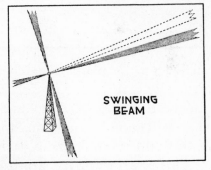

SWINGING BEAM

upon which they are located. They send out an identifying letter in code. Very often they are located at the intersections of beams from two radio stations. They are then tuned to the frequencies of both beams and serve as a reminder to pilots on the range going either way that it is time to tune to the frequency of the new range. These radio marker beams are equipped for two-way voice communication and weather reports can be obtained from them upon request.

The minimum equipment for a private pilot to fly the range is a receiver, a pair of headphones and an antenna in-

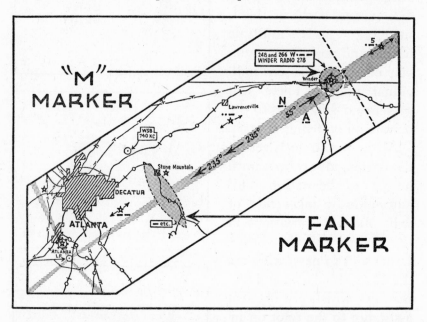

stalled on the plane. The cheapest receiver is the portable dry cell set already mentioned. This costs around $40 and can be had with headphones at slight extra cost. The salesman will install an antenna for a few dollars. You are then equipped for simple radio navigation.

This set, since it has a broadcast band in addition to the range band, and a built-in loop-aerial, can also be used on the road or on the water. In the home or office it can be plugged into the regular house current, which automatically disconnects the dry cells. It is a very versatile little outfit.

This matter of wave lengths, frequencies and bands that

you hear a great deal about these days can be cleared up quite easily. These are merely radio standards of measurement. If you throw a stone into water you cause a disturbance that manifests itself by waves going in all directions from the disturbance. These waves gradually diminish in height until

WAVE LENGTHS

their energy is entirely dissipated. But the distance from top to top of the waves is the same as long as they last, whether near or far away from the disturbance. This distance is the wavelength.

Radio waves are also caused by a disturbance. But the disturbance is in the ether and the waves are invisible. Their length may be measured in meters. We are not greatly concerned with this for that is an obsolete method of measuring radio waves. Today they are measured in frequencies— the number of waves passing a given point in space per second. The frequency also equals the number of cycles, or complete oscillations, per second. But because the radio waves have thousands of cycles per second we speak of their frequency in terms of thousands of cycles, or kilocycles. Ultra high frequencies are in terms of millions of cycles or megacycles. If you will look at your house radio you will see that its broadcast range is from 55 to 160, which means 550 to 1600 kilocycles, the final zero having been left off for easy reading. This is the American broadcast band and these frequencies have been assigned by the Federal Communications Commission. The band assigned to the ranges and for airway traffic control is from 200 to 400 KC (kilocycles). The band from 2000 to 6000 KC is given to aircraft communication such as airlines, military and other aircraft. These are subject to modification as conditions demand. The bands we are interested in here are the 200-400 band for radio range, weather and airport traffic control, the 550-1600 band for broadcast and radio-compass work, and the 2000-6000 band for aircraft communication.

Radio is a fairly complicated study and something about which the average man knows little. About all he wants to do is turn a knob and have music or signals, or whatever it is he is looking for, pour forth without further effort on his part. He must, therefore, depend to a considerable extent upon the judgment of the salesman he is dealing with for the selection and installation of his aviation radio apparatus. The equipment available today is well engineered, reliable, and very sensitive. It is a waste of money to buy good equipment and then provide such poor accessories, or do such an unsatisfactory installation job, that the full possibilities of the apparatus are not realized. Each set is built to be used under certain circumstances and with a certain type of antenna. The results obtained depend upon the selection of the various pieces of equipment, the care with which it is installed, and the manner in which it is maintained.

Antennas are divided into several types and the best performance of the set depends upon their proper selection, location, and installation. Receiver antennas come in two T-types, those running along the top of the fuselage and those

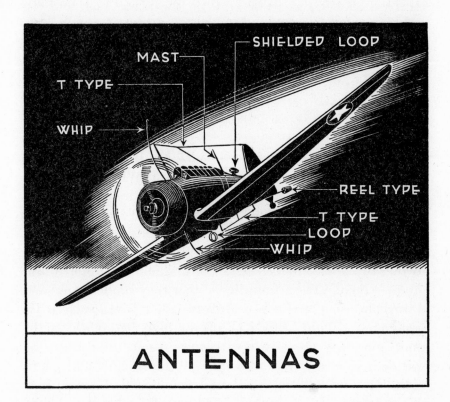

ANTENNAS

attached to the underside of the fuselage. Other styles are the *whip type, vertical mast* and *trailing antenna.*

In addition there are the fixed and rotatable loops which we shall cover when discussing homing and the radiocompass.

Transmitting antennas are usually the trailing type and the triangular type which runs from the tail to the wing tips.

When the plane is in the air its metal parts pick up charges of static electricity. Usually the various metal parts have unequal charges and there is a tendency for current to flow from one part to another. If they are not connected the current may jump across in the form of small sparks that are heard in the receiver. Sparks also occur between the plane itself and the outside atmosphere. This can be tolerated under good weather conditions, but when the weather gets poor and there is more electricity in the air the static may become so bad that signals are blotted out. This can be largely corrected by connecting the various metal parts together with wire so that the charges can be equalized. This process is called bonding and should be done by the service man at the place where you buy your set. Airplanes may be bought bonded by the factory.

Yet another factor that must be taken into consideration is the ignition system. The sparks in the engine plugs set up high frequency oscillations that make a great deal of noise in the receiver. To prevent this all the high tension circuits must be confined within a metal case or shield which is grounded to the airplane. This process, called shielding, absorbs and grounds the electrical impulses so that they cannot cause any disturbance in the receiver. Because other wires, such as instrument and light leads, pick up the high frequency oscillations and relay them to the receiver, these should also be shielded. The only way to do the job thoroughly and guard against any noise from the plane's own electrical system is to shield completely all electrical equipment and wires. Again, unless you are a radio specialist, this is a job for the radio service man.

There is a great deal of equipment now available for radio navigation and new methods and applications are continually appearing on the market. So many combinations of apparatus and procedures can be used that it is practically impossible to cover them all adequately. Certain basic equipment has been selected and will be mentioned briefly to illustrate the uses of the general types and their applications to navigation.

There is included a picture of a popular receiver compact enough for the light airplane, yet built to meet the most severe conditions. Because of its few controls it is as simple to operate as a home radio. The knob in the left-hand corner turns the set on and controls the volume. The center knob is the station selector for the 200-400 KC band on which the range signals and weather reports are received. Of particular interest is the traffic control switch in the lower right corner. Almost all airport stations that direct traffic by radio are set on 278 KC. In using this set when you get near the airport you merely flip the switch off the beam over to 278 and then receive landing instructions from the operator in the control tower. This receiver should have a horizontal antenna which can be mounted either above or below the fuselage.

Let's assume that we are flying on the range over Daggett, California, eastward toward Albuquerque, New Mexico. We know that we have just passed over the town of Daggett because we have just finished checking our position on the chart.

Yes, we still have our charts and we plotted our courses before we started out. This is because radio should be considered as an aid to navigation and not be depended upon entirely. The beam might stop working for some reason, or your set might get out of order when you least expect it.

From the sectional chart we know that the Daggett beam is on 365 KC so our radio is tuned to this frequency on the dial. The call for this station which comes through every 30 seconds is DG or dah dit dit space dah dah dit. The magnetic bearing leading out on the east leg is shown on the chart as 71 degrees. Of course deviation and wind have changed this to a different compass heading but it is near 71 degrees. With the compass pointing near this heading, and the radio tuned

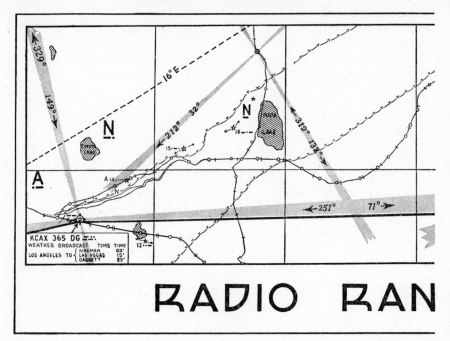

on 365, as long as a steady hum is heard we are on course or on the beam. If we start hearing A signals or dit dahs we know we have gone off the beam to the right and merely turn left until the steady hum reappears. If N signals or dah dits are heard we are on the left side of the beam and turn slightly to the right to get back on course. As far as the beam is concerned it does not matter at what altitude we fly as the beam extends from the ground as high as you would want to fly.

The chart also tells us that weather reports are issued from Daggett. At two minutes past the hour we shall receive Los Angeles to Kingman weather. We are very much interested in this as Kingman is our next range. Las Vegas and Daggett weather are transmitted at 15 and 29 minutes after the hour, respectively. These weather reports come in right over the range so that you do not have to hunt for them. Incidentally

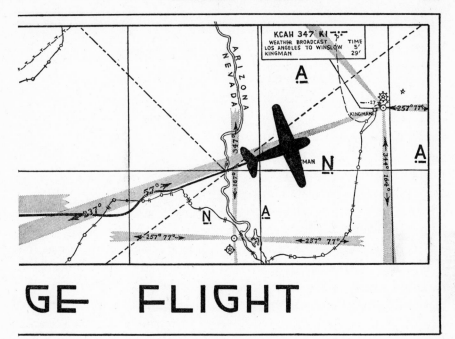

GE FLIGHT

these weather reports are now given in code and will be for the duration. This code is available to military pilots and others authorized to have it.

After flying on the Daggett range until the signals have gradually become weaker and we conclude from study of the chart and from our speed calculations that we are near the intersection of the Daggett and the Kingman ranges, we must change our receiver setting. Looking at the chart again we see that the Kingman range is on 347 KC so we tune our set to this frequency. As the new beam bears slightly more north than the Daggett beam we shall probably hear A signals first on the Kingman beam. The procedure here would be to continue straight until a clear on-course was heard, then make a left turn that you estimate will coincide with the beam. In a short time the signals will indicate whether you are on course or not. After settling down so that you are on course the compass should be read. By using the compass in conjunction with the radio you will soon be able to fly the ranges accurately. As you approach the Kingman range the signals gradually get louder. The best practice is to turn the volume control so that the signals can hardly be heard. Just as you get to the station the volume surges and then dies out as you pass over the cone of silence. Another surge and you will probably find yourself in the N sector on the east side of the station. A right turn will bring you back to the beam and on course again. The identification signals for the Kingman beam are KI or dah dit dah space dit dit. Weather reports for Winslow, which is another range on our course, come in at five minutes after the hour. When flying ranges pilots should fly on the right side of the beam. Periodic 10-degree turns to the right should be made until the off-course signal just begins to come in. An immediate turn should then be made back to the on-course.

It becomes apparent that successful radio range flying depends upon a knowledge of each range, particularly where the N and A quadrants are. This information, given on the aeronautical charts, is greatly amplified in the government publication *Air Navigation Radio Aids*. Of particular help for instrument flight, this pamphlet also contains a wealth of information of interest to the pilot who flies contact. Published regularly by the Civil Aeronautics Administration and kept current in the *Weekly Notices to Airmen* it tabulates all of the radio facilities available to pilots. The *Weekly Notices to Airmen* are reports sent to airports and others interested, listing changes in maps, radio facilities, airports in repair, danger areas, and anything else of general interest to the aviator. With all of this help available to the pilot aerial navigation becomes practical and safe.

These reports are now restricted to military and other authorized personnel and will be for the duration. After the war they will again be made available to the public.

Wartime restrictions have considerably limited the privileges of the private pilot and have placed strict regulations on civilian flying. As these change frequently, you will have to depend on your local airport manager for advice. Military pilots of course receive all necessary information through service channels.

There is no substitute for study and practice in these matters. Navigation, whether it be piloting, dead reckoning, celestial, or radio, can only be learned through actual experience. While it is easy to explain how to use the radio ranges, the actual flying of them becomes simple only by doing it. The best way to become familiar with the different signals is to practice on the home range until familiarity with the system is obtained.

29

THE RADIOCOMPASS AND
DIRECTION-FINDER

A N extremely interesting and highly practical instrument is
shown in the illustration facing p. 341. It represents one of the
greatest advances in navigation systems and equipment since
the early development of radio. Used as a receiver it has three
bands, the 200-400 KC or X band, the 550-1600 KC or A
band, and the 2000-6000 KC or B band. With the addition
of a loop antenna it becomes a *radiocompass,* and as such it
makes possible another kind of radio navigation known as
homing. If the loop antenna is of the rotatable type yet another branch of radio navigation called *direction-finding* is
possible.

With the normal fixed antenna, either the horizontal T-type
or vertical mast, this set operates as an aural receiver, on all
three bands. To use it as a range receiver the switch in the
center is set at Beacon Weather Regular, the knob on the left
turned until the pointer is on the X or beam band, and then
the range is selected on the frequency scale on the right side.
The volume is regulated in the conventional manner with
the volume control. To receive entertainment broadcasts the
band selector is changed to the A or broadcast band and the
desired station selected on the tuning dial. If you want to

remain in touch with your ground station or would like to listen in on the weather reports of the airlines covering the territory over which you are flying, the B band can be used.

When the set is used as a radiocompass, which is its primary purpose, a loop antenna is required in addition to the regular aerial. The loop is placed so that it is secured directly across the plane parallel with the wings and is called a fixed loop because it is not movable except by moving the plane. The

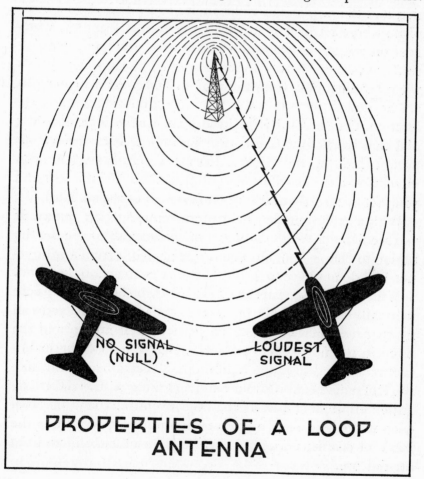

NO SIGNAL (NULL)

LOUDEST SIGNAL

PROPERTIES OF A LOOP ANTENNA

loop itself is electrostatically shielded in a streamlined housing.

The properties of a loop are such that no signals are obtained when the plane of the loop is at right angles to the direction of the transmitter to which the receiver is tuned. In this "null" position the airplane is headed directly toward or directly away from the transmitter. Maximum signals are obtained when the loop is in line with the broadcasting station and the airplane at right angles to it. Therefore an airplane whose receiver is tuned to a certain transmitter, when kept on a heading where the signals are "null" will head directly toward or "home" to that station. The same effect exists when heading away from the station. You know whether you are heading toward or away from a station by your relative location. On the AVR-8 the heading is usually indicated on a dial that works just like a turn indicator. After the set has been tuned to, and headed toward a certain station, you merely keep the needle centered on the visual indicator and you will fly directly to the antenna system of the station.

With a radiocompass you are not limited to the ranges. If you are flying to a city that has a range station you can use the station to "home" on, but you can approach it from any direction and do not have to go out of your way to get on the beam.

If there is no range at the city to which you want to fly there is usually a commercial broadcasting station which you can select. Frequencies of these stations are well known and are listed in the newspapers and pamphlets given out by manufacturers. The use of the radiocompass is confined to the 200-400 KC radio beam weather band and the 550-1600 KC standard entertainment band. The high frequency band of 2000-6000 KC is not available for radiocompass operation as the inherent characteristics of these frequencies make them unfit for this use.

An interesting feature of the radiocompass is that you can receive simultaneous visual and aural signals. When flying a course to or from a radio range beam station you can fly by visual indicator and still receive the weather broadcast. When homing on a broadcast station with the visual indicator, you can at the same time enjoy the program of the station toward which you are headed.

When homing correctly the nose of the airplane will always be pointing toward the station being received. If there is a side wind blowing, the airplane will be carried with the wind along a curving, steadily changing course towards the station. This change in heading automatically takes care of drift. It might appear that the airplane is going considerably out of its way flying in this manner. As far as the time is concerned, it works out about the same as if a drift correction were made and the airplane "crabbed" on a more direct course.

Although we may be pretty certain that the radiocompass will bring us in all right, it is always advisable to plan the

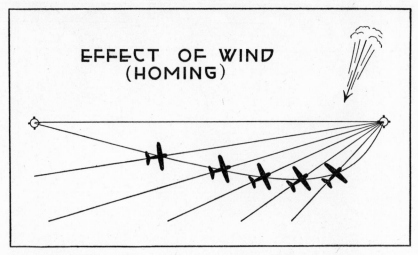

EFFECT OF WIND
(HOMING)

course regardless. We will not bother about the wind direction and velocity other than to notice its direction and estimate its strength, and make a mental note of its effect on the course. If the wind is too strong the flight should not be made. If it is moderate the radiocompass will automatically correct for wind without any difficulty.

Of course full consideration must be given to the terrain conditions and the weather before taking off. Next a radio station at the destination is selected. In case we wanted to fly from Winston-Salem, N. C., to Roanoke, Va., we could use either the Roanoke range station on 317 kilocycles or the commercial broadcasting station WDBJ on 930 kilocycles.

To fly the course by radiocompass the ship is first taken into the air, and after a safe altitude is reached it is headed in the general direction of Roanoke, which is 15 degrees with slight variation for estimated wind effect. The headphones are adjusted over our ears and the set is turned on. If the range station is to be used the band selector is set to the X position, or if the commercial station is desired, to the A position. After the tubes have warmed up the volume is ad-

RADIO COMPASS

RADIOCOMPASS
INDICATOR

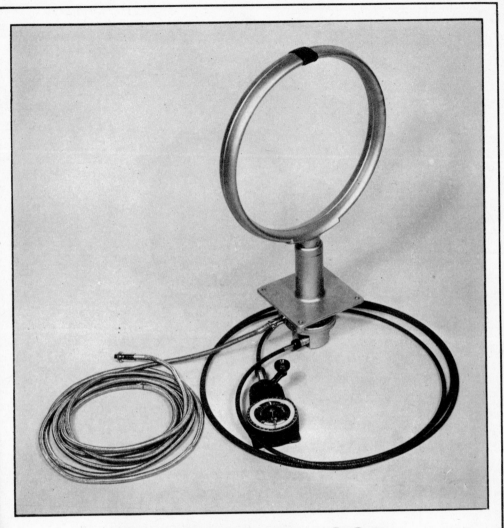

ROTATABLE LOOP

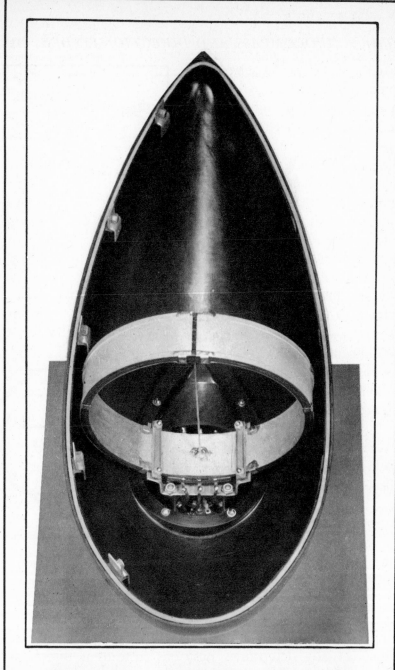

SHIELDED LOOP
(OPEN)

justed and the station selected is tuned in on the tuning dial. The Operation Selector must be on the Beacon-Weather-Regular position, while the tubes warm.

When the desired signal is tuned in so that the station is being received the volume is reduced to a minimum. The Operation Selector is then turned to the radiocompass position and the volume again adjusted so that the signal is at a comfortable level in the headphones. With adjustment of the sensitivity control on the indicator head the set is completely adjusted. Then, by heading so that the needle is centered, you will fly directly to the station in Roanoke to which you are tuned.

When this set is used as a radiocompass the antenna is a fixed loop. That is, the loop remains stationary and its plane is parallel with the wings of the airplane. A rotatable loop is one in which the whole loop rotates when a hand crank or knob attached to it is turned. When the airplane has a rotatable loop this same radiocompass may be used as a direction finder.

This term direction finder is not exactly accurate for the system actually determines positions instead of directions. Directions can be found from one or more positions but only

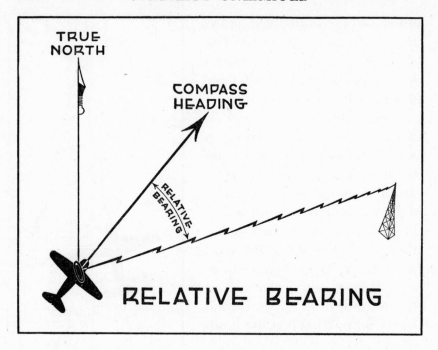

after the positions are located. The principle of direction finding is to locate the position of the airplane at different times. From these successive positions the airplane's direction of flight can be determined and its relation to a pre-planned flight course can be seen. If the airplane is making good its course no adjustments need be made. On the other hand if the various positions of the plane indicate that it has varied from the course the necessary corrections are made in the compass heading to bring the plane back on course.

To determine the plane's location or position the radio set is tuned to some radio station on the side of our course. The location of this station, of course, is shown on the chart. The loop is then rotated until the visual indicator is on zero. If the set does not have a visual indicator the loop is turned,

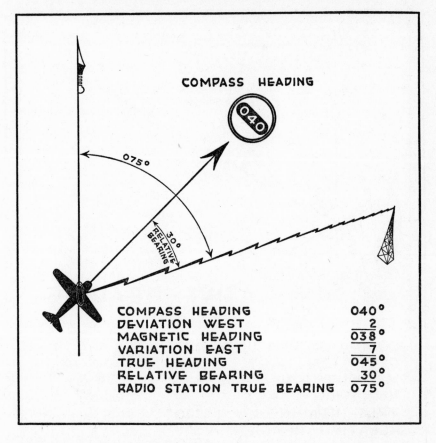

COMPASS HEADING

COMPASS HEADING	040°
DEVIATION WEST	2
MAGNETIC HEADING	038°
VARIATION EAST	7
TRUE HEADING	045°
RELATIVE BEARING	30°
RADIO STATION TRUE BEARING	075°

after the station has been tuned in, until the signal is at its lowest volume or at the "null" position.

At this point the airplane is heading in one direction but the plane of the loop is turned so that it is perpendicular to the radio station selected, which is in another direction. Attached to the shank of the loop is a circular scale called the *azimuth scale*. A pointer on this scale will now indicate the number of degrees between the compass heading of the airplane and the radio station. This is called the *relative bearing*. It is *not* the bearing of the airplane to the radio station.

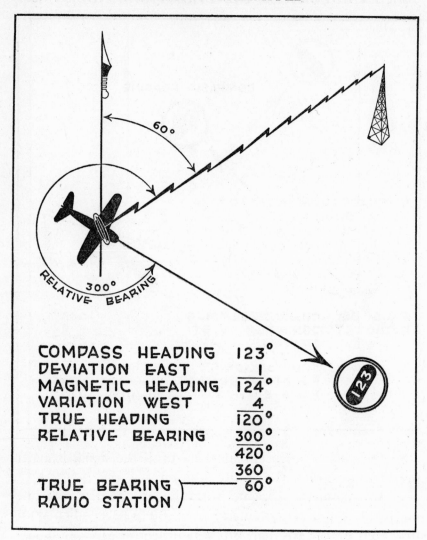

COMPASS HEADING   123°
DEVIATION EAST   1
MAGNETIC HEADING   124°
VARIATION WEST   4
TRUE HEADING   120°
RELATIVE BEARING   300°
                       420°
                       360
TRUE BEARING)———   60°
RADIO STATION)

To obtain the true bearing of the airplane to the radio station we read the compass and then apply the deviation correction for that heading and the variation correction for that locality. Remember that in this case we are working from

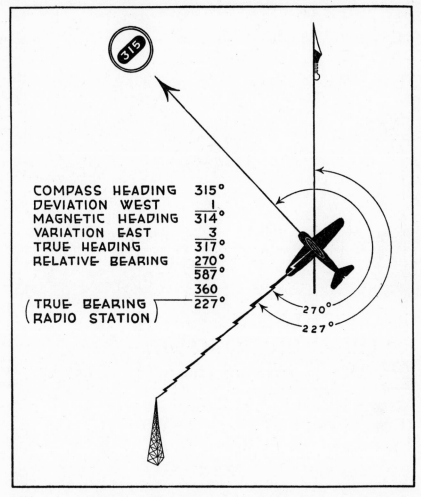

COMPASS HEADING 315°
DEVIATION WEST   1
MAGNETIC HEADING 314°
VARIATION EAST   3
TRUE HEADING   317°
RELATIVE BEARING 270°
                 587°
                 360
(TRUE BEARING) 227°
(RADIO STATION)

compass heading to true bearing, or really backwards, so our rules given earlier are reversed. This will now give the true heading of the airplane. The true heading is now added to the relative bearing. If as frequently happens the total is more than 360, then 360 must be subtracted. This might prove a bit confusing at first but study of the illustrations will make it clear. Now we have the true bearing of the airplane

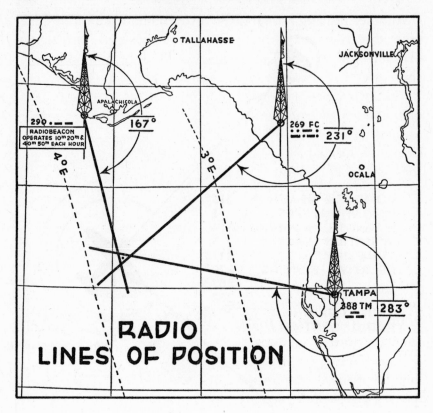

to the radio station and this can be plotted on the chart.

It is much easier, however, to plot the bearing of the radio station to the plane, since we know where the station is while the location of the plane is what we are trying to find. We merely use the reciprocal of the plane-to-station bearing to get the station-to-plane bearing. This is obtained simply by adding or subtracting 180 degrees. When the bearing of the station to the plane is obtained it is plotted from the point representing the station on the chart. This then represents a radio line of position and the airplane is somewhere along this line.

Another bearing is then taken on a different station in some other direction and a line of position determined in the same manner. This second line of position is plotted on the same chart and the airplane is somewhere along this line also. If the airplane is somewhere along both of these lines it *is*

obvious that the exact point on both lines where the airplane is located is where they cross. This point then fixes the location of the airplane and is known as a *fix*. In practice, bearings are usually taken on three radio stations for accuracy. A fix is marked on the chart with a small triangle and the line of position is marked with the time at which it is taken.

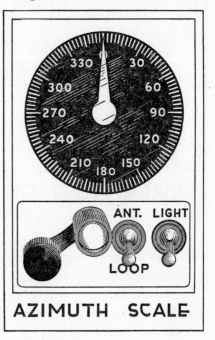

This taking of bearings and plotting of position looks and sounds complicated but it can be done easily and quickly with practice. Once facility has been gained all these operations can be performed much quicker than they can be explained.

A very convenient chart that saves considerable work in plotting bearings is the DF (Direction Finding Chart) of the Coast and Geodetic Survey. This is on a Lambert Conformal projection at a scale of 1 to 2,000,000 and six charts cover the entire United States. An index of these maps is shown on page 322. As radio bearings follow great circle courses, and a straight line on the Lambert is approximately a great circle, the scale error of this chart is negligible. Around each range

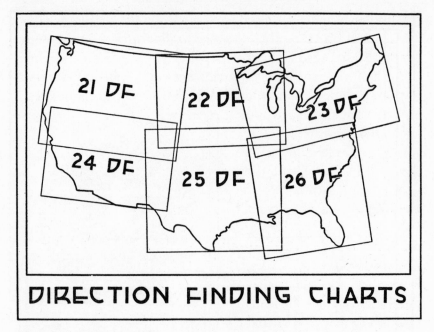

DIRECTION FINDING CHARTS

station, and other important stations, are compass roses oriented to the magnetic meridian. There are two rows of figures, or scales, on the compass rose. The inner figures form the conventional magnetic scale. The outer figures start at zero at the south and show reciprocal magnetic bearings of the station concerned.

In using the DF chart it is not necessary to do much figuring. As the compass roses on the chart are magnetic we can use the magnetic heading instead of the true heading to get the magnetic bearing of the station. Nor is it necessary to calculate reciprocals as they are given on the compass rose of each station.

Let us take a practical example and see how the chart can be used. We are flying from Dayton, Ohio, to Evansville, Indiana, and would like to locate our position. First we read the compass and find we are heading 244 degrees. As the

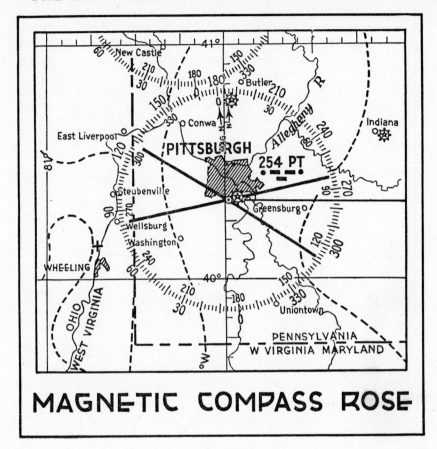

MAGNETIC COMPASS ROSE

deviation on this heading is 2 degrees west our magnetic heading becomes 242 degrees. Tuning our set to 266 KC we find with the pointer on zero that the Indianapolis range shows a relative bearing of 86 degrees. When this is added to the magnetic heading of 242 we obtain 328 degrees, the magnetic bearing of our plane to the station. We draw a line from the Indianapolis range station through the outer 328, giving a radio line of position. Next, tuning the set to the Cincinnati range 335 KC we see that the relative bearing is 210 degrees.

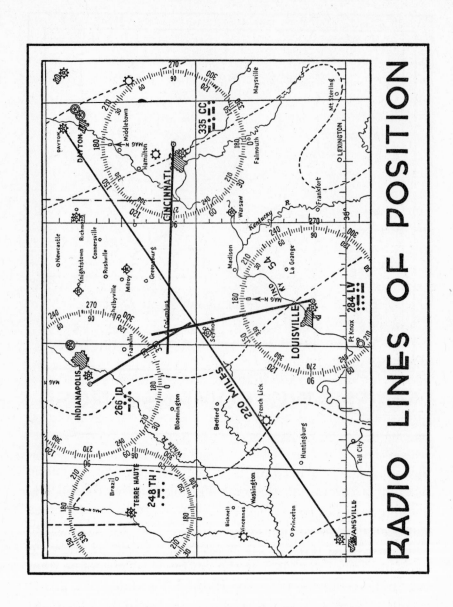

When this is added to the magnetic heading of 242 the sum is 452. Subtracting 360 the magnetic bearing to the Cincinnati station becomes 92 degrees. The next step is to draw a line from the Cincinnati range through the outer 92 point, and the second line of position is completed. The point at which these lines cross represents our position, but for confirmation we will take a third bearing.

Tuning to the Louisville range on 284 KC our relative bearing is 286 which added to the magnetic heading of 242 becomes 528. Deducting 360 leaves 168 and we draw our third line of position from Louisville through the outer scale at 168. If our calculations have been very precise this line will pass through the intersection of the first two lines. More likely it will be somewhat off and the intersections will form a small triangle. Our position may then be taken as the center of the triangle, which is just south of the little settlement of Columbus.

This indicates we have traveled off the course by about 6 degrees, which amounts to about ten miles in this case. By modifying our compass heading and taking later bearings it is possible to get back on course and to remain there.

If the set does not have a visual indicator the null position can be used to take bearings. Bearings can also be taken with a fixed loop, but the whole airplane must be turned in order to locate the null position.

Because the radio bearings follow great circle lines a correction must be made when a Mercator chart is used on long courses. This correction may be ignored if the radio station is known to be less than 50 miles away. There are other details that come to light in further study and practice, that when observed will make for more precise results.

In the earlier explanation of a fix it was assumed that the cross bearings were taken at the same time. Under favorable

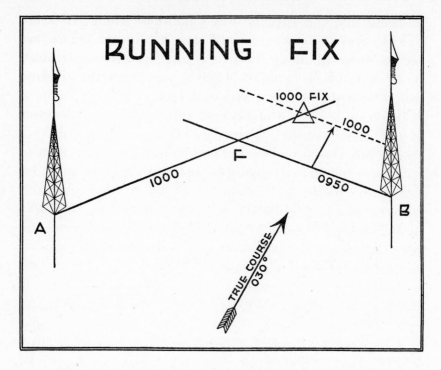

RUNNING FIX

1000 FIX

1000

F

1000

0950

A

B

TRUE COURSE 030°

conditions and with modern equipment two or three bearings can be taken within a minute or two. This is so close that they may be considered as having been taken at the same instant. Often, however, a substantial time interval may occur between the taking of bearings. The position of the airplane is then determined by what is called a *running fix,* which involves moving the lines of position to the same moment in time.

For instance, A and B are radio stations and AF and BF are radio lines of position from them intersecting at F. Bearing BF was taken at 10 minutes before 10 o'clock and bearing AF was taken at 10 o'clock. As the plane was making good a course of 030 degrees at a ground speed of 85 miles per hour it is obvious that it could not be at F at 10 o'clock. But knowing that the airplane was somewhere along AF at 10 o'clock, and somewhere on BF at 10 minutes before, we merely move BF along the true course the distance traveled in 10 minutes, or 14 miles. Then at 10 o'clock the airplane would be at the point marked *1000 fix*.

Direction finding is of extreme value in flying over water or unfamiliar territory where landmarks are either unavailable or unsatisfactory. Position finding is of great help in dead reckoning and an extremely valuable aid to instrument flight. But owing to the amount of work, equipment, time, and space required, it is of more practical value where personnel to do the work is available. It is practiced extensively in the Navy, where a radioman and navigator are normally included in the crew of the larger planes.

30

THE VOICE OF THE AIRWAYS

TRANSMITTING equipment for airplanes is more and more in demand. With a transmitter a pilot has a voice in addition to ears. He can keep in touch with airway traffic control operators, report his position, announce arrivals, and in case of trouble request assistance. Even for contact flying the Civil Air Regulations require a two-way radio for flights above 3500 feet on the airways. More and more large airports require two-way radio.

Anyone can own and operate a receiver as he pleases. When an aircraft has a transmitter, however, it becomes a mobile station and both operator and station must be licensed by the Federal Communications Commission. An examination must be taken and passed for the operator's license, but this is made up of common sense questions and presents no great difficulty. Applications for both kinds of licenses and sample questions and answers from which the examination is made up are obtainable from most radio dealers. If not available locally these may be obtained by writing to the Federal Communications Commission, Washington, D. C.

The average person stands somewhat in awe of radio and the very thought of transmitting raises a mental hazard. This anxiety is needless. The smaller sets are usually set on 3105 KC and this frequency is guarded by all stations that maintain listening watches. This means that these stations always have their receivers on and tuned to 3105 kilocycles. All you have to do is turn your set on and when the tubes are warm press the microphone button and talk. You will be heard by all the stations within the range of your transmitter that are tuned to the frequency you are using.

An excellent transmitter is the RCA Model AVT-15 which is a companion set to the AVR-15 receiver previously described. When these two sets are used together the same power supply operates both. This combination eliminates the need for an extra panel and controls as the receiver off-on switch lights the filaments of the transmitter tubes and places the unit in readiness for instant operation. It becomes a two-way system with but two controls.

The antenna supplied with this set is of the reel and conduit type. This is of a predetermined length depending upon the frequency, and is reeled out after the plane takes off and reeled in prior to landing. The reel is unwound by the pull on the drag unit attached to the end of the antenna. As the pull exists only when the plane is in flight the reel cannot be accidentally unwound on the ground.

Since unsystematized broadcasting would clutter up the air with confusing messages a definite procedure has been established. If you are a private pilot you will be calling either the Civil Aeronautics Authority communication stations located at range stations or local airport traffic control towers. When calling communications stations they are addressed by name—"Atlantic Radio" or "Denver Radio"—rather than by call letters. In calling either radio or tower you use your transmitting frequency, which will probably be 3105 KC. The radio range facility will answer you on the range to which you are listening, but you will have to switch over to 278 KC, or some other local frequency, to hear the tower reply.

An incoming pilot should call the control tower for landing instructions when about 10 minutes away from the airport. After the plane is on the ground the tower will continue to give instructions in regard to taxiing until the plane is parked. Before taking off a pilot must contact the tower for permission to take off and instructions or information as to traffic, runway to use, etc. He should continue to listen on the control tower frequency after take-off until certain that it is no longer necessary.

In order that the station operator may understand you it is important that certain procedures be followed. These come naturally to the trained operator, but are very likely to be overlooked by the amateur. Speak clearly and distinctly, pronouncing every syllable and with the microphone in the same position and distance from the lips during the entire transmission. Speak at the same rate as ground operators who are experienced in communication. Care should be used in transmitting digits. The cipher is always "zero," and where similarity of sound exists digits should be spoken in two syllables —3 should be th-ree, 4 fo-wer, 5 fi-yiv, and 9 as ni-en.

Each message is made up of three parts, the preface, the body, and the end. To establish communication the station being called is mentioned first, followed by your identification. Contact should be established by a preliminary message before any request for information is made.

A normal sequence of messages may go like this: On approaching an airport the pilot establishes contact by calling, "Wichita Tower from NC, two, eight, zero, one, two, answer." The tower will come back and say, "NC, two, eight, zero, one, two, from Wichita Tower, go ahead." Contact having been established, the pilot gives his position and makes his request,

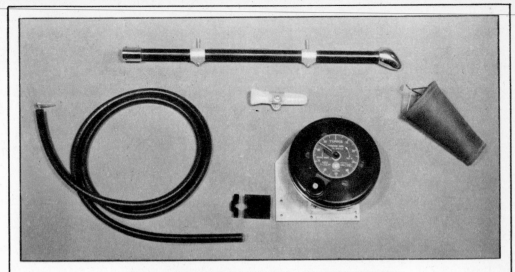

TRANSMITTING ANTENNA

TRANSMITTER

AUTOMATIC DIRECTION FINDER

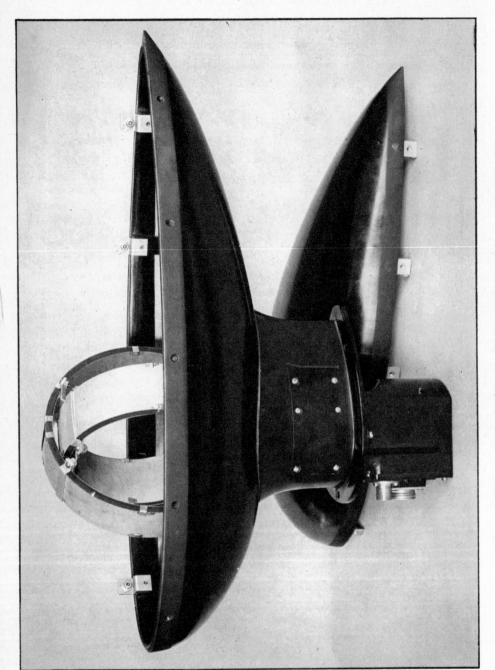

SHIELDED DOUBLE LOOP

as follows: "I am one five miles northwest Wichita Airport, request landing instructions, go ahead." The tower will then give instructions that may run like this: "Approach airport, circle to the left until I contact you, go ahead." The "go ahead" requires a reply so the pilot can answer the word "received," "roger," which is an acknowledgment, or "wilco," meaning, "I will comply." Then, of course, the tower will call the plane when it gets to the airport and give it further instructions and information regarding runway, traffic, obstructions, etc.

One thing to remember is that when you are ready to transmit be sure your receiver is tuned to receive the station you are calling before you start to talk. Always listen before talking. It may be that the ground operator is carrying on communication with another plane and your call would break in on them.

31

NEW DEVELOPMENTS

A MONG the other new developments constantly appearing, an extremely valuable device is the *automatic direction-finder*. When the finder is tuned to a certain station, a motor automatically rotates the loop to the null position. A pointer on the dial indicates the direction of the station and continues to do so regardless of the heading or changes of course of the airplane. Because the pilot does not have to rotate the loop by hand to the bearings, he is relieved of a number of time-consuming motions and can therefore devote more attention to his other duties.

Another advantage of this instrument is that it is free from 180-degree ambiguity. The ordinary loop, when on the null, places the station either in a certain direction, or its reciprocal. The automatic direction-finder, when used with the shielded double loop provided with the set, points in one direction only—toward the broadcasting station.

Navigation scales are provided from which the relative, magnetic, and true bearings can be obtained quickly without calculation. The instrument operates on both the range band and the broadcasting frequency. It will show the bearing of the station at the same time that signals are being received through the headphones. No time is lost when several bearings are required as the needle swings quickly to the station bearings with an accuracy of one degree and without overswing or oscillation (hunting). It can also be used as a range receiver, a radiocompass or a manually operated directionfinder.

Another outstanding development in navigation instruments is the *Learmatic Navigator*. This instrument combines the functions of the automatic radio direction-finder and the directional gyro. The instrument case, which is connected to an automatic radio direction-finder, contains a conventional directional gyro. A circular 360-degree azimuth scale set in a horizontal position on the top of the case is coupled direct to the gyro shaft. The horizontal scale rotates with the conventional scale so that both indicate the same heading in relation to the lubber line. A double-lined reference scale, called the desired-track index, can be turned to the course to be flown on the azimuth scale and then set so as to rotate with the scale.

In operation, the pilot needs only to set the desired-track index to the course he wishes to follow with respect to the radio transmitting station, and to tune the automatic radio direction-finder to the frequency of that station.

This instrument can be used in quite a number of different ways and under varying conditions. A straight course can be flown along any desired track either toward or away from a radio transmitting station. Drift is constantly corrected and the position of the airplane in relation to the track flown is automatically given. The instrument can also be used in navigating to points not having radio transmitting stations. Instrument approaches and landings can be made at fixed or temporary bases, by land or sea aircraft, under an infinite variety of conditions.

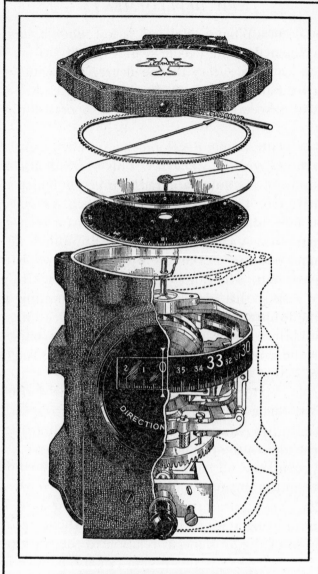

LEARMATIC
NAVIGATOR

And so it goes. What is modern today is obsolete tomorrow. The development tempo in aviation is such that it is very difficult to keep up with everything that is going on. Some of the standard equipment we see on private planes today could be afforded only by the airlines and the services just a short time ago. The equipment used by airlines today will be on the private plane of tomorrow.

The airlines and the services are the proving grounds for new equipment and systems. They have the money, the access to inventive minds, and the vision to carry on the work. Airlines are now using double automatic range-finders which further simplify navigation. Equipment is available for absolute automatic directional control by radio. This device brings the airplane in to a radio station by radio without help from the pilot. A radio altimeter indicates the actual height of the airplane above the ground over which it is traveling.

The ultra-high frequency radio bands now being tested in experimental work will soon be in common use. Certain ranges, as well as the Z-type markers, already operate on these frequencies. Blind landing systems utilizing the ultra-high frequencies can no longer be considered in the experimental stage.

There are so many new developments under way that it is impossible to keep up with them. No one can predict what will come in the future.

32

PRACTICAL FLYING

WE have taken several flights together. I hope they have
been enjoyable and instructive. Before closing I would like
to make just one more flight with you. On it we shall sum
up and use all the experience we have tried to acquire. We
shall go through all of the actual steps of a flight from New
Orleans, Louisiana, to Pensacola, Florida, using a combination of the various methods and facilities at our disposal. On
this trip we may use a Navy plane for a change. The prin-

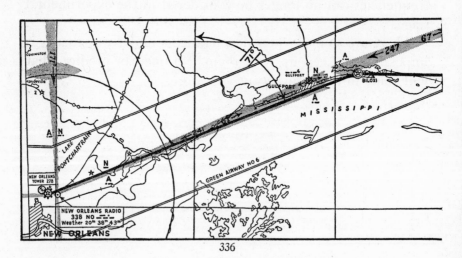

ciples remain the same regardless of the type of plane used.

The first thing to do is to lay out and study the Mobile sectional chart on which our course is located. It is obvious that a direct course here would take us so far out over the Gulf of Mexico that we could not reach land in the event of motor failure. It would not be good judgment to follow such a direct course. On the other hand, there is no need to go any farther out of the way than necessary. As the proposed track follows the shore line of the Gulf, it would be a simple matter to fly the course by piloting if we so desire. But the weather may be bad somewhere along the trip, so this is not a safe procedure. From an analysis of the chart it appears that the best thing to do is to break up the flight into two parts. The first leg will be from New Orleans to Biloxi, Mississippi, and the second from Biloxi to Pensacola. The distance of these two flights is 171 miles, against 168 miles if the flight were made direct. This extra distance of only three miles is a small price to pay in order to remain within gliding distance of land.

We draw in the two true courses, measure them and find

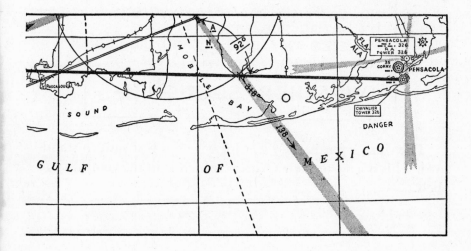

them to be 69 degrees and 92 degrees, respectively. The distances are 71 miles and 100 miles. The variation on the first
part of the course is 6 degrees east, giving a magnetic course
of 63 degrees. The variation on the second leg of the course is
5 degrees, also east. The magnetic course on the second
leg of the course is therefore 87 degrees. This information,
with the mileages, is noted on the log of the plotting board or
on the chart itself. At this time it is a good idea to mark off
mileage units on the chart so that the ground speed can be
checked later while in flight. A good unit, easy to use, is ten
miles and this should be marked off near the start of the
course.

The next step is to take our plotting board and go to the
office of the Weather Bureau. The weather sequence has just
come in. From the chart we see that the stations we are interested in, other than New Orleans and Pensacola, are Biloxi
and Mobile. The actual reports are given in the illustration.
You should be able to read these by now, but I will check
them over with you just to be sure.

NO C -◍/16◔ 200/55/45↓↘20/011
OX E12⊕9 200/54/48↓14/012
MS E12⊕ 196/55/49↓↘15/010/C1G RGD
NC E35⊕14◔ 183/61/56↓↘10/006

WEATHER SEQUENCE

The time given is 1430 E, which is 2:30 P M eastern standard. This is 1:30 at New Orleans, which is in the central time
belt.

NO, or New Orleans reports as follows:

CONTACT—CEILING UNLIMITED—HIGH THIN BROKEN CLOUDS, LOWER SCATTERED CLOUDS AT 1600 FEET—"VISIBILITY UNLIMITED"—BAROMETRIC PRESSURE 1020.0 MILLIBARS—TEMPERATURE 55 DEGREES, DEW POINT 45 DEGREES—WIND NORTH NORTHWEST 20 MILES PER HOUR—ALTIMETER SETTING 30.11.

OX, or Biloxi:

CEILING ESTIMATED 1200 FEET OVERCAST—VISIBILITY 9 MILES—BAROMETRIC PRESSURE 1020.0 MILLIBARS—TEMPERATURE 54 DEGREES, DEW POINT 48 DEGREES—NORTH WIND 14 MILES PER HOUR—ALTIMETER SETTING 30.12.

MS, or Mobile, reports:

CEILING ESTIMATED 1200 FEET OVERCAST—"VISIBILITY UNLIMITED"—BAROMETRIC PRESSURE 1019.6 MILLIBARS—TEMPERATURE 55 DEGREES, DEW POINT 49 DEGREES—WIND NORTH NORTHWEST 15 MILES PER HOUR—ALTIMETER SETTING 30.10, CEILING RAGGED.

NC, or Pensacola, weather is as follows:

CEILING ESTIMATED 3500 FEET OVERCAST, LOWER SCATTERED CLOUDS AT 1400 FEET—"VISIBILITY UNLIMITED"—BAROMETRIC PRESSURE 1018.3—TEMPERATURE 61 DEGREES, DEW POINT 56 DEGREES—WIND NORTH NORTHWEST 10 MILES PER HOUR—ALTIMETER SETTING 30.06.

The winds-aloft report gives us the wind only at 1000 feet as there was a low overcast at the time of the last observation. At that time the wind at 1000 feet was 20 miles per hour from 355 degrees. The general weather reports are not bad. The ceiling is low at Biloxi and Mobile, but higher at Pensacola, at the end of our flight. The temperature and dew point begin to get close together at Biloxi, Mobile, and Pensacola, but not close enough for precipitation. The pressures are high at all points which, of course, is very much in our favor. A look at the weather map shows nothing disquieting. The meteorologist tells us that the weather will gradually clear and be even better in case we wish to return the same day.

So, despite the low ceiling, we will plan to start our trip. The ceilings and visibility are good enough so that we can make a contact flight. Since the Civil Air Regulations require

	1st LEG	2nd LEG
TC	069°	092°
Var	-6°	-5°
MC	063°	087°
WC	-7°	-8°
MH	056°	079°
Dev	+1°	+2°
CH	057°	081°
GS	140	150
Miles	71	100
Time	30	40
Dep	1345	1415
ETA	1415	1455

NEW ORLEANS   PENSACOLA
LOG

that an airplane on a contact flight keep at least 300 feet below the overcast, our flight will be planned for 900 feet. We will use the 1000-foot level wind for our vector diagram, however.

With the wind direction and velocity known we find by using the plotting board, or computer, or by drawing out the triangle of velocities, that the wind correction angle is 7 degrees for the first leg and 8 degrees for the second. The wind being on the left this correction is subtractive. Our magnetic headings then become 56 degrees and 79 degrees, respectively. Measuring the ground speed we find it to be 140 miles per hour for the first leg and 150 for the second. The above information is entered in the log. We will wait until we get back to the ship to find the deviation in order to get the compass heading.

Now, we will cross the corridor and drop in at the office of the Civil Aeronautics Administration, Communications Division. Here we will file a flight plan. We give the operator our name, plane number and type, altitude and route, speed, radio equipment, departure time, and estimated time to make the trip. Either he or we will make out the form shown in the illustration on page 342.

With this information the operator waits for our plane to take off. At the time of our departure he will put this message on the teletype so that Pensacola and Biloxi and Mobile, the chief airports along the route, will be informed of our flight. As we progress along the course we report our position by radio at specified places. In this manner a record will be kept of our progress and if we should get into trouble rescue parties would know where to look for us. Once you make a flight plan these position reports are very important, particularly the arrival report. This arrival report can be made by radio after landing, or by phone. The important thing is that it be done *immediately* upon arrival. If no arrival report is made it is assumed that the plane is down somewhere and unable to communicate. Rescue planes and parties are sent out and if it is later found that the pilot just forgot to file an arrival report he is billed for the trouble and expense of the search.

When the arrival report is properly filed the message goes back all along the line so that all concerned are notified of

Filing time (Received)	DEPARTMENT OF COMMERCE CIVIL AERONAUTICS ADMINISTRATION WASHINGTON FLIGHT PLAN Form ACA 398 (Rev. 9-1-40)	Delivery time (Transmitted)

ADDRESS ....
(Circuit number/s)

TEXT (APREQ) ~~NC~~ AR NA NO   *01639   BEECH   LIEUT. VETTER   NEW ORLEANS*
(Aircraft identification mark)   (Type aircraft)   (Pilot)   (F. P. number)   (Point of departure)

CFR   NO-OX-MS-NC   PENSACOLA   150   ⬭3105⬭ 495 6210 RONLY NORDO
(Proposed altitude/s and route)   (Point of first intended landing)   (Speed)   (Transmitting frequency)

P   *1345*   D $1^h + 10^m$
(Proposed time of departure)   (Actual time of departure)   (Estimated elapsed time)   (Alternate airport)

REMARKS: ....

.... SIGNATURE .... Filed by ....
GPO   16-9035   (Station identification and number)   (Name)

the plane's safe arrival. With this service your family can be informed of your safe arrival by calling the communications office after a reasonable time has elapsed.

With the flight plan filed we go down to the ship and make a quick inspection, taking particular note that our gasoline tanks are all full. We check our compass for the deviation correction and quickly note our compass headings on the plotting board. Deviation on our first magnetic heading is 1 degree west. Our compass heading for the first leg then becomes 57 degrees. The deviation on the second leg is 2 degrees west so the compass heading for that leg will be 81 degrees.

The engine is started and while it is warming up the radios are turned on in order to have the tubes warm when needed. The receiver is set to the New Orleans Control Tower frequency of 278 KC and the transmitter is ready to broadcast on 3105 KC.

Before going any further let us clear up one point on which there is considerable confusion. This has already been covered, but it will bear repeating. Several control tower operators and communications men have told me that many pilots use procedures in transmission which are not conducive to efficient communication. When your call goes out on the air both the traffic control tower and the C. A. A. communication stations hear you. They both maintain a listening watch on your frequency. So be sure to state clearly whom you are calling. Most all busy airports have both tower and communication stations and sometimes others besides. To the pilot they are all radio stations, but there is a big difference to the operators who must keep order on the air.

The tower that you talk with has a low-powered receiver and transmitter located on the premises. The purpose of this station is to direct *local* traffic on and around the airport. The range of such stations is only around 15 miles. They are always referred to as "Tower" and identified by name—"New Orleans Tower," "Philadelphia Tower," etc.

When you want to talk with the C. A. A. communications you refer to them as "Radio," identifying the one you are calling by name—"New Orleans Radio," "Mobile Radio," etc. The communications stations have powerful receivers and transmitters and control long distance traffic. A common mistake of pilots is to call "Radio" when they mean "Tower." When "Radio" is called he has to answer, and if it was the tower that was wanted confusion results and time is wasted.

Well, to get back to our flight . . . we were in front of the hangar with our engine warm and radios ready.

Listening through the phones to be sure we will not interrupt another conversation, we pick up the microphone. The air being clear, we press the mike button and call, "New Orleans Tower from Navy, zero, one, six, three, nine, answer."

Instantly we hear the voice of the tower operator: "Navy, zero, one, six, three, nine, from New Orleans Tower, go ahead."

Since communication has been established and the operator can see our ship on the ground, there is no need for going through the calling procedure again. We merely say, "Flight plan filed with communications for flight to Pensacola, request take-off instructions, go ahead."

The answer comes right back, "You may taxi out to runway on 330 degrees, wait for Eastern Airliner to land."

We taxi out to the edge of the runway and wait while the airliner comes down. After it is out of the way we hear the tower operator say, "O.K. Navy, you may take off when ready."

With a hurried, "Thank you," we note the time, roll out on the runway, take off, and are on our way.

After getting away from the airport we settle down at our previously determined altitude of 900 feet and compass heading of 57 degrees. We set the gyro at the same heading and tune the radio to the New Orleans beam frequency of 338 KC. We ride the beam, occasionally checking with our compass and directional gyro for our heading and continually with the chart for our position. Traveling right on course we find it took just above 4 minutes to fly the 10 miles between our predetermined check points. The computer shows we are making a ground speed of 146 miles per hour. This is a little faster than we calculated on the ground, but we will make no change in our plans as this slight extra speed will allow for our climb out of the field and slight variations in flying.

In just twenty-nine minutes we are over the Biloxi Airport and the first leg of our trip is completed. We turn the ship to the compass heading of the second leg, or 81 degrees, wait until the compass settles down, and reset the gyro. The radio is then tuned to the Pensacola range frequency of 326 KC. As soon as the signals are right we turn the Operation Selector to Radio Compass and adjust the visual indicator to "home" on Pensacola. We put the phones down and use the Radio Compass for the rest of the flight as the Pensacola beam is not on our course.

Again, after settling down on our course, we check the ground speed. As we covered the 10 miles in just under 4 minutes our ground speed is about 152 miles per hour, or just about what we figured it would be.

By this time we find that we are about to enter the Mobile Control Zone of Intersection. When flying on a flight plan we are expected to notify the communication stations in all Control Zones of Intersection that we are passing through. This is done when the zone is entered. So we turn the Operation Selector back to Beacon Weather Regular and tune in the Mobile Range station at 248 KC.

When we are sure we will not break in on some other call we pick up the microphone, press the button, and call, "Mobile Radio, from Navy, zero, one, six, three, nine, answer." Mobile comes back saying, "Navy, zero, one, six, three, nine, from Mobile Radio, go ahead." We reply, "Reporting position—just entered Mobile Control Zone of Intersection at juncture of Alabama-Mississippi border, true course 92 degrees, go ahead." The range station will acknowledge our message by repeating our position. He will say, "Your position is at edge of Mobile Control Zone of Intersection on Alabama-Mississippi border, true course 92 degrees, go ahead." Again we come back, saying, "That is correct—roger," which terminates the message. But, if the operator knows the ceilings are low, he may add, "Navy, zero, one, six, three, nine. Will you give me a ceiling check? Go ahead." Our reply is, "I am flying at 1000 feet, estimated 300 feet below the overcast, *visibility unlimited,* go ahead." He terminates the communication with, "Thank you—roger," and we go back on our radiocompass course toward Pensacola.

As we approach Pensacola we are both very alert for training planes, as there is a great deal of traffic in this vicinity. Within a few miles of Chevalier Field we call the tower and listen for them on the beam frequency on 326 KC. This being a Navy tower, it is not on 278 KC as are most civilian stations. After requesting and receiving landing instructions we come down and taxi up to the line.

Here there are three ways of making our arrival report. Since this is a Navy Base we can report to the Operations Department and ask them to do it. We can phone the radio station, or call them on the plane radio. The most convenient procedure is by radio before we leave the airplane. As we are tuned to the station, we merely call, "Pensacola Tower from Navy, zero, one, six, three, nine, answer." The reply comes, in the prescribed manner, "Navy, zero, one, six, three, nine, from Pensacola Tower, go ahead." Our last message is, "Reporting arrival, from New Orleans 1407 central standard. Please notify New Orleans and intermediate stations—go ahead." The tower answers, "wilco," which means "I will comply" and closes the matter. We switch off the radio and our trip with *VISIBILITY UNLIMITED* is over.

INDEX

347